Pull up a Sandbag and pass me a lamp

Or life in the Royal Air Force Regiment during the Flower Power years and beyond

John C Harriss

To Richard & Lesley,
You know, this is what it
was like!

JayCeePress

Best wishes,

John Harriss

1 NOV 2011

1st Edition

Published by JayCeePress

ISBN 978-0-9570380-0-4

Copyright © John C Harriss 2011

The moral rights of this writer have been asserted

Printed by **OlivePress** Ltd
www.olivepress.co.uk

About the Author

Bought up as the son of an RAF Pilot, the author went on to join up himself at the age of seventeen and a half. Unlike his father though, he joined the Royal Air Force Regiment. Most of his father's comments on hearing the news were unprintable. 'My son, a Rock-ape,' he cried, diluting his beer with his tears. 'I must not let my colleagues find out.'

The author went on to serve for 24 years, which indicates an inability to accept that, perhaps, this Regiment life wasn't for him. One day, whilst spinning a yarn over a beer, someone said, 'You tell so many stories, 'why don't you write them down before old age causes you to forget'!

So here we are.

Forward and thanks

All of the anecdotes in this narrative really happened and whilst some of these might seem bizarre or unreal, the general rule of thumb is that 'truth is sometimes stranger than fiction'. Currently, most dates and places are unchanged so that any readers who were there at the time will remember the incidents set down in this story.

The young airmen, whose fortunes are followed in this novel are real people. All names, however, are entirely the author's imagination and are made up deliberately to cover up the true identity of any person. No-one connected with any anecdote could therefore be connected by the closeness of given names to real names.

Thank you to all those who were there at the time because without you there would be no book.

My special thanks go to, Professor Peter Herbert for the hours spent proof reading and editing my work.

Contents

Chapter 1 – Basic Training

Matt got off the train and glanced up at the late summer sky. It was like this when he left this part of the world, a few years and a lifetime ago. A lot had happened since then, not least, he'd joined the Royal Air Force. Best not let on about his background, he reflected.

It was September 1964 and having 'joined up' he found himself posted to the 'No 7 School of Recruit Training' at RAF Swinderby in Lincolnshire.

Situated on the A46 halfway between Lincoln and Newark, it was well known to Matt. He had lived in and around that area for six years as a child. It used to be 'No 11 Flying Training School' and the home of the Vampire T11. His father was a flying instructor then and indeed, was still in the RAF serving as a pilot on a Communications squadron at RAF Andover.

Matt had got off the train at Newark station but there had been nothing resembling RAF transport waiting there. There was just an old white coach sitting in the corner of the car park. No sweat he thought as he stuck his thumb out. Within thirty minutes he was walking through the gates of RAF Swinderby. There was a coach parked up outside the guardroom full of young chaps like himself looking awkward and dressed in civilian clothes. Come to think of it, he thought, it resembled the coach he'd seen earlier, outside the station. He climbed aboard and asked if the coach had just arrived from Newark station. 'Yes,' said one of the occupants. 'We were held up because some bloody fool went 'A-WOL' and didn't turn up.' Matt gulped and quickly sat down. The person in charge might not notice an extra body if he kept quiet.

A large man dressed in blue wearing a peaked cap and sweating profusely climbed on board and as Matt recognised the two stripes on each arm the corporal, recognised that an extra passenger had climbed aboard. 'Who the hell are you and where the fuck did you come from?' screamed the corporal. 'Get off, now.' Matt hurried to comply. 'Name?' shouted the corporal. 'Matt' replied Matt. The corporal got redder in the face and said in a very quiet voice, 'Your fucking surname laddie.'

The first thing that everybody learnt early on was that 'initiative' was definitely 'out of order'. They were paid to do as they were told, not to think and certainly not to contemplate initiative.

On day two Matt found out, again, just how stupid it could be to use his initiative. They were marched to the hairdressers. 'Right you lot, form an orderly queue and get your hair cut, report back outside immediately you're finished.' Matt had gone to the trouble of getting an extra short haircut only the day before travelling to Swinderby. He informed the corporal that he didn't need a haircut as he'd only just had one. Wrong move again. He was marched to the front of the queue and dumped unceremoniously into the waiting chair. 'Give him a short back and sides,' said the corporal and short back and sides is what he got. The sting in the tail was that he had to pay again as well. It was time to get smart and stop this initiative nonsense.

There was a strict hierarchy at Basic Training or square bashing as it was known. The recruits were the lowest of the low. They lived underneath the cow-pat. Warm smelly and kept in the dark. Just like mushrooms really. The corporals on the other hand were the Demi-Gods and only spoke to the recruits at 100 decibels or above. The Sergeants only spoke to the corporals, never the recruits and they were the Semi-Gods. The Flight Sergeants lived somewhere in the heavens and even the sergeants stood to attention when addressing them. They were almost Gods.

There was one Warrant Officer, he was the Station Warrant Officer and he *was* God. If he ever had cause to speak to a recruit then that recruit knew a bolt of lightning was going to come out of a

2

cloudless blue sky and smite him between the eyes. There were commissioned officers but they never bothered with the recruits. These officers lived somewhere in the stratosphere and were seldom known to touch the earth. Aloof and distant, these were the 'chosen ones' and the recruits were taught to salute them even if they crossed paths 50 miles away.

Friendships were quickly made in the billets which fourteen men, or to put it more accurately, boys shared. Matt teamed up with two other lads who were going to the RAF Regiment after basic recruit training. Matt, Luke and Bill looked out for each other whilst at Swinderby and soon became firm mates. They learnt to march and drill with the Mk4 Lee Enfield rifle. They learnt to endure the screaming, yelling and pointless exercises that the drill corporals made them carry out. Most of all, they learnt to keep a low profile. They learnt that 'Bullshit baffled brains' and they could get away with most things if they went through the movements. Indeed, they were taught during rifle drill that if they dropped anything, they were not to attempt to pick it up. Just go through the motions as if you still had the bayonet or rifle or hat said the drill corporals. The corporals were of course priming them to win the drill competition for them, hoping that the judges would not notice an empty arm where there should be a rifle - or even a spare arm on the ground still clutching a rifle - after they'd marched off.

During the eight weeks they were to spend there the recruits were allowed one 24 hour pass and one 48 hour pass. Most of the course chose to go into Lincoln on their 24 hour pass. Matt decided to revisit old haunts and walk to North Hykam. If he walked along the main road, it would take two hours. He had walked it many times in the past. If he took the back roads, it would take one hour. It was a nice day and Matt chose the back roads.

Down past the 'Sheepwalk' Matt wandered. Past the Mill where he and his sister used to swim in the summer as kids and on into

Hykam. There was no hurry and after a while, he found himself standing outside the house where he used to live. The memories came flooding back. The gut wrenching divorce his parents went through. The overwhelming sadness he felt when told by his mother that his parents would never get back together. The cruelty of his mother during those years and the glorious day when his father arrived out of the blue and took all four brothers and sister down to White Waltham. He smiled as he remembered Wendy. The 'nice' lady around the corner where he used to babysit. He willingly donated his 'cherry' to her at the grand old age of 14 whilst her husband was asleep upstairs. A thought formed in his head. I wonder if they still live there. Hmmm. Matt walked around the corner. Things were not quite the same. Where the house used to be, there was a Fish and Chip shop. Ah well thought Matt, might as well get some whilst I'm here. He walked in and joined the queue. More people came in and joined the queue and then, there she was, 'The Cherry Picker'! It was her, standing in the queue, chatting to a friend. She's still pretty he thought, still a nice figure, wonder if she still needs that padded bra, must be 28 now and look at that, butter wouldn't melt in her mouth. Matt had left there three and a half years before, he had grown to twice his former size and he was dressed in RAF uniform. He didn't expect to be recognised and he wasn't. He glanced across and thought, she hasn't changed a bit. I wonder what the old man's doing nowadays. Matt took his fish and chips and wandered outside. Parked there was a white van. Inside were three children and Ron, the husband. A feeling of mischief came over Matt as he walked over to Ron, who was sitting behind the wheel. 'Hello Ron,' he said. 'I expect you don't remember me. I used to babysit for you and your wife a few years ago when I was much younger.' 'Good Lord,' said Ron, 'I do remember you, how are you doing?' 'Fine,' replied Matt, 'as you can see, I'm in the Air Force now based at Swinderby. I just thought I'd wander down memory lane and see where I got to. How about you?' 'We live at

Waddington now,' said Ron. 'We still come back from time to time. This place does the best fish and chips around. In fact, the missus is in there right now getting some for us.' 'Oh well,' Matt said, 'pity I've got to rush, I've got a bus to catch, shame I'll miss her. Give her my best won't you.' 'Sure thing,' said Ron. 'All the best.' Glad he never found out, Matt thought, as he walked away wondering how she'd react when he tells her who he's seen. Matt disappeared around the corner and headed back to camp. The sun shone, the birds sang and as he strolled along with his memories, he had a broad grin on his face. All in all it was a grand day.

Near the far end of the airfield was a wood. Nobody took any notice of it until one morning near the end of the course when they were briefed about a night exercise that would take place, that night, in the wood. Guarding an ammunition dump. Containing nuclear bombs. The day was taken up learning to erect tents, dig in fire extinguishers, operate the 'Lazy man boilers' and turn blankets into sleeping bags. They arrived at the wood during the late afternoon and set up camp. It soon became obvious that there was no ammunition dump and certainly no nuclear bombs. 'Who did they think they were kidding?' Luke asked. 'Dunno,' said Matt 'but if brains was dynamite, they wouldn't have enough to blow their ears apart.'

The night was spent guarding the camp bounds. Always two men at a time, each man on for two hours. The off going man would wake up the oncoming man who would then spend the first hour on guard getting used to being awake. After that hour, his mate had finished his two hours and became the off going guard, and so it continued in staggered fashion throughout the night. There were three teams or pairs guarding the camp and one extra team who's job it was to keep the boiler going throughout the night. The corporals insisted, under pain of death or even worse, that they wanted hot water in the morning for their tea and shaving. Matt and Luke, of course were detailed for one duty looking after the boiler and one at the perimeter guarding the notional nuclear bombs at the notional ammunition dump. It became very cold so having stoked up the boiler, Matt and Luke sat looking out with their backs towards the heat, leaning against a sapling. Soon the fire warmed them and they dreamed the dreams of the just and brave. Matt awoke with a start. 'Bloody hell, quick Luke, you wake up the next guard and I'll relight the boiler,' whispered Matt. They must have slept for a good few hours. The boiler was out. Matt soon got it going though, the wood near it was quite dry. Luke had the foresight to wake up the two correct guards in the pattern and Matt and Luke beat it back to the tent as fast as they could. About half an hour later there was a roar from the corporals tent. The water was still cold, so no hot tea. All trainees were paraded. A field investigation was carried out as to who let the boiler out but nobody was forthcoming. Oh dear thought Matt, we might have to go and have a hot breakfast back in the main camp. They struck camp and piled the equipment on to the lorries that had arrived. The lorries left and Matt gazed after them, watching the potential lift disappear towards the main camp. All right, get fell in you lot, came the order and so it was with rifles held above their heads that the erstwhile group of men found themselves doubling towards the main camp a mile away. Despite the physical effort, they were all smiling at the thought of a decent breakfast until they came to a halt outside the gym. The corporals left them to the tender mercies of the RAF physical training instructors and went on to their own breakfast and hot tea.

It was the final night before the Passing Out Parade came. The drill competitions and rehearsals were over. The next day was the real thing, the big day.

The now, senior recruits were busy in their billets shining their boots for the passing out parade and were rubbing buckles, badges and anything else that could be made shinier. Best uniforms were being pressed and an air of subdued excitement was present. The recruits sat on their beds hoping not to see the Demi-Gods or 'drill pigs' come in. Their kit would be thrown out of the window at the slightest provocation. The lads sat and made the magic circles on their boots necessary to create the mirror finish demanded, they chatted and white blanco'd belts and rifle slings which lay on pristine yellow dusters. A scene of domestic contentment ensued as they cracked jokes and told stories whilst they worked.

The door opened and Matt just had time to catch a glimpse of a somebody in uniform entering the room when the yell 'OFFICER PRESENT' caused a moment of chaos. Every man dropped what he was doing and sprang to attention at the bottom of his bed. Head and eyes to the front, body rigid, thumbs down the side seams of the pyjamas. There was a stunned silence. This was unprecedented. 'Chosen ones' just did not work after 16:00 and it must have been pushing on for 20:00. Matt's peripheral vision showed this unidentified person disappearing behind him, and he gulped.

'Stand easy, relax and carry on with what you were doing,' said this voice behind him. There was something familiar with that voice. 'Dad,' he blurted out and turning around, Matt saw his father. Removing Matt's 'General Service Knowledge' book from underneath the pillows, his father said, 'That's just where I used to hide mine when I was doing my square bashing.' 'But dad,' 'what,' 'I mean.' 'Relax son,' said his father with a smile. 'I thought I'd come and watch my son pass out tomorrow.' He looked the part, Matt noted. With his rows of medal ribbons and his pilot wings. None of the 'chosen ones' here had any of that real RAF stuff on their uniforms. The rest of the lads in the billet were dumbstruck and Matt tried hard not to smile. The door opened and a drill pig Demi-God stuck his nose through the door. He was about to start on them when he spotted a 'chosen one'. The drill-pig withdrew swiftly and closed the door quietly. Matt's cup flowed over. Yes...... he thought:

Brilliant. His dad sat on the bed and they swapped yarns about square bashing and different terms and types of bullshit for a while. At about nine or so, Matt's dad left to a silent and stunned room who had hung onto every word between 'chosen one' and son. Matt's mates came up and said, 'Is that your old man then?' Matt nodded and could only feel .... PRIDE...in spades.... as he carried on making 'magic circles'.

The new day dawned grey and blustery. Dark clouds scudded across the countryside with the promise of rain later. The recruits didn't care. This was their last day at this God-awful camp and the weather could do as it liked. Nothing could alter the fact that they wouldn't be here tomorrow.

The Passing Out Parade came and went. They marched on to the parade ground, which was really an open piece of concrete that once used to have Vampires parked on it. They wheeled and turned into position, stood at ease and waited. Eventually, they were called to attention as the reviewing officer arrived in his staff car. They were inspected by the reviewing officer in open order whilst the band played. It took forever. They marched past then went forward the regulation 14, one-two, paces in review order. They pretended to listen to the reviewing officer's chosen words, all the time wishing that he would bloody well get it over with and let them get the hell out of this cold place. It was November now and gone were the warm dry days of September. Eventually they marched off and handed in their rifles and white webbing. They made their way back to the billet to collect their luggage and rail travel warrants. There was a coach leaving the guardroom in an hour heading for Newark train station and and 'Don't be late,' growled a drill-pig.

Matt made his way to the 'Meet and Greet' venue (Airmen's Mess) where the families were gathered. His father was waiting for him. 'Have you got all your stuff,' he asked. 'Yes,' said Matt. 'Good,' his father replied. 'We need to get away, got a bus to catch.' 'What's happening,' asked Matt. 'We're going to RAF Waddington. I flew down in an Anson yesterday and we're returning to RAF Andover. I might add that you are the only man on the parade today to fly home. Even the reviewing officer has to travel by staff car. The weather's to bad to fly from here. It's better at Waddington because it's on top of the hill. He's got a fair way to go as well,' said dad, 'he's the station commander of RAF Abbingdon. He hurt himself in a parachuting accident which gave him that permanent stoop. We call him Bent Fred. Not nice I know, but that's his nickname.'

An hour later they climbed out from RAF Waddington, out of the grey overcast and into a clear layer between the clouds. Matt's father set the course due South and invited Matt to fly. 'You have control,' said his father. 'I have control,' said Matt, repeating the mantra drilled into all pilots and aspiring aviators. 'Just keep it on one eighty for now,' said his father, as he pulled out his pipe and stoked it up. He next pulled out a newspaper and after checking the time on his wristwatch, settled down to read.

Matt had spent some years as an ATC cadet before joining the RAF. He had been a staff cadet at RAF White Waltham for a couple of years. That meant attending each weekend to help with briefing the cadets who had come for 'Air Experience' flights. He helped them into and out of the Chipmunks and when they shut down for refuelling, made coffee for the pilots. The reward for doing this was flying. Usually half-a-hour on Saturday and the same on Sunday. Most of the pilots lived on the same 'Married Patch' and knew each other well. He flew up and down the country on various trips with various pilots getting the odd 'go' now and then. He also used to get to fly quite a bit with his father (night flying included) and by the time he was 'driving' the Anson home from Waddington, he had about 55 hours dual flying time on Chipmunks and Ansons.

His father glanced at his watch again and talked to a ground controller. 'Bring it round to one six zero now,' he said. 'One six zero,' said Matt and commenced a gentle bank to the left. He straightened out on the new course and noted that the cloud was starting to break up beneath them. Below, he could see a railway line and noted that he was flying Southwards, down the righthand side of the track. The Anson landed at Andover in the early afternoon in totally different weather to Lincolnshire. Warm sunshine and woolly white cumulus sat still in the sky, with the windsock hanging at 45 degrees indicating about eight knots of wind. As they touched down he noticed that the runway was grass and that the airfield had a slight hill or hump in the middle of it. Hope there's nothing waiting on the other side of that hump, he thought. There wasn't and they taxied in and shut down.

The drive from Andover to home at Everleigh took about thirty minutes. Matt reflected on how lucky he was to have a father who was able to conduct a training exercise in one of Her Majesty's aircraft which could include collecting an airman at the conclusion of his square bashing and delivering him home. How considerate of the Queen to keep this private flying club going for such eventualities. 'When do you have to report to RAF Catterick?' asked his father as they got in the house. 'A week on Sunday,' said Matt, 'The course starts on the Monday.' 'Hmm, okay,' said his father, 'we'll see what we can do to get you up there in time, no promises mind.'

Chapter 2 – RAF Catterick

It was a good leave period. His brothers came home from boarding school and listened to his tales of 'bravery and initiative' with suitable awe. Matt's stories of being out in the dark with a rifle, guarding the bomb dump all night in case enemy intruders should attempt to blow it up, were met with suitable jaw-dropping gasps of hero worship. In reality, of course, he and the other recruits had expended much more time taking it in turns throughout the night to tend the corporals' wood-fired, hot water boiler. Remember, the corporals insisted, on pain of death or worse, to being woken up in the morning with hot water for shaving and tea. Although it was the truth, it didn't have quite the same ring to it as the bomb dump story - so the bomb dump it was. All too soon leave came to an end and Matt found himself, on a Sunday morning, standing on the concrete apron outside a hanger at RAF Andover. His father climbed into the Anson and Matt followed. Stowing his bag, Matt went 'up front' to the 'office' and sat in the righthand seat. They took off and headed North once more.

In the RAF, aircraft movements were notified to various authorities and agencies by means of 'signals'. These took the form of typed communications which were sent out and received by teleprinter. One copy of an aircraft movement signal, for 'notification only', went to RAF Catterick. This ensured that there would be 'no surprises' when the aircraft landed there. This was standard procedure. The airfield was not a full-time active airfield and was only used to land aircraft 'for the last time': aircraft that the RAF Regiment Fire Service would use for ground training purposes. Matt's father drafted the signal and handed it over to the civilian operator who would send it. RAF Andover was at the time an RAF Staff College and the lowest rank on the station was a Sergeant, who worked in the General Office. The teleprinter operator had never heard of the rank of A.C., the abbreviation for Aircraftsman.

The operator therefore used his initiative. The signal was sent informing RAF Catterick that a certain Air Commodore Jenkins would be arriving by Anson on Sunday afternoon at 14:00. The signal, which was not urgent, arrived at RAF Catterick late on the Friday afternoon - too late, in fact, to make many enquiries as to who this Air Commodore was and why he was being delivered to the station. It was assumed, because the Air Commodore had not spoken to the Station Commander, that the visit was informal and that the dignitary had made his own onwards, transport arrangements. The station was obviously being used merely as a 'staging post'. The Station Commander briefed the Orderly Officer detailed for that weekend who, in turn, had a quiet word with the Station Warrant Officer.

After an uneventful flight North, Matt's father made a let down at RAF Catterick using the RAF Leeming Radar's 'Extended Runway Centerline'. As they crossed the river Swale and the runway threshold, Matt could see that the tarmac was wet. The windsock showed about 20 knots of wind. 'Looks like you've got a welcoming committee,' said Matt's father. Indeed, there was a staff car and a Land Rover waiting at the far end of the runway. The aircraft swung around at the end of the runway ready to taxi back in preparation for the take off. Matt threw out his bag, then jumped out resplendent in his best uniform denoting the (non) rank of an Aircraftman. Holding his hat in his hand Matt gave a 'thumbs up' to his father who nodded then taxied away. A small crowd formed around Matt: a distinguished man in civilian clothes, who Matt later discovered was the Station Commander; a Pilot Officer who, it would seem, was the Orderly Officer; the Station Warrant Officer or SWO; and bringing up the rear, the Orderly Corporal and two Airmen. 'Who on earth are you?' said the SWO. 'A.C. Jenkins, Sir,' gulped Matt. 'Sort him out corporal,' said the SWO. And sorted he got. After all the vehicles had sped off, the Orderly Corporal and escorts looked at each other, then at Matt. 'You can carry your own kit,' said the corporal and so it was that Matt found himself carrying his luggage and running with the escort towards the accommodation a mile or so away.

The transit accommodation housed, amongst others, his three mates from Swinderby who, of course, noticed Matt's arrival. He came to a steaming, panting halt in front of the accommodation block and to the jeers and cheers of the occupants. For them, a boring Sunday afternoon had just been livened up with Matt's arrival. Matt 'fell out' as ordered and walked into the block to find a spare bed space. 'I see you've already made an impression then,' said Bill. 'What on earth have you been up to, and what was all that about?'

Matt knew, he just knew, that he was a marked man. Word was out and life would get more demanding from now on. So much for trying to keep a low profile.

Bill, Luke and Les were almost crying with laughter when they heard the story of Matt's arrival. 'By God, you don't things by halves, do you,' said Luke. 'and do you remember your arrival at Swinderby, trying to sneak onto the coach as if you'd been there all along?' said Les. 'You do better entrances than a Prima Donna,' said Bill. 'In fact, that can be your nickname, we'll just call you 'The Diva' for short.' God, thought Matt. As if things couldn't get any worse, they've nicknamed me the bloody Diva. How will I ever live it down?

The next morning dawned cold and wet. It was November and still dark when they came back from breakfast. A 'permanent staff,' Senior Airman was waiting for them. They were about 25 in all now and followed the Senior to their new accommodation, then to the General Office to collect their blue arrival chits. Arriving on an RAF Station was a pain. They had to go to every department to obtain a signature showing that the person in charge had registered their presence. At Stores there was yet more kit to draw, including the standard working dress of blue shirt with black tie, one-piece

13

overalls, boots, gaiters, web belts and beret. They got changed and went for lunch.

They paraded outside building 159 at 13:30 and were introduced to their directing staff for the duration of the course. There were two corporals, one sergeant and a Flight Lieutenant, the course commander. It all seemed very civilised after square bashing. The course commander had a few words then left. The sergeant told the corporals to carry on but, just before he left, he stopped, faced the course and said, 'So which one of you is Jenkins then?' 'Here, sergeant,' said Matt, gulping. 'Hmm,' said the sergeant, staring. At that he turned on his heel and left. They were marched into a classroom where the rest of the afternoon was taken up with course administration which included instructions and a one-sided discussion of the timetable.

Back in the billet they discussed the events of the day and prepared their kit for the following day.

Matt soon fell into the swing of things and indeed, began to enjoy the course. There were lessons in field craft and map reading, patrolling and stalking. They learnt and practised 'stripping and assembly', along with weapon drills, on the Self Loading Rifle or SLR and the Light Machine Gun or LMG.

The SLR, unlike the .303 Lee Enfield they had trained on at Swinderby, was operated by means of a gas recoil system. The gases were used to drive a short-stroke, spring-loaded piston housed above the barrel. The breech locking mechanism had what was known as a *tilting breech block*. To lock, it dropped down into a solid shoulder of metal. The gas system was fitted with a gas regulator behind the front sight base, allowing adjustment of the gas system in response to environmental conditions, and it could be closed completely by rotating a 'gas plug' one hundred and eighty degrees. This allowed for the firing of 94mm 'Energa' Anti Tank grenades from rifles. The magazine capacity was 20 rounds. The bullets travelled at 2756 feet per second and the effective range was 300 meters using the iron sights.

They learnt how to fire the 94 Energa anti-tank weapon, a rifle grenade launched from the SLR. A blank round filled with Ballistite was used to give the High Explosive Anti Tank, or HEAT, round its ballistic flight.

One day, they went out on to the airfield and erected a bed sheet between poles for a target. They were told that the Energa rounds they would fire that day would be inert and free from explosives. The idea was to get them used to firing the weapon and hopefully, hitting the sheet. The two best shots would get a go at firing the real thing, the HEAT round, when they next went to the ranges. At a cost of £ 100.00 each they were not to be wasted. The weapons range was between 50 and 90 meters, and Matt wondered about the wisdom of leaping out in front of a tank and pointing this peashooter at the aforesaid tank with it's large gun and heavy machine gun aimed at him. True, the Energa would penetrate seven to eight inches of armour - but that was if it hit the thing at 90 degrees. If the round hit at 45 degrees, the penetration would be three to four inches. Given that the armour of the day exceeded this depth many times over, it seemed like a suicide mission. It occurred to Matt that should he ever have to fire this weapon in anger he would not be leaping out in front of 'bleedin' tanks. No, he'd leap out behind them, pull the trigger, then 'Foxtrot Oscar' as fast as he could.

Another of the weapons they had to master was the two inch mortar. Latterly, the name was changed to the 51 mm mortar but it was the same thing. This was a man-portable mortar system used throughout the British Army, for which smoke Illuminating or High Explosive (HE) bombs were available. The HE bombs had a small, ring-pull safety pin on the side of the nose fuse. The fuse remained unarmed until the pin was withdrawn and the bomb was fired. The illuminating rounds, when fired, were a bright magnesium flare suspended beneath a parachute. They turned the night into day for a minute or two and were extremely effective. The smoke bombs were also effective given the right conditions but the best, thought Matt, were the High Explosive rounds. Each contained just over two pounds or 920 grams of high explosive and were deadly when used on hard ground.

Training expanded to cover the Bren Gun. The Bren, they learnt, was a modified version of a Czechoslovak-designed light machine gun, the 26 ZB vz, which the British Army had tested during a competition in the 1930's. The Bren featured a conical flash hider and a quick-change barrel with a gas regulator.

At that time, the Bren was a fully automatic machine gun capable of firing 600-800 rounds a minute. Originally, it fired a 0.303 round using a 'rimmed' cartridge case, but was later modified to fire the standard NATO 7.62mm rimless round. The bullets were fed by means of curved magazines, and each patrol would carry as many of these as they could. The magazines were distributed amongst the section. Each time 10 magazines were fired at 'rapid', the call 'Tenth magazine, change barrels!' was made: the barrel had to be changed due to the heat generated before they could recommence firing.

The Mills 36 Hand Grenade was yet another weapon taught on the basic course. It was a classic design with a grooved, cast iron, pineapple-shaped body. It had a central striker held by a close hand lever and secured with a pin. Although the segmented body helped to create fragments when the grenade exploded, according to the Mills 'notes' the casing was grooved to make it easier to grip and not as an aid to fragmentation. The Mills was a defensive weapon. After throwing it, the user had to take cover immediately. A competent thrower could manage 30 metres (98 feet) with reasonable accuracy, but the grenade could throw lethal fragments further than this. It was normally fitted with a flat base and could be fired with a blank cartridge from the old 303 rifle with a 'cup' attachment, giving it a range of around 150 meters. The grenades could be fitted with two types of fuse, one of which was the seven-second fuse to accommodate both hand and rifle launch. Early in the Battle of France, in 1940, this delay had proved too long: it gave the defenders time to escape the explosion, or even to throw grenades back. So, the fuse timing was reduced to four seconds. As both types of fuse were still in circulation, Matt and his colleagues learnt that the four-second fuses had a band around the fuse itself, whilst the seven-second fuse did not. It was an important point because the fuse timing often had to be checked, by feel, in the pitch dark.

Range firing was part of the training and when all had passed their weapon proficiency tests, they fired at the 600 yard gallery ranges of Deerpark and Whipperdale. As they became more proficient, their confidence grew. They threw live grenades at the grenade range and watched as the two Energa Anti Tank HEAT rounds were fired at the range designated as Catterick 6E.

A little more mundane perhaps, but equally as important, was the use of spades and pickaxes. They were taught how to dig different types of weapon trenches and how to protect themselves from fire and overhead debris. Gradually, it all started coming together and exercise followed exercise. The one most people enjoyed was the night time 'Lamp snatch'. Each man had to crawl up to the lamp, in the dark, and leave their name underneath it without being seen or caught. Of course, everyone *was* caught but that didn't detract from the fun. At this stage of the course, it was getting quite cold and snow was appearing as light dustings on the ground.

One cold morning they were marched to the armoury and issued with two Bren guns each. There were 20 of them and as they 'fell in' outside the armoury, Matt hoped that the corporal marching them would not try and take chances with patches of ice laying around: they were carrying a lot of weight. They approached the hanger and whilst marching, tried to keep their feet on the ice. They couldn't use their arms to balance, they were full of Bren guns. The command came to 'HALT' and 20 pairs of hobnailed boots flailed and back-peddled as the men fought to keep their balance. The air turned blue as every man hit the freezing cold, unforgiving, iron hard ice whilst tangling intimately around and through his Bren gun. They crawled to the edge of the ice and cursed as they inspected the deep scratches on the bulled shine of their boots – they would take hours to re-polish. Gingerly, they felt their bruises. There were two who had broken their wrists and had to report sick, while the rest of them nursed only anger as they cursed the corporals and pushed on towards the nice warm hanger.

It was about halfway through the course, in September, when it became Matt's turn to be interviewed by the Course Commander, Flight Lieutenant Willoghby. Matt marched in and stood to attention in front of the desk. The course commander told him to stand at ease, then easy, so Matt stood in a relaxed posture, feet apart and with his hands behind his back. Glancing at the slim pile of documents in front of him, the course commander noted that Matt was doing well on the course. Indeed he was above average. He asked Matt if there were any problems that he might wish to air and on the whole, there weren't. Apart from one small thing. When could he leave and start his trade training for Air Radar Technician? 'What on earth are you talking about?' said the Flight Commander. Matt explained that when he joined up he wanted the trade of Air Radar. Indeed, he'd passed the tests. He was told at the recruiting office that the course wouldn't start until the December but that if, in the meantime, Matt signed up to join the RAF Regiment, once in, he would be able to 'change his trade' and join the Air Radar course when it started. The course commander went red in the face and explained to Matt that this wasn't going to happen. He had joined the Regiment and there he would stay. Matt had two options, he was told. One, he could try and buck the system and lose or, he could use the system, keep his nose clean, apply himself and get promotion, more money etcetera. Matt's heart sunk. The interview was over and Matt was marched out. He felt angry, resentful and let down by the 'Brass necked con' that had been perpetrated. He became quiet and withdrawn. The course commander must have had a word with the course directing staff because, a few days later, one of the corporals singled him out for a run around the airfield. Halfway round, they broke into a walk and chatted about what had happened to Matt. No, life wasn't always fair, it was agreed and Matt was gently told to to 'put up with it and get on with enjoying life now'. He had signed on for five years, and a quarter of the first year had passed already. Matt agreed and over the next few days came to realise that what had been said made sense. He was grateful for the empathy shown to him by a fully fledged RAF Regiment Corporal no less. Can't all be bad, he thought, he's got my vote and so it was that he learnt his first lesson in leadership.

A few days later, when the course had finished for the day and their kit was ready for the morning, the lads were sitting around idly chatting. Bill told them about a group of chaps he had heard of who were on a different course. They were, so the rumour went, dabbling with life after death or the occult. They got together regularly and contacted the dead through an Ouiju board.

And so it was, a few nights later, that Matt found himself up in the roof space above one of the rooms in the block opposite. Half a dozen or so people had gathered below. He could hear them quite plainly and he grinned in anticipation whilst rubbing his hands against the cold. It went quiet and then a whisper from below, 'Is there anybody there?' Matt waited. 'Is there anybody there?' came the whispered question again. Matt leant forward to knock on the ceiling. Then he slipped. 'Ahhhhh,' he yelled. From below came screeches of surprise and fear at the scream from above. His hand on the ceiling, Matt was now carrying most of his weight and as it gave way, he yelled again, 'Ahhhh'. A large lump of plaster and years of accumulated dirt fell away and hit the Ouiju board below with a crash. The plaster split into a thousand pieces and its dust billowed into the room. Matt saved himself, just, and peered through the hole. At the same time as he looked down, the unfortunates below looked up at the hole in the ceiling. Matt's face was so black that all they could see were two white eyes, wide with fear, peering out of the darkness above. They'd had enough. 'Ahhhh,' they screeched, even louder this time, as they ran and disappeared through the door. Matt finally lost his balance and fell through. The table broke his fall but it was still a tremendous crash. The mess was incredible. There was plaster and black dust everywhere. Matt was up and out of there in a flash. Limping, he hobbled away at top speed. Down the stairs, out through the main doors and across the road to his own block. His mates were waiting. 'Quick, into the shower and get cleaned up,' said Luke. 'We'll sort out your clothes,' said Bill. Five minutes later, the Orderly Sergeant arrived, along with the guard, and disappeared inside the block. Matt was soon out of the shower and into a track suit. He and the rest of the billet peered out of the windows, politely enquiring as to the cause of the disturbance opposite. Soon the Sergeant came out and it was obvious that he'd caught some very dirty and dusty looking Airmen in the block. They stood on the road as, with a look of thunder, he proceeded to rant and rave at the hapless perpetrators of the barrack room damage. 'If he carries on like that, they're gonna think the roof's fallen in on them,' said one of the onlookers. The victims were doubled away by the guard while the Sergeant made his way across to their block. He came into their room and looked around at a scene of innocent domesticity. Each man was sitting quietly on their beds or in some cases whistling tunelessly, as they bulled their boots, darned socks or just read. 'NCO present,' yelled the senior man as they jumped to the position of 'Attention'. 'Stand at ease, stand easy,' said the Sergeant. 'Does anybody here know what's been going on across the road tonight?' asked the sergeant. 'We heard some crashing noises like furniture being broken,' volunteered one of the men, 'but we kept out of it.' 'Hmm,' said the sergeant. 'Carry on,' and he turned on his heel and left. 'What was that all about?' said one of the lads. 'Dunno,' said Matt turning down his bed. 'Anyone got any indecent reading material?'

The pace of training quickened and exercises on the Gandale and Feldom training areas became more frequent. Ambushes in the 'Land of Nod' quarry and night exercises in 'Lamp snatch wood' became commonplace. Autumn turned into winter and snow fell deep and cold onto the training areas. The final exercise was held on the moor top, where the course spent the night in freezing cold trenches. The dawn attack which signified the end of the exercise was late, but soon they packed up their kit, filled in their trenches and made their way to the waiting transport.

Matt was at the rear carrying the Bren gun when, all of a sudden, he lost his footing and slipped. Down he went, into a deep ditch, and disappeared under a covering of snow. He floundered, crawled and dragged himself back up the sides of the ditch along with the heavy gun. The patrol had by now stopped and alerted by the curious muffled noises coming from the rear, watched with interest. Spitting snow and resembling a snowman, Matt emerged covered in a thick layer of white. 'What do you call a Yeti with a gun?' Bill shouted. 'Sir,' shouted Luke and the patrol collapsed with laughter. 'Come on Jenkins,' shouted the corporal, 'Stop playing the bloody fool and get on the truck.' To say he was cold was an understatement - the snow had found its way into places he never knew he had!

A few days later, the course sat their final written and practical tests. Matt and his mates all passed and were told to clear the station and be ready to move the next day. They were promoted to the dizzy heights of 'Leading Aircraftman' and posted to RAF St Athens, in Wales, for a driving course. 'Where the hell's Wales?'

remarked Luke, as they collected signatures on their blue 'Clearance' forms. 'Dunno,' said someone. 'Somewhere down past Crewe' offered Matt? 'Whatever, let's just get cleared and on our way. The transport leaves for Darlington station in an hour and we still need to finish packing and hand in our bedding.'

Chapter 3 - St. Athens

The train journey was long, overnight, uncomfortable, tedious and unpleasant. They had to change trains at Crewe (wherever that was) and after they got off they discovered that the wait for the connection would be an hour. The connecting train was, of course, leaving from a different platform and so, at two in the morning, they carried their heavy cases over the footbridge. It was cold and raining and the station shone bleakly in the wet glare of the sodium lights. It was almost Christmas but they still had to report to their new unit before going on leave, if they were going to be granted leave. At 03:00 their train pulled in and they gratefully climbed into a warm, dry carriage dragging their cases with them. The train was empty. Hooray for small mercies they said as they thankfully claimed a seat each. They awoke to the sight of sodden grey countryside slipping past in the cold wet dawn. Soon they were in a built-up area and the train stopped. 'Cardiff, this is Cardiff,' announced the station tannoy. 'Passengers wishing to travel to Barry must change here.' 'That's us,' said Bill. Cursing, they got off and dragging their baggage along the platform once more, they enquired as to the correct platform for the train to Barry. Of course, it was over the footbridge! And the train was waiting, about to leave. All thoughts of sleep were now gone as, red-faced and panting, they raced for the train and caught it ... just. At Barry there was a bus to catch and eventually, four very tired and travel worn airmen got off outside the Guardroom of RAF St Athen.

Having reported and signed in, they were shown to the transit accommodation. As it was only eight in the morning, the bedding store was not yet open. 09:00 said the sign and so, after following a crowd of people all heading in the same direction, they found themselves in the breakfast queue at the airmen's mess. 'Cor, would you get a load of that,' said Bill, 'they've got WAAFs here.' 'I've just died,' pronounced Luke. Matt could only stare. At that stage in their lives, females were as rare as 'Rocking Horse Droppings' and females in uniform even rarer. It didn't matter that some of them must have been attested because of their ugliness or that a good few were ill-proportioned. Here were pheronome transmitters and the boys' receivers were receiving, loud and clear. They had been starved and now could not believe their luck. Yes, thought Matt as he mentally punched the air.

The boys didn't know it but they were the 'Lambs being led to the Slaughter'. The girls who seemed to be coyly eyeing up the new boys were, in reality, working out the order in which they were going to 'Think of England'. Provided, of course, the boys promised to make the supreme sacrifice and get engaged first. This was one of the unwritten rules in the sixties and no-one would be allowed to break it.

After breakfast they reported to the 'General Office' where they were given their blue 'Arrival' forms. This took all day, as the camp was vast. There were two camps really. They were named West camp and East camp. They were connected by a regular RAF bus service. They collected their course information from the general office once the arrival procedures had been completed and made their weary way back to the transit accommodation. Tea and an early night beckoned. The next morning they were given leave passes and sent home until after Christmas. The course would start in January and there was nothing to do until then. Back on the bus and back to Barry train station they went. It seemed like only yesterday since they were last there.

It had been a good Christmas for them all. Matt had driven back from his home in Everleigh, Wiltshire to St Athen on his motorbike. The journey took 10 hours. He had to travel via Gloucester as there were no road bridges in those days. When he went home for a weekend, if he was 'with funds', he would go via Chepstow and catch the train that went through the tunnel under the river Severn.

The bike and Matt would travel in the guards van and the cost was seven shillings and eleven pence. Arriving at Bristol, he would set off and get home within four hours. Sometimes, it was so cold that Matt couldn't use the bike and had to thumb a lift; that could take anything from 10 hours upwards.

Most were excited to get back from leave and start the driving course. Those that were there met in the NAAFI club that evening and compared notes. They had moved by now from the transit accommodation to the more permanent, course accommodation. The course started and on their first day, they filled out their applications for provisional licences. Matt didn't need to as he already had one. The course would consist of 90 hours of theory before being allowed to get into a vehicle. The theory consisted of the Highway Code and mechanics. They learnt about engines, transmission, brakes, steering and suspension. There was a test at the end which they had to pass before they could get onto the driving part. Eventually, after nearly three weeks, the great day arrived. They met their instructors and clambered into the passenger seat of a truck. They were taken out to the 'nursery' area; a vast expanse of aircraft pan or parking area which could have swallowed up Wembley stadium and then some. Parked in one corner out of the way, whilst awaiting work, were a couple of Vickers Valliant 'V' bombers. After an explanation as to what was required, Matt got into the driving seat of the truck. It seemed very big and unwieldy at first but he soon got the hang of the gears. Next, it was in and out of the cones then, all to soon, it was late afternoon and time to finish for the day. The instructors drove the trucks back to the driving school and parked up. Matt and company were dismissed until the morning. That evening, in the NAAFI club, they compared notes. A largish group had formed consisting of the current course members and Matt found himself sitting next to a girl. She introduced herself as Pauline. 'My initials are PLJ which stands for Pauline Linda Jones, and that means you have to squeeze me, because I'm a lemon.' Her Welsh voice carried the lilt from the valleys but he didn't care. His receiver was receiving overtime and as he got up to play the latest tune on the jukebox, he put out his hand and said, 'Come on then, if you want squeezing we'll have to put some music on to squeeze to.' 'What do you fancy?' 'Unit 2 plus 4,' she said. 'Concrete and Clay.'

The next morning followed much the usual pattern but they were taught to carry out 'Daily Inspections' before moving out. They arrived at the nursery area and for the first half hour did the same work as the previous day. Then came reversing. The way to do this was demonstrated by the instructor. You hung out of the cab, with your right hand holding the open door for support, whilst you looked behind you. Your left hand was kept on the wheel to steer. You let the vehicle tick over and slowly reversed. To stop you only had to depress the clutch then the foot-brake, sit upright, close the door and apply the hand-brake. You could then select neutral and relax. Matt had no problems with the technique. He had just stopped when he noticed his instructor looking the other way. He switched the engine off and jumped out. As he followed the instructor's incredulous gaze, he saw a three-ton truck at the far corner of the pan reversing slowly - by itself. The instructor was helping a girl up: obviously, she had just fallen out of the cab whilst reversing. The rear of the truck hit the wing of the V bomber and kept going. The damage was later estimated at millions of pounds. No blame was attached to 'PLJ' - for it was she who fell out of the cab - but an interview 'without tea and biscuits' was a certainty for the instructor. She was simply too small to carry out the manoeuvre as demanded. That night she and Matt had a long squeeze as consolation for falling out of the truck and egged on by the rest of the course, re-enacted the events of the day once more.

The days passed and their proficiency grew. They now drove into Barry amongst the traffic and practised hill starts and turns in the wide back streets. The big day came when they had to take their driving test. They all passed and graduated from three-ton trucks to Land Rovers. Barry was now left behind as they progressed to Cardiff. They drove around Cardiff in the rush-hour traffic and after a couple of weeks, took another driving test. Matt passed, as did most of the course. The course now stepped up a gear and they started night driving and convoy driving. They covered most of South Wales during the day and night until, one day, the course was finished.

The WAAFs on the course were posted off to their new units. Tearful goodbyes and promises of faithfulness were given in the full knowledge that things would be different next week, whilst the erstwhile RAF Regiment lads were sent to wait on the 'Holding Flight' until their postings came through. There was not much doing at the holding flight. Their numbers varied but, on any given day, there were about half a dozen or so waiting around to be given jobs. They were farmed out as and where necessary. A Flight Sergeant ran the holding flight and as long as his mug of tea was kept full, he was okay. One day, Matt had to report to the driving school. They needed a driver to run some equipment over to the West Camp. He duly reported and set off. On arrival at the West Camp Stores, he was met by a WAAF. She had blond hair, blue eyes and great big knockers. They got chatting and he found out that her name was Gloria. She came from Birmingham or Brum as it was known. They arranged to meet in the Red Lion in the village that night. She was definitely not backwards at coming forwards Matt decided and on the way home, PLJ became a distant memory. A week went by and Matt and Gloria applied for leave passes. She had a flat in Brum and they were going for a long weekend after work on the Friday. Not due back until Tuesday, Matt tingled in anticipation.

Friday morning saw Matt and his mates 'bumpering' the lino floor at the holding flight. The phone rang. It was answered by the corporal who said 'Yes, sir,' and passed it on to the flight sergeant as if it were a hot potato. A minute or two later the phone was replaced in the holder. 'Jenkins!' yelled the flight sergeant. 'Flight!' replied Matt. 'Get yourself in here now,' shouted the corporal, not wishing to miss the fun. 'You are to go back to your billet, pack up your full RAF kit into your RAF holdall and bring it back here,' said the flight sergeant. 'Yes, flight,' said Matt, 'but could I ask why?' 'Yes,' said the flight sergeant, 'You're going to have a full kit inspection.' This was odd in the extreme. A full kit inspection and over here as well: it was normally laid out on the bed. A puzzled Matt made his way back to his billet and packed his kit. He returned 20 minutes later and the rest of the lads helped him lay out his kit on the highly polished floor. The flight sergeant inspected Matt's kit and sent him off to stores to buy a new 'collar unattached'. Seven shillings and sixpence was deducted from Matt's clothing allowance before the flight sergeant was satisfied. 'Okay, pack it up and come into my office,' said the flight sergeant.

Matt was detailed to be over at the West Camp, at the Visiting Aircraft Section, at 14:00. 'Don't be late,' said the corporal. 'You are going to be met by an 'owficer' and before you ask, no, we don't know his name.' This was all a great mystery to Matt, who wandered what the hell was going on. There wasn't even time to get hold of Gloria and tell her he'd be late. He climbed on to the bus dressed in his 'Best Blues', carrying his RAF kit in his RAF holdall. At the Visiting Aircraft Section the penny began to drop and sure enough, at 14:00, an Anson landed and taxied up. He removed his hat. It was normal practice in the RAF to take your hat off when near to aeroplanes with engines running. If you didn't, it could get sucked up by an engine and cause thousands of pounds worth of damage. His father opened the door and seeing Matt said 'Hello, don't you salute an officer when you see one?' Matt gulped and replaced his hat. He threw up a snappy salute and red faced, climbed aboard. There were two other passengers on the aircraft so

Matt took an empty seat near the front of the cabin. Matt's father climbed into the pilot's seat. The navigator was already in the right-hand seat. They started up, taxied round to the runway and took off. Matt's despair knew no bounds. His father had arrived to take him home for the weekend as a surprise. He had obviously 'phoned the holding flight with the intention of letting Matt know. The flight sergeant, not knowing who he was talking to and being 'old school to boot', wasn't going to let one of his men be seen by an officer unless he was ready for inspection - in all respects. That explained the events of the past few hours but no explanation was going to be good enough for Gloria who, it would transpire, was about to be stood up, spectacularly. It's a good job I couldn't get hold of her, he thought. 'I'm going to be late' would sound a bit lame by this evening. Of course he was grateful that he had been collected and taken home for the weekend but, at eighteen, this just wasn't the same as being up to the armpits in a buxom blond called Gloria.

Matt's brothers were home from boarding school. His father's girlfriend was there as well. Thank God he had some civilian clothes at home. Matt had to make a bed pack with his blanket and sheets and lay out his kit each morning to demonstrate to his brothers 'the neatness of service life'. I get enough bullshit back at camp, Matt thought, without it happening at home. He was starting to discover that having an officer for a father had its drawbacks. He didn't mind to much though. The bullshit was as nothing compared to his agonies as he lay in bed listening to his father and the girlfriend giving it 'root-te-toot' in the other room. He fell asleep thinking of Gloria and England. On the Monday, he was flown back by another pilot conducting a 'navigation exercise'. On arrival he said his goodbyes and 'thank you's and caught the transport back to the East Camp. He reported to the holding flight, only to be told to report to the general office. The postings had come through. They were posted to RAF Innsworth in Gloucester, and needed to get around RAF St Athens as soon as possible with their blue clearance forms. They didn't know it yet but they were heading for another holding flight.

Chapter 4 – To the Far East

It was a sunny day as the train chugged along towards London. It was May 1965, and they were travelling from Gloucester to London at the start of a big adventure. There were four in their compartment and in a state of high excitement they played cards, chatted and watched the countryside roll past. It was the start of their big trip, first to Singapore and then to Penang in Malaysia. The culmination of months of training.

'All right you lot, shut up and listen in.' Matt, Luke, Bill and Les shut up and gave the Demi-God their undivided attention. They were in the RAF Innsworth orderly room receiving their final instructions and travel documents. Surprisingly for them, they were dressed in civilian clothes for the first time in months. They had had to wait for two dreary, wet and cold months for this moment. Briefing over, haircuts inspected and baggage weighed they climbed onto the back of one of the most uncomfortable forms of transport known to man; the three-ton truck that was waiting to take them to the railway station. Goodbye Innsworth, hooray.

With nothing to do for the last two months, they had been made to undergo enforced occupational therapy. This took many forms of torture, like painting huge piles of coal white. This was done because it was easy to see when coal was nicked and during the inevitable search, it was easy to spot the culprits. Their pot-bellied stove burnt like billy-oh. It was so hot they had to sit away from it most of the time. Needless to say, they had some black paint to hand just in case they hadn't been able to burn the white stuff before room inspections. On occasions they painted kerb stones white and as a reward for being good boys, were detailed to paint or mark out the parking spaces in the car park or work on the dustcart emptying the bins around the Married Quarters.

One of the low points of their lives was being detailed for Fire

Piquet duties. Scattered around the Station were Fire Hydrants. When called out, the four men propelled a red painted wooden cart with large spindly wheels, rather in the manner of a Rickshaw, but with Bill and Les at the front 'T' bar. A large transverse box at the back housed a standpipe, a 'T' piece or turnkey and the hoses. The idea was that, in the case of a fire being reported, the team directed by a Demi-God, galloped to the scene of the reported fire, fitted the standpipe and hoses to the hydrant and fought the fire. The reality was that the Piquet arrived at the scene only to discover they'd run out of hose, forgotten the turnkey or needed to move the whole 'spaghetti nest' to the next hydrant. The Fire Piquet duty lasted for 24 hours and as it was deemed a sleeping duty, no time off was given in lieu, no matter how many times they were called out. Particular Orderly Officers used to take a sadistic delight by practising the Fire Piquet and calling it out to the hydrant furthest from the Guardroom - at about two or three in the morning. It seemed that this sadistic pleasure was reserved for the four lads so they swore that, one day, they would get even.

There was no regret in leaving the holding camp which had looked after their welfare and kept them occupied for so long. There was no regret in getting out of the three-ton truck that took them to the station and no regret in exchanging their green travel forms at the ticket office for return tickets to London. Wait a minute, return tickets? They were only valid for three months and they were going away for two-and-a-half years. Demi-God had got them once again. They would have to pay for their tickets when their tour ended. 'Ah well, c'est la vie, let's get on the train chaps,' said Luke. So they did and though it seemed to take forever, eventually they steamed into London.

Assembling at a bus stop, they kidded each other that they knew where they were and which bus to catch. They had to report to the British Eagle Air Trooping office in Knightsbridge and of course, no-one had a clue how to get there - so they used their, so far, suppressed initiative and found a pub. Using their initiative had not been encouraged by the Demi-Gods during their short careers thus far, so they discussed whether they should risk using it again. Should they hail a cab or ask a policeman? The cab won and took them straight to the British Eagle office. Having presented themselves and their travel documents, they were ushered straight on to a coach taking them to Heathrow and their first flight on a Bristol Brittania.

In 1952, the Bristol Britannia prototype suffered from undercarriage problems and on more than one occasion, narrowly avoided disaster while landing. On another occasion, in 1954, the test pilot, Bill Pegg, suffered an engine fire on number 3 while flying the second prototype. The problem was caused by the failure of the reduction gearing to the propeller, which permitted the compressor turbine to over-speed and disintegrate. The test pilot successfully landed the aircraft, with the wheels and flaps up, on the mud between Avonmouth and Sharpness.

After delivery to BOAC, the aircraft continued to be plagued by problems with its Proteus turbines.

In 1957, a Britannia was lost when it dived into a wood near Bristol. The pilot and test crew of 14 were killed. Shortly afterwards another pilot, Godfrey Auty, was involved in another incident which very nearly claimed more lives at Brownsville, Texas. The fault was isolated to the autopilot which was disconnected. Redesign followed, which cured that particular problem.

All the lads had ever seen regarding the Britannia were the Pathe newsreels of the 'Whispering Giant', showing how quiet and vibration free it was. It was claimed you could stand a threepenny bit on its edge without it falling over, such was the steadiness of the aircraft. So, the lads were blissfully unaware of the aircraft's chequered past as they eagerly climbed aboard to surrender their lives, virginity or anything else required, to the tender bosoms of the nubile, gorgeous, young girls who made up the cabin crew. They took off into the late afternoon setting sun, lovestruck, en route to Istanbul and the far East.

Women and children sat at the rear of the aircraft, whilst serving 'singlies' were up near the front. It was quieter up front because the children's screams and crying could not be heard against the engine noise. A meal was served, hot and quite tasty compared with the British Rail sandwich some hours before. A short doze followed, before being woken up to be told they would be landing shortly in Istanbul. They would be on the ground for between four and six hours and would be escorted into town to have a look around and stretch their legs. It never dawned on them that something might require fixing on their aircraft and so they filed off, innocent and excited, to see the sights. They visited a bazaar realising, on later reflection, that it must have been the renowned Grand Bazaar. They walked around for an hour amazed at the sights and smells. There were goods on display and there was the wafting of strong Turkish cigarettes and coffee. The richness and opulence of it all was almost too much to take in. Years later, Matt visited a Souk and discovered that whilst there was a similarity between the two, the Turkish Bazaar was by far the most spectacular. They returned to their coach. They had been on the ground for about four hours and it was time to return to the aircraft.

They took off once more and headed out towards Bombay. As the aircraft droned on through the night, they quietened down. Card games were abandoned, books fell to the floor. Cigarettes were extinguished as, one by one, they fell into that shadow world of being half asleep and half awake. Matt could not sleep at first and would never cease, thereafter, to be amazed at the sights he saw outside the aircraft window. They were flying at about 19,000 to 20,000 feet and he could see the sky being lit up by lightning as they flew above the cloud tops. Sometimes they flew around the tops and he saw the most spectacular sights as the clouds were illuminated from the inside. There was no noise of thunder, just the incessant droning of those four Proteus turbines as they turned that reduction gearing that caused the propellers to go round. Matt must have slept eventually because he was woken by an announcement that they would be landing shortly in Bombay. Wow, were there no borders to their adventure? Where the hell was Istanbul in Turkey, anyway? As for Bombay, the group agreed they had seen it on the school atlas, albeit some time ago. It was a smooth landing, for which they gave the captain eight-out-of-ten, then the doors were opened......MY GOD!.....The heat came in and hit them as if they had climbed into an oven. Instantly they were drenched in sweat and found it difficult to breath. Nothing could describe how they felt when the heat hit them as they moved from air-conditioning at English temperatures to no air-conditioning at Bombay temperatures. They were given chits to exchange for drinks in the airport terminal and disembarked. The walk across the concrete apron sucked every little bit of moisture from their bodies. They could see whirling fans in the airport building which beckoned to them as they arrived in a molten lather. The fans gave the illusion of cooling by stirring around the hot air. A choice of drinks consisted of water or bottled orange. Matt chose the orange drink. Who, he thought, in their right mind would pay for water? Big mistake. The orange was too fizzy, extremely sweet and hot. The bottle was sticky and dirty but the walk from the aircraft ensured that the drink was necessary. There was no choice. He belched from the gasses in the bottle as he took the sugar overload, and felt sick. If he could only keep it down, he would be ahead. About an hour later, and soaked in sweat, they re-boarded the Britannia once more and took off. As the aircraft climbed out they succumbed, once more and thankfully, to the air-conditioning and gradually, they dried out. The wiser folks in the rear of the aircraft formed a queue for the lavatories whilst the lads stayed where they were. They might have been smelly but they were cool. Goodbye Bombay and good riddance .

After Bombay came the hours of tedium. Some of the hours passed in sleep and some in other pursuits. Matt even went down to the rear of the aircraft with the intention of chatting up the hostesses. They provided Matt with a beer and smilingly, sent him back. He didn't care. It didn't matter. He'd spoken to them and he was in lust once more. The hours droned on as over the Indian ocean they flew. Eventually they made landfall, just as the sun was setting for the second time and lost height as they flew over Jahore Baru and came into land at Singapore. The total flying time was 19¾ hours. They had cramp and were shattered. God knows what the aircrew felt like and they were flying the thing, thought Matt. Thank God they want to live as much as me. The doors opened and the Singapore evening air flooded in.

It was hot, *and* humid unlike Bombay. But it also stank. There was this smell pervading everything, it was a cloying sickly smell that Matt learnt later was the odious stench of the Durian fruit. They had landed at RAF Changi which housed the RAF Transport Squadron, the New Zealand Transport squadron, a maintenance unit and a parachute training school. The airfield was vast. They completed their formalities and were ushered onto an RAF white coach. Typically, the last passengers boarded half-an-hour later, while Matt and the others endured the claustrophobic wait before they set off. Five minutes later they stopped and were ushered into a mess-style restaurant. The last thing they wanted was more food so they waited around outside in the relative cool, and smoked. Eventually, they were told to get into a minibus and were driven to the Transit accommodation.

They stopped outside and their escorting airman, the driver, told them to report to him at the general office at 08:30 the following morning. 'Bring all your documentation including 'Pay books',' he said. He pointed out the general office, the Malcom club, the mess and the swimming pool. 'You'll be here for about three or four days then you'll be going 'up country' to Butterworth.' 'Apart from the morning where we have to clear up a few formalities, the rest of the time will be yours for acclimatisation.' 'Accommodation, first floor,' he said and drove off. They carried their luggage inside and up a flight of concrete stairs. There was only one room with beds in it and for once, the bedding was on the bed. It consisted of two sheets, one pillow and one pillow case. They dropped their gear and having unpacked their towels headed for the showers. One cool shower later they crawled into bed and slept the sleep of the just. To say that they needed no rocking was an understatement. Sleep came instantly but then, so did the morning.

Chapter 5 – Changi

The first thing Matt noticed in the morning were the huge windows. The sunshine was streaming in. The windows were just large holes in the walls, with no glass or window frames. There were storm shutters and Matt guessed that it might rain a lot here. Feeling surprisingly light-headed, Matt grabbed a towel and headed for the shower. After a cool shower and a shave, Matt walked back into the room brushing his teeth. He stopped dead. His bed was made and a dark gentleman was sitting on the floor making magic circles on his shoes. 'Who are you?' asked Matt. 'I'm the bearer and my name's Freddy,' said Freddy. 'You each pay me two dollars a day and I look after you. Any laundry, any errands, anything,' said Freddy. 'What nationality are you?' asked Matt. 'I am Tamil, Singaporean Tamil.' 'Uh, okay, er, thanks and yes, er, yes,' said Matt, who was by now quite lost for words. Freddy collected up the shoes and left the room. The other lads now woke up and sleepily grabbing their towels, headed for the wash rooms. Freddy came back in and made the beds. He then placed the shoes by each bed and waited for the lads to return. They each fell for his well-rehearsed bit of 'fait accompli' and agreed to let him be their bearer while they were in transit. Breakfast was called and as they made their way to the mess, they realised just how hot it had become out in the sunshine. By the time they got to the mess they were soaking with their own sweat. Their shirts had dark patches. Being conscious of their white colour, they joined the breakfast queue of night-shift workers who had just finished and shuffled up to the servery. 'Just got 'ere then,' said the cook as he ladled the beans onto their plates. 'Just 'elp yourselves to the fried bread. Eggs are over there.' 'Thanks,' said Matt and as they went over to the egg counter, he looked at his watch. It said 12:30. Sod it, thought Matt. Still on UK time. 'What time is it?' asked Matt. 'Six thirty,' came the reply. Bloody 'ell thought Matt, this must be what 'Jet Lag' is all about. They sat down with their plates at a table which was almost directly under one of the revolving fans. The cool air felt wonderful on them as they started to eat. 'Pass that red sauce over,' asked Matt. Luke passed the sauce. 'Don't look like tomato to me,' said Bill. Matt shook it liberally over his eggs and then shoved them into his mouth with relish. As he swallowed, he knew he'd made a big mistake. It was chilli sauce. Choking violently, he sprinted for the cold drinks counter. It took two large mugs of iced 'jungle juice' to restore calm to his mouth and throat. Matt returned to his table. Bill and Luke were laughing fit to bust. Indeed it would be more accurate to say that they were crying. 'Okay, okay,' said Matt, 'anyone can make a mistake.'

After breakfast they had a couple of hours to spare before reporting to the general office, so they decided to find out where things were on the domestic side of RAF Changi. They walked past the Malcom club with the netball courts outside and up towards the swimming pool. On the way back, birds flew amongst the palm trees and sprinklers watered the grass. People started going about their daily tasks and it was like walking through one gigantic park or garden that was just waking up.

At 08:30 they went across to the general office where they met their escort from last night. He gave them a brief and took their pay books and passports. 'You have to collect paperwork from here before you fly up to Butterworth in three days. You'll get these back then.' 'Report here at twelve hundred, you'll be transported over to the airfield and to a Bristol Freighter flown by the Kiwis. Wear civvies on camp till then but report with all bags packed ready to fly, in uniform.'

'Oh, and just before you go, I need to warn you that we have a professional con man or thief hanging around the transit block. He calls himself Freddy. He offers to be your bearer for the duration of your stay, to make your beds and clean your shoes. Trouble is, he also helps himself to any of your valuables not nailed down. That's the reason I've taken your passports and pay books. I'll lock them in the safe until you fly.'

'But he's there now,' said Luke. 'Yes I know,' said the escort. 'We took the view that if he stayed there, he couldn't be causing harm somewhere else. So we warn everybody to make sure he can't do any damage. Remember, when you take your watch off to wash, put it in your pocket. Don't leave money lying around. Go out tonight and buy a money belt and use it, even in bed. Follow a few simple rules and be aware. Let's keep him where he is because he's been here a few years and he's too smart to be caught.'

'One last thing.' 'Don't get caught out with sunburn. Stay in the shade. Twenty minutes in direct sunlight without sun cream and you will get badly burned. You will also be charged with 'Self inflicted injury' when you've recovered enough to be charged, that is. Don't forget, especially at the pool.'

'Right, that's enough from me,' said their escort. 'I'm off this afternoon so I'll see you on Friday at twelve.'

And there they were. Three days off with nothing to do, in a strange new country, with everything so different from home. 'Let's go and have a look at the Mallie,' said Matt, 'and see if there's any crumpet about.' Red faced and sweating in the heat, they made their way back to the Malcom club. They found a shaded table on the veranda and sat down. Bill was delegated to get the cold drinks, so they sat listless in the shade and waited. As they waited Matt checked the time. He had set his watch in the general office. It showed 10:00. As he looked around for Bill, he noticed a group of women walking through the club and out onto the courts. It seemed as if they were trying to out-do each other in the shorts and tops stakes or rather, lack thereof. They were confronted with two teams of very scantily clad, beautifully-shaped women who proceeded to play netball with a gusto. Bill came back and nearly tripped. He wasn't watching his feet, in fact they were the last thing on his mind. The drinks were placed on the table as Bill slid into his seat without taking his eyes off the proceedings going on a few feet away. It was as if they had arrived at the gates of heaven. 'I think I like Changi,' said Luke. "Hear, hear,' said the others as they drank in the shade of the veranda. The Mallie was getting full by this time. It was 'NAAFI' break and the Mallie was a popular spot. The other tables soon filled up, with the veranda tables proving to be the most popular. At 10:30, the people on break drifted back to work and the club emptied. The girls finished their netball and came inside for a cool drink. Once again, the veranda proved popular. The boys sat entranced, pretending not to look at the perspiring women as they chatted and drank. They had never seen so many hot women trying to cool off like this. The break crowd had left and the place was pretty deserted. The netball players were lifting up their tops trying to get the cooling air to evaporate the sweat. There were flashes of boobs, and giggles all over the place. The problem the boys had was that they needed to sit there feigning conversation until the girls had finished and left. They didn't dare get up out of their seats until all excitement had subsided. Too many 'Sweaty Bettys' for one day they decided. 'I know,' said Matt. 'Let's go down to the pool and cool off.'

The pool was brilliant. Plenty of shade, with the water being just cool enough to be refreshing. There was a bar which also did snacks. 'It's the best holiday venue I've ever been to,' said Matt, 'and it's free.' They laid their towels down in the shade and hit the pool. The lifeguard came up to them after a while and asked them if they had just arrived. He gave them some sunscreen and sent Bill down to the Sick Quarters to get some more. It was free but limited to one tube each at a time. Luke and Matt waited in the shade for Bill to get back and idly chatted while they kept a look out for crumpet. Bill soon arrived with the sunscreen, which they applied liberally. Even with their bravado, they realised that severe sunburn was a very real danger for the new arrivals. Lunchtime came and went and soon the pool began to fill up. Everyone worked from seven in the morning until one in the afternoon. They all worked for six days a week, but the hours worked were a great way of avoiding the worst of the heat. Especially if you took the family to the pool in the afternoon. Soon the water was crowded with children enjoying themselves. It was getting noisy. 'Let's go back to the transit block and grab a few 'zeds' before tonight,' said Luke. 'Yeh, good idea,' said Matt, so they gathered up their meagre possessions and set off through the heat of the afternoon towards their billet. The fans were off and the air was stifling when they arrived back. They soon worked out the controls and got the cooling air circulating. They lay down in their underpants and thankfully, let the cool air play over their bodies. They fell asleep and woke up in the dark. It was seven in the evening. After a shower they dressed and donning shining shoes, they ventured forth for their first real night out abroad. On arriving at the camp gates, they explained to the RAF policeman on duty that it was their first night and where would be the best place to go to see some night life, eat and buy money belts. They were directed to turn left outside the gates and walk for a little way into the village. 'Be careful of any traffic,' the policeman warned. 'Get off the road when a vehicle comes along or you'll end up as another statistic.' They thanked him and proceeded in the direction he had indicated. They could have just followed the noise or the smells. It would have been the same thing.

 On arriving, they could see that all down the right-hand side of the road was a constant succession of eating houses. They were mostly curry shacks judging by the smell. Down the left-hand side, it was all 'Duty Free' shops. Radios were booming out Indian music at full volume among the startling bright, garish lights. It seemed that each shop was in competition with each other in the noise department. Those who were loudest were best, seemed to be the rule. Grinning shopkeepers and touts tried to get the lads into their shops to 'only see' the 'best genuine bargains in Singapore'. They soon learnt that the locals called them 'Johnny'. It didn't matter what their real names were, here they were 'Johnny'. They also worked out that the best eatery was the one (anyone) that was situated opposite their choice of music. The cacophony of sound couldn't be avoided, so they would have to make the best of it. They chose an eating place opposite the Nancy and Frank Sinatra duet which proclaimed that 'Boots were made for walking' and ordered a beer. A couple of seconds later, the Chinese girl had poured them each an ice-cold Tiger beer and demanded 'dolla ea'. When they asked for a menu the girl pointed to a sign at the counter. Matt went over to have a look. It was a menu which proclaimed in the best Queen's English that Fishes Balls were one-dolla-fifty, whilst fried Fishes Fingers were only two dolla. Matt ordered Beaten Fishes and chips for three, for six dolla, and wandered back to the table. It was a real show watching people along the street. Taxis would stop and blow their horns in the attempt to get fares. People were grabbed by touts and steered into shops. The music changed to reflect the type or race of customer 'pulled', as all the time their restaurant tried to 'out volume' the shops opposite with Chinese music. Nancy and Frank died out and was replaced by the Amsterdam Mouse. After another two beers each, the fish and chips arrived. As Matt suspected, the 'beaten fish' were actually battered. Not bad either. 'Got any ketchup darlin'?', asked Matt. 'Over there,' she said, pointing with her nose at the counter. 'I've got it,' said Luke. 'Don't forget the salt and vinegar,' said Bill 'and give us another round of beers,' he directed to the waitress. 'Dolla ea' came the reply, so Bill sighed and gave her the three 'dollas'.

They had underestimated the strength of the Tiger beer. At least that's what Luke said in the morning. Matt had vague recollections of them paying the food bill and weaving their way home. With an exaggerated sobriety they walked past the guardroom and produced their 'twelve fifties', or ID cards. They got back to their accommodation and once more slept the sleep of the dead.

43

The next morning, with thumping heads, they woke up in the bright sunlight and realised after a while that there was no Freddy. There were no wallets either. He had cleaned them out.

After breakfast, they decided to go to the general office and report the theft to their escort. At 08:30 they were there recounting their tale of woe. 'Unless you can prove that Freddy took your money,' he said, 'you can't do a thing.' and of course, there was nothing to prove that Freddy had pinched their money. They were incensed, broke and still had two days to go. They made their way back and spotted Freddy going into the transit block. 'Hey, there he is,' said Matt excitedly. All hangovers were forgotten as they ran towards the block. They caught him at the top of the stairs. 'Hey Freddy,' they shouted. 'Where's our bloody cash?' Freddy responded, 'I've got it here. You were all asleep with your valuables spread all over the locker tops. If I hadn't taken them and locked them away, they would have been lost by now.' 'Come with me and we'll get them.' Freddy led them into his broom cupboard and unlocked a steel locker. He took out the neat piles and distributed them out to the lads. 'Count it and make sure it's all there,' said Freddy. 'Thank you,' said Matt, feeling a bit sheepish. 'Here, take this,' handing over a five dollar note. 'We could have lost the lot if you hadn't looked after it,' said Matt. 'Yes,' said Luke and Bill simultaneously, as they handed over a couple of notes. 'I think we'd better get over to the general office,' said Matt, before any hue and cry starts.

It took a little while to get used to the insect and animal life that seemed to surround them. There were huge 'Stag' beetles that flew around. Sometimes they would fly into the fan which would hit them with an almighty crack. When this happened everybody ducked and waited for the piece of deadly shrapnel to fly across the room and bounce off something or someone. Sometimes it went flying out of the window and sometimes it hit something within the room. Waiting to be hit after the crack caused a few nervous twitches but nobody suffered a hit whilst they were there. Lizards or 'chit chats' were another source of fascination. They would crawl around the walls and ceilings searching for any insects to devour. This they did with a dedication that demonstrated to the lads that their room would be an insect free zone if they were just left alone to get on with it. At first, the lads chased a chit chat and having caught it, held on to the tail. The lizard of course had other ideas. When Bill grabbed it, the tail came off in his fingers. The tailless lizard then bounded away as Bill stared at the still twitching tail between his fingers. He dropped it on the floor and watched it twitch, in macabre fascination. The others were equally fascinated but resolved to leave them alone to carry out their insect clearing duties in the future.

Each day now followed a set pattern. First breakfast then back to the block. Get over to the Mallie to 'bags' a table by 0945. Get settled and watch 'erotica' netball. Next, the pool, until the families invaded at 14:00. Siesta followed, then more exploring down the village. They came to know the places that served the best food and soon realised that the beer needed to be treated with respect. All to soon Friday morning came. Having had breakfast and packed, they paid Freddy and made their way down to the general office. The transport was waiting and having detoured past the transit block to collect their bags, they headed out towards the other side of the airfield.

At the Royal New Zealand Air Force squadron H.Q. their paperwork was checked. They were told to leave the baggage on the transport and follow the 'loadie' out to the aircraft. They took off their berets and wandered across to the aircraft the loadie had indicated. They could see their transport with their bags and as they watched, the bags flew off and landed on the steel mesh that formed the aircraft park. The transport went off in a cloud of dust and they were left to the tender mercies of the RNZAF. 'Blimey,' said Matt quietly, 'I wonder if this thing will get off the ground.' He looked up at the aircraft. It had a fixed undercarriage and there were soot stains down each side of the engines. It had that 'well used' and 'a bit worn' air about it. 'Jump on,' said the loadie. 'I'll be up when I've finished my checks out here.' Inside the aircraft it was hotter than hell. The merciless sun had been beating down for hours. The nose doors were open, along with the rear passenger door, and the small breeze that there was gave a welcome relief to the heat. The loadie jumped on and gave each airman a small wad of cotton wool.'Stick these in your ears,' said the loadie. 'You'll need them when she starts up.' The pilots climbed aboard and disappeared 'upstairs' into the office. The front, clamshell doors were closed and locked and the engines were started. With great belchings of smoke and exhaust flames they caught one-by-one and developed a rhythm that Matt could only assume was tick-over. By now, the sweat was freely running and their shirts had become dark with moisture. The engines revved and they moved forward. Trundling along, the lads peered out of the window and noted that they were following the sea around to the end of the runway. Lining up, the pilot opened up the engines then let the brakes off. They bumped and jerked across the uneven airfield. Alive with vibration, the aircraft seemed to be one huge sound box. Matt now knew why they had been given the cotton wool. He waited for the vibrations and bumpings to stop, which would signify that they were airborne, and realised that they hadn't yet. Surely we must be running out of runway by now, thought Matt. He looked out of the window again and realised that they were 500 feet up and climbing. It would seem that this aircraft, named the Bristol Freighter, should have been called the Bristol Vibrator. They climbed to about five or six thousand feet. Into the blissful cool air. It was a wonderful relief after the heat of the past few days and nobody cared about the noise. As they lurched their way northwards across the morning sky, Matt grinned. Arriving once more in one of Her Majesty's aircraft. Can't be bad, eh.

Chapter 6 – The New Boys

The flight covered 500 miles and took two-and-a-half hours. They were all grateful for the coolness that the cruise at 6000 feet gave. Matt looked down frequently but the only thing to see was the reflection of water underneath an endless canopy of trees. There were no discernible features until they turned east then northwards to follow the coast. The engine note eased as they started their descent. The 'loadie' motioned for them to sit down and strap in. They landed on a long tarmac runway and taxied around to the visiting aircraft section. They passed F86 Sabres of the Royal Australian Air Force and Gloucester Javelin FAWs of the Royal Air Force. Matt reminded himself that his home for the next two-and-a-half years was on this Australian base. They stopped and the engines were switched off. The silence was deafening. They removed the cotton wool from their ears and moved towards the rear door. It was opened from the outside, and they were pointed in the direction of a hut on one side of the aircraft pan. As they made their way across, a vehicle arrived to unload the aircraft. They were met by the RAF Regiment squadron duty driver and as they waited for their luggage, they questioned him about the base and the general set up. It was hot on the edge of the pan but not quite as humid as Singapore. It seemed more bearable somehow. Eventually their bags arrived and they were taken to their billet and shown their rooms. The accommodation was 'bungalow' style with the ablutions in the middle part. Set in a palm grove with a coarse grass on the ground, the rooms were airy and cool. 'Okay,' said the driver, 'get yourselves settled in and follow the lads to the squadron in the morning. You'll be in Control and Reporting flight, commonly known as C&R flight, so you'll need to report there. Dress will be the Khaki Drill you're wearing now with 'Hose Tops', boots and putties. Bring your UK blues with you as they need to be dry cleaned, packed up and vacuum-sealed in polythene. Okay, see you later,' and with that he was gone.

They were told that they were joining a 'Light Anti-Aircraft' Squadron or LAA which, together with a Battery of Guns from Treble One, Royal Australian Artillery, made up the defence of the airfield.

The guns or cannons were Bofors Forty Seventies and Forty Sixties. The RAF Regiment had the Forty Seventies and the Aussies had the Forty Sixties.

The job of the C&R flight was to man observation posts (OPs). These were pushed out forward of the airfield perimeter by a couple of miles. It was their job to maintain radio communications and report any aircraft by type, course and height to the guns. The last part of the equation was a radar at the airfield to warn of possible targets. An RAF Regiment (Canadian) gunner manned the radar and through a dedicated phone line, communicated with the command post (CP). The CP controlled the gun and OP orchestra. All of this was run and manned by the Airmen and Officer Gunners of the Royal Air Force Regiment No 1 (LAA) squadron.

At that time, the president of Indonesia, president Sukarno, was rattling his sabre. He was generally making a nuisance of himself and misbehaving over Malaysian sovereignty so that, until the Tunku Abdul Rathman of Malaysia decided otherwise and Sukarno ceased his sabre rattling, the No 1 Squadron (LAA) RAF Regiment would remain in Butterworth. Just like the apes of Gibraltar it would seem.

The incumbents of the block now started to arrive after finishing work for the day. There were quite a few of the chaps who had been on the same course as them back at Catterick. The handshakes and smiles were genuine as they sat around, smoked and generally caught up on who had done what and when. 'Hey,' said one of the lads, 'do you remember that business back at Catterick with the block opposite and the ceiling coming down?' 'What about it,' said Bill. 'Well, they got done £300 for barrack damages. The funny thing is, they swore it was a black ghost that caused it.' 'I'm surprised that they weren't medically discharged,' said Matt, keeping his face straight. The other two snorted, then were unable to hold it back. Between tears and laughter they told the tale to an audience who were once innocent witnesses to the real events and who laughed until it hurt as the tale unfolded. 'Hey,' said one of the older hands, still laughing, 'you guys didn't get caught out in that Freddy scam in Singapore did you?' 'Er, what Freddy scam is that then?' said Matt. 'It's where he nicks your money when you're asleep then tells you that he was just looking after it for you. When the grateful owner gets it back he usually doesn't realise that there's a dollar or two missing. He's even been known to have been given a couple of dollars as a thank you.' 'I guess that's us then,' said Luke. 'Yup,' Bill agreed, 'I guess that's us then.'

After a shower, the lads unpacked and stowed their kit. The wardrobes, they noticed, had light bulbs in the bottom. They were there to stop the clothes going mouldy whilst hanging. They were shown to the mess and after tea, they sat on the veranda of the billet and watched the sun go down. It got dark quickly in the tropics and within 30 minutes it was pitch black. Matt looked up and stared at the unfamiliar constellations. The stars were bright, as there were very few lights around. The lads accompanied the rest of the crowd and were shown, in turn, the NAAFI club and the WRVS lounge. Matt settled for the lounge and perused the few books available. The lady that ran the lounge was called Doreen and she was an amiable, plump, middle-aged woman. Rather like a mother figure to the lads who hung out there.

Matt discovered, many years later, that Doreen was a widow whose husband had been a Royal Air Force pilot. He'd been killed in a flying accident whilst on approach to RAAF Butterworth, and Doreen had elected to remain. She died there many years later, always a surrogate mum to the lads who were so far away from

50

home.

The next morning they reported to the C&R flight building. All were made to stand to one side as the morning muster parade took place. Matt was mortified. He had never seen so many corporals on one flight, let alone in the same place at the same time. This must be the birthplace for corporals, thought Matt. He counted the airmen and worked out that there was one airman for each corporal, without taking the newcomers into account. The set up consisted of the flight building and the store *cum* radio repair workshop. They were called up one by one into the flight office where the flight sergeant and sergeant had their office. After a brief but amicable interview with the flight sergeant, they were marched, individually, into the flight commander's office. There followed the normal chat about the trip from the UK, what you did before joining the Regiment and not to rock the boat whilst living under the invitation of the Royal Australian Air Force umbrella. Matt noticed that the flight commander was a Flight lieutenant and wondered what he might have done to be such a senior person, in such a junior position. After all, his father flew and examined other pilots to maintain their currency in their flying proficiency, and he was a flight lieutenant. It's not as if Matt's flight commander had that sort of responsibility.

'Right,' said a corporal with a clipboard 'you need to see the CO.' 'Report to the SWO at the following times.' 'After that, report to the squadron Mechanical Transport or MT section at the following times for your driving familiarisation and tests.' Every new driver had to get familiar with the local roads and the different styles of local driving before they could be let loose and still live. Matt knew it made sense. The corporal then proceeded to read out a list of names, times and venues. Who was supposed to be where, when and doing what. Matt realised that he was due at the squadron MT section five minutes ago and so, asked where it was situated. Fortunately, the office was only 100 yards away and Matt arrived breathless. Corporal Jones was in charge, and he took Matt out to a Bedford three-ton truck. Matt climbed into the driver's seat and they set off. It was a good familiarisation of the airfield set up. They were out for about half-an-hour and upon returning, Matt's RAF driving licence, known as a 'form 1629', was stamped up as being fit to drive for 1 Sqn at RAAF Butterworth. It was break time now and Matt made his way back to the flight office. A cool veranda ran round each of the squadron buildings and the C&R building sported an iced-water dispenser. Heaven, thought Matt, as he drank. He looked around at the crowd that had gathered around the machine and spotted a few familiar faces from Catterick. Waving his hello's, he made his way across to the squadron HQ and reported to the Squadron Warrant Officer. The SWO introduced himself as Warrant Officer Silvers and told Matt to wait outside. After a few minutes, he was called in and was marched into the holy of holies, the inner sanctum, the Squadron Commander's office. Matt halted and came to attention in front of the desk. Stood at ease then easy, Matt took in the office and the man behind the desk. The squadron leader looked at Matt and asked the predictable questions about the flight, first impressions on the station, not getting into trouble etcetera, then he was marched out. Back in the SWO's office he was invited to sit down. Luke was already there and was marched into the CO's office. Presently, he came out and was told to sit. The SWO took off his hat and placed it on the desk. 'Right, now that we've got the formalities out of the way, here's some of the realities.' They were told in no uncertain terms that they needed to keep their noses clean and their wits sharp. When questioned about their financial state they admitted that they were broke and yes, they knew that it was another week until pay day. The SWO pulled out his wallet. 'I'm going to lend you forty dollars each. It should be enough to last until pay day as long as you don't go mad. I expect it back the minute you've been paid,' he said. They stammered their thanks and were shown the door. Their surprise was absolute, this was the second time in Matt's short career that an unexpected gesture of humanity had been demonstrated. 'He's got my full attention,' said Matt, and Luke agreed. They reported back and were told what the breakdown of duties would be. Normally, it would be two days of normal work from seven till one, then two days on OPs. This would be from three-thirty in the morning until about eight at night, then two days off. There would be twenty-four hour periods of squadron duty driver which would occur periodically, once every few weeks. For the rest of this week they would be on normal working hours, starting OPs on Saturday morning. Matt was assigned to corporal Crow, who took him to one side in the shade and explained more about the job, the area and the station. This went on until lunchtime, when the single men went to the dining hall and the married men went off to catch the coach home. It was one o'clock in the afternoon and work was over for the day.

There was a long queue. It stretched from the doors, along the veranda and around the corner. Past all the sinks and towel dispensers. There was a sink situated about every two feet along the veranda, and the queue was about 20 or 30 yards long. At the head of the queue was a corporal from the RAAF, inspecting hands. Matt couldn't believe it. They were being treated like children. It seemed that no matter how clean your hands were, if you were not subservient enough or if he just took a dislike to you, the corporal sent you to the back of the queue. There was no argument. If you tried to argue, back you went. Matt ensured his hands were well scrubbed by the time he got to the 'hand inspection' and with the nod and the words 'no worries', he passed through. He continued in the queue, which still had another few yards to run before it got to the servery. Matt made a mental note to get there early next time to be at the head of the queue. The food was excellent. Steak if you wanted it, omelette, stew, curry along with chips, vegetables, boiled potatoes and rice. At one end of the dining hall were the cold drinks dispensers. Matt learnt that fresh milk was flown in from Australia, on Tuesdays and Thursdays. They would be rationed to one pint per man but it would be fresh and ice cold. On the sweet counter there was a selection of various sponges with custard or ice cream. Matt opted for the ice cream, then, having taken his used plates to the washing area, wandered outside. It felt cool on the veranda after the heat inside the dining hall but, as he walked back to the billet, Matt felt the full heat of the Malaysian afternoon sun as it beat down. It felt like he'd been hit on the head with an iron bar as he made his way along the path. Arriving back at his room he savoured the coolness of the fans and the veranda. It really was a picturesque spot, thought Matt. The billets were set in a palm grove. He could see the sea on the other side of the road and the medical centre to his left. He sat on the veranda and enjoyed a cigarette before his shower. He had to wait because the rest of the lads had got there before him, so he idled away the time chatting to the two bearers. He discovered that they were called Philip and Mansa and they would look after him for five dollars a week.

Luke came out of the room. 'Have you seen this?' he said, stroking a piece of grass. 'What?' said Matt. 'Look,' said Luke. Matt looked, and to his amazement the grass fronds started to move and close up. 'It's called 'Nerve Grass',' said Luke. 'Well I never,' said Matt, 'I've never seen plants move by themselves.' Matt moved to the edge of the veranda and looked closer at the grass. It wasn't grass at all: it looked like a miniature fern. He touched it and sure enough, it closed up. 'Well I never,' said Matt again.

Chapter 7 – Learning the Ropes

The shower was long, cool and refreshing. The siesta was cool and punctuated only by the gentle thump, thump, thump of the fans as they stirred the air and evaporated the sweat. The afternoon passed and as it got dark Matt woke and looked at his watch: it was 18:30. The sun had set and the world was bathed in a red light. Philip and Mansa were long gone so Matt, bored, wandered outside to the notice board to see if there was anything of interest. There was nothing but Station Routine Orders. Everybody had to read them, so Matt thought that he might as well get it over with. There was the usual uninteresting stuff until he got to the orders about not being in an 'Out Of Bounds' area. That sounds interesting, thought Matt, and a few enquiries confirmed that the Royal Australian Air Force had placed all houses of ill-repute out of bounds. That these houses were on Penang Island and that they were all brothels only made the prospect of a visit more interesting. Having only 40 dollars mattered not a jot. He could look in the windows, couldn't he?

Matt teamed up with one of the chaps who'd been on his Basic Course back at RAF Catterick; his name was Bob and he had been there for a couple of months. An old hand in fact.

They walked out of the main gate wearing long-sleeved shirts buttoned at the cuffs, along with long trousers. Dress at night was mandatory and shorts and T-shirts were definitely out. It was an anti-mosquito precaution, they were informed. Taxis were waiting expectantly outside the main camp gate, so Matt and Bob jumped in the first in line and haggled over the price to the ferry terminus. Once agreed, they set off. Matt looked out at a landscape that was vastly different from England. Palm trees were a novelty and coconuts were not as he remembered them from the fairground. The buildings were completely different. They didn't need to keep out the cold, for a start. They only needed to keep out unwanted insects and people. At the ferry terminus they got out and bought return tickets. The ferries left the Butterworth side every 20 minutes and the trip across took 20 minutes. The last ferry back sailed at midnight and Matt resolved to be on it. On the Penang side they were hustled off with the crowd and after some strong bartering, managed to get a reasonably priced 'trishaw' ride each into town. 'Another dollar if you get to the Tiger bar before him,' shouted Matt. 'Two dollars if you beat him,' shouted Bob. The drivers redoubled their efforts. It became an honour thing, and Matt sat exposed at the front. He soon realised that he would be the first to be hurt if they hit anything and closed his eyes each time a car came towards him. Matt hung on grimly as they raced through the evening traffic, up past the prison and on to the High Street. There were several heart-stopping moments before they slid into the side of the road and stopped outside the brightly lit Tiger bar. They paid the trishaw drivers off and climbed the stairs to the bar. The coldness of the air-conditioning hit them as they opened the door. Outside it was clammy and hot but here, inside, it was delicious. It was brightly lit with harsh strip lights mixed with UV. It made people look green but who cared. People? They were the only ones there. They ordered pints of Tiger from the waitress, who set them down on the zinc-covered tables. She went back for beer mats and salted peanuts, as the bar resounded with overly loud music. It came from the jukebox sitting in the corner of the concrete-floored room. Matt noticed the white tiles on the walls and thought that it was like drinking in a public toilet. Still, it was a relief after being outside.

A young lad, who must have been about ten, offered to clean their shoes. Once more a price was negotiated and the shoe-shine boy set to work. After a couple of pints and with shoes clean, they both felt ready for the main entertainment of the evening. It was now nearly ten-thirty, so they needed to get a move on. They paid up and walked out into the hot, damp night. Outside, the same trishaw drivers were waiting so, once more, a price was negotiated. This time they were going to Mamma San's. At this time, all brothel keepers were called Mamma San, as in that all white European males were called Johnny or Chonny.

After a few minutes the streets became narrower and the houses smaller. They had entered a 'Jig a Jig' town – a sort of town within a city where there were no cars, only trishaws, small motorbikes and brothels. They stopped outside one of the two-story wooden shacks and were ushered in by a woman who appeared to be about forty years old. They were invited to sit down and bottles of Anchor beer arrived. The lights were dim and red and as Matt and Bob watched, a dozen girls were paraded in front of them. Each one wanted the business and each one was smiling enticingly. 'Which one you wan?' said Mamma San to Matt. 'Enny one you wan,' she said. Matt got up and went to one wearing a green dress. She took him by the hand and led him upstairs. He was in lust and his eyes devoured her derrière as he followed her up the tiny staircase. They went into the first room. It contained a double bed and a wardrobe. There was another door on the opposite side of the room and the only light showing was coming from between the slats of the shuttered window. She stripped off as quickly as if she'd peeled a banana. She jumped on the bed then laid on her back with her legs apart. Matt had never witnessed anything so clinical before. He undressed, with his manhood starting to relax as he wilted under her scrutiny. Once he was on the bed, she jumped up and inspected the end of his manhood closely. Apparently satisfied that he was disease-free, she lay back down and grabbed his (by now) 'little willie'. Her energetic massaging soon revived it back to manhood status but, as he rolled over onto her, she froze. 'What's up?' said Matt. 'Fuckie red hat,' she said as a squealing of brakes outside the room was followed swiftly by the banging of Land Rover doors. 'Shit,' said Matt, 'it's the Military Police.' Known colloquially as Red Caps, these were the bad boys and Matt and Bob were in trouble. Matt grabbed his clothes and ran to the other door. He guessed they'd be coming up the stairs judging by the noise outside. He opened the door just as the occupant ran in to Matt's room. Wasting no time, she got into bed with Matt's girl. Matt ran into the next room, up a ladder which went through a skylight and out onto the roof. He noted that Bob had beaten him to it as he pulled the ladder up and closed the skylight. As they waited, they could hear the commotion below. One of the MPs had walked into the room containing the two women locked in the throes of passion and had beaten a hasty retreat, his ears ringing with the screams.

Matt looked at his watch. It was half-eleven and there he was, stark staring naked on a roof top somewhere in Penang, with a ferry to catch within 30 minutes. It started to rain and the Red Caps, to Matt's eternal relief, decided there was no trade worth getting wet for right then and so, after a couple of minutes, they sped off and left the lads to it. Dressed by now in wet clothes, they made their way back down the ladder. They tried to get out but found their way blocked by two girls demanding their money. Matt and Bob were relieved of 10 dollars each before jumping into the trishaws which were still waiting expectantly. Again, fare negotiations took place before the 'ride of death' commenced towards the ferry terminal. They made it, just. The rain had stopped and pulling thankfully on a cigarette, they stood outside on the deck to watch the black water slide past and the lights of Penang recede into the distance.

The Butterworth routine consisted of two days on Observation Posts (OPs), two days normal work, then two days off. A twenty-four hour spell as Duty Driver came round every couple of months or so.

The OPs were situated outside the airfield and were there to inform the airfield guns, by radio, of any aircraft movements inbound towards the airfield. The Indonesian confrontation had been going for some years by this time and whilst an air attack could occur, several layers of defence screened the airfield. Combat Air Patrols were flown by the Australian Sabres whilst English Javelins took over during bad weather. The ring of OPs was one part of the overall picture. OPs meant long days for anybody manning them. Up at four in the morning and back to bed by ten at night. During the monsoon season it was hot and damp although punctuated by cool, lashing rain each afternoon. Each onslaught of rain was preceded by a blast of cool wind. For the rest of the time it was just hot and damp. Humidity ran at about 90 percent, with daily temperatures at on or about 100 degrees. There was no sleep whilst on OP duty and a listening watch needed to be kept on the radio at all times. An early-warning radar operator warned of approaching aircraft via the radio.

One of the OPs was situated at a Fire Station in a local village. Look-out was kept from the top of the fire tower. Another was situated on the roof of the Penang ferry terminus building and always seemed to be downwind of the stink of Durian fruit - the offensive odour which seemed to smell of a rank mix of vomit and garlic.

On both these OPs, a local lad had been employed to help with cooking and washing up duties. These boys made the tea during the day and were both named 'Shithouse'! It wasn't as if they'd ever meet. and anyway, if they did they'd probably use their proper names to each other. 'Shithouse squared' were taught to change the radio accumulators when they ran low. Attempts were made to teach them to answer the hourly radio checks, but they proved abortive because their strong local Indian accents caused the command post staff to smell a rat. Usually, within half-an-hour of a suspect reply on the radio, a visitor in the form of a corporal (or worse) would arrive and demand to know what was going on. Innocent expressions of bewilderment at the unjustness of it all usually carried the day and caused the suspicious visitor to leave, having first been calmed by the mandatory brew of tea.

The two days on normal duties were from seven in the morning until one in the afternoon. The day normally began with morning muster parade, where duties were given out. Matt and his mates usually ended up on Accumulator duties. That meant going to the battery charging section and collecting 140 steel-clad 75 amp hour accumulators, loading them by hand up onto a truck and then taking them around to all the airfield guns, the command post and radio servicing section. As they dropped off the freshly charged accumulators, so they collected the discharged ones. Eventually, they arrived back at the battery charging section and unloaded the 140 depleted accumulators for recharging. It was hot, backbreaking work. The team of three would drip with sweat after the first minute and gulp water from jerrycans as the morning progressed. They grew callouses on their hands and developed muscles in places they did not know they had. Twelve-forty-five usually saw them back at the Flight hut donning shirts and berets. Tidy now, they made their way to the Airmen's mess.

Lunch over, the day was their own. A cool shower, followed by a laze around for an hour, clad only in a towel or underpants, laying on the bed, with the fan going full belt was normal. Then it was dress, in civilian shorts, shirt and shoes, grab a costume, grab wallet and get down to the swimming pool. Oh heaven.

The swimming pool was situated about fifteen minutes, hot walk away. It was adjacent to the Married Quarters, set near the beach in a palm grove. It was idyllic, with a sea breeze and bronzed Australian mums looking after children whilst covertly eyeing up any new talent arriving. The drill was to get changed, showered and in the pool in the shortest possible time. Having cooled off, there was nothing for it but to go to the bar and order an icy, pint glass of draught Tiger beer. 'My God, it just doesn't get any better,' thought Matt. 'I could stand this sort of life,' quickly forgetting the purgatory of the morning. Cor-blimey, look at the tits on that, thought Matt as he clocked the mum in a bright red bikini bending over to scoop up her child. She was oblivious to Matts' gaze, or perhaps not as she glanced up and smiled at him. Instantly, he was in lust. Pure, naked lust. He knew he had to do the chat-up thing first. Make her laugh whilst uttering undying platitudes of love, but somehow he just couldn't bring himself to do so. How could he walk over and talk to her and make it casual like James Bond when he had developed, in the flash of an eye, an embarrassing bulge big enough to trip over? He flashed a brave smile back (he had been practising, in front of a mirror, in case this moment ever arose) then realised that she was smiling at someone behind him. Another mum waved back, while Matt sat in his chair feigning nonchalance. Back in the pool quick, Matt thought, and turning his back he attempted a flip which ended as a very painful flop.

The sun eventually lost its heat and at six, the pool closed. Matt, along with his mates, wandered back. 'Anybody got any smokes?' asked Matt. 'No, but we're going past Ismael's shop in a minute. He lets you put stuff on account until pay day.' 'Great,' said Matt, as they filed into the shop and started their accounts. I'll have to be careful, thought Matt, or I'll have nothing left on pay day when I pay off my tab.

Matt soon discovered that Ismael knew everything about everyone. He discovered that if he wanted to know where and when they were going on exercise, he could find out from Ismael. Anything he wanted to know about the base, the units and the people in them could be found out from here. Matt was amazed at the amount and accuracy of the information Ismael seemed to have at his fingertips. Matt was to discover much later, however, that there were some critical gaps in Ismael's knowledge.

The two days off were great. Most of the time was spent at the pool. Lunch usually consisted of steak sandwiches purchased at the pool bar. They were cheap and saved the hike back to the Airmen's mess - besides, the Airmen's mess didn't serve pints of Tiger beer.

The days rolled into weeks and the new boys found themselves meeting new people and making new friends. The camp cinema was fun. Each alternate Thursday, either Pathe news was shown for the Brits or the Aussie equivalent for the Aussies. If Pathe news came on there was a great booing from the Aussies. If the Australian 'ABC' news came on, the Brits demonstrated their enthusiasm in the same manner. Empty beer cans were thrown at the screen by both parties and all in all, the cinema kept everybody out of mischief for the evening.

Trips on the ferry to Penang on days off provided hours of fascinating entertainment. There were many different cultures to view. The Chinese, mostly Hok-En with a sprinkling of Mandarin, behaved totally differently from the Tamils. The Tamils, in turn, differed from the Sikhs who, once again, were different from the Malays.

By now, Matt had bought himself a motorbike. One of the Aussies he knew was due home and arranged with the shop for Matt to take over the monthly payments. It was a bargain and Matt jumped at the chance.

Returning late in the evening, there was nothing better than to stop for a curry take-away on the way back to camp. It was served in a rinsed out 'Beans' tin, wrapped up in a banana leaf tied up with raffia instead of string: a tied raffia loop was provided to hang over the handle bars and thus transport the scalding hot concoction.

Sitting on the veranda back at his billet, eating the hottest Keema curry ever, scooping the sauce up with fresh chapattees, and trying not to hiccup at the spiced heat of molten rock was a memory that would stay with Matt forever. The heat stayed in his mouth which, quite soon, became numb and nothing eaten before or since had ever been quite as hot.

One evening, whilst listening idly to a radio playing in the background, Matt heard the announcer say that they were listening to Radio Butterworth, the voice of the Royal Australian Air Force broadcasting on a frequency of 1445 kilocycles in the 208 metre band in Malaysia. I'd like to get involved in that, thought Matt, and inquiries found it to be coming from the camp opposite the guardroom. The next afternoon off found Matt in the reception area of the radio station. Wishing to help and willing to 'start at the bottom', Matt was introduced to a couple of people and given various menial tasks. It was 'policy' to see if people really wanted to carry out a useful function or whether they just romanticised about being an instant announcer. Matt wanted to be an announcer and was willing to do whatever it took to get there. After several weeks of working in the record library, he was allowed to sit in on 'live' evening programs and watch the dials and switches being manipulated by the announcer while records were cued and held on felt mats with miniature crocodile clips on chains until needed. A xylophone was used for the station jingle before the station identification was announced and although seeming crude, it sounded, in reality, quite professional.

Matt progressed to training sessions and recorded tapes for critiques. A new studio was almost finished and it was in this studio that he did most of his training. The day eventually came when Matt was told he would be reading the English news. It would be typed by the station secretary from the BBC world service and given to Matt for broadcast. As he went on air, he realised he had never felt so nervous in his life. It went fine and indeed, he was congratulated by people who wanted to know how he had got his English accent!

Matt moved on from reading the news to getting his own show called 'Nightbeat'. He occasionally stood in for other people and when not on duty, helped out with the Saturday night 'Party Time'. These shows were great fun because all sorts of girls 'phoned in with requests. They usually wanted to chat with the DJs and a great many dates were there to be had, for the willing.

And so came the evening when Matt arranged to meet May Yong outside the cinema on Penang Road at six thirty pm. She had 'phoned in during the Saturday night show and made a request for any Beatles record. She ended up making a date, which was the original intent anyway. A couple of hours later he had made another date, with Mee Soon. She had also 'phoned in with a record request. The trouble was that he had committed the cardinal error of making the second date for the same time and day as the first. His only saving grace was that he would meet Mee Soon opposite the cinema, instead of outside. Matt reasoned that as they didn't know him, he could eye up the talent and drive past if it didn't come up to scratch (so to speak!), all the time forgetting that white European men on Penang Road, on a Wednesday evening at six thirty, were as rare as shoe repair men on a beach. I'll wear my crash helmet, reasoned Matt, so how could they recognise me? That all the rest of the motorbike riders would have no crash helmet at all didn't enter his head; he had told them his name was Johnny so he reckoned he'd be safe!

The time for a romantic date arrived and Matt savoured the thought of a 'Chinese Takeaway'. He drove off the ferry and headed towards the cinema. He arrived a few minutes early and was surprised to see a girl on each side of the road, both obviously waiting for something or someone. He had to stop as the traffic lights were at red. Waiting and praying for the lights to change, he noticed that both of the girls were overweight, over-age and over made-up. Just then three things happened at almost the same time. Both girls spotted him and yelled, 'JOHNNY,' and started to run towards him. The lights changed from red to green and Matt let out the clutch and opened the throttle to make good his escape. Alas, it was not to be. At the point of the front wheel lifting off the ground, the chain snapped. Noooooooo !

Grabbing the chain, Matt pushed and ran for his life. Around the corner he went and as the road started to run downhill, Matt leapt onto the saddle and watched with anxious anticipation as the hue and cry was gradually left behind. The two girls, sensing their quarry had escaped, had now stopped and were shouting and waving their handbags. Having done little to cement Chinese - English relations within the last few minutes, and sweating profusely, Matt free-wheeled down the hill. Still panting heavily, he waited for a while before looking out for a motorcycle repair shop. Fortunately they were numerous in this country, where everybody seemed to get around on motorcycles. Half an hour later, Matt was on his way. 'God, I need a beer,' said Matt to no-one in particular and so it was that he made his way to the 'Oasis Cafe'. The Oasis was a favourite haunt of Matt and his group of friends because it was ice-cold inside, with potted plants instead of plastic and barmaids who were pleasant as opposed to pushy. 'A pint of Tiger, please,' said Matt as he sat at the bar. Phew, he thought, as he went over the events of the last hour. The lads should be coming in any time now. Better not say anything, they'll only take the mickey. He caught the barmaid looking at him distastefully as she banged his pint onto the counter. His gaze went down to his hands. He'd better get washed up he thought. His hands were black with oil from the chain. By the time he got back from the gents, some of the motorbike gang were in. Good natured banter and stories were exchanged, and people came and went until Matt decided it was time to say his goodbyes. He went out into the hot, steamy night rain ... followed by the barmaid. 'Why you no wanna see me at the cinema tonight but can drink here, OK?' Matt did a double-take and realised who the barmaid was. Fuuuuuuuuck! Enough was enough so, while being slapped around the head with a wet bar towel, Matt started up, revved up and sped off at high speed to catch the ferry back to the mainland and bed.

Chapter 8 – The Experienced Hand

Just before leaving work one afternoon, Matt was pulled to one side and told to report to the Flight Sergeant. Remembering his last unpleasant meeting with a certain Flight Sergeant at St Athens, Matt gulped and ran to stand outside the Flight office. 'Jenkins,' yelled the Sergeant, 'Get your horrible body in here.' 'Yessarge,' yelled Matt in return. He marched smartly in and halted in front of the desk. The Flight Sergeant viewed the specimen in front of him and while playing with his moustache, told Matt to 'Stand Easy'. Matt relaxed. 'Your turn at Squadron 'Duty Driver' has come round,' he said. 'You're to report to the Squadron Warrant Officer, or SWO, at 06:30 tomorrow.' Matt nodded and said, 'Yes, flight.' 'You haven't done this duty before so this afternoon I'm putting you with Noriss to learn the ropes. Stay with him until the meals and the mail have been delivered this evening to the guns. He'll be collecting you from the billet at 13:00 and you should be done by 21:00.' 'Yes, flight,' said Matt. 'Okay, dismissed,' said the Flight Sergeant.

Matt headed straight for the mess hall, went to the front of the queue and told the corporal he was on duty and asked to be allowed to jump the queue. The corporal was unmoved and pointed to the back of the line. It went around the corner and out of sight. Matt sighed. Any hopes of getting a meal today evaporated and he headed towards the billet for a shower and a change into fresh clothes instead. At 13:00 the duty Land Rover pulled up and Matt jumped in. 'Hello Nifty,' said Matt. 'Eh up lad,' said Nifty. They headed off towards the North edge of the airfield passing the refuelling point on the way. As they moved around the airfield, Nifty explained the duty, the routes and who expected what, where and when. By the evening, Matt felt confident enough to take over. As he was dropped off at the billet that night, Nifty told him to make sure he was five minutes early the next morning. 'The SWO expects it,' said Nifty.

The next morning at 06:25, Matt reported to the SWO. He signed for his vehicle and was told to go to the battery-charging section and collect one of the squadron airman who would be waiting. As it was a squadron parade day, Matt was dressed in his best working uniform. His webbing belt was freshly blanco'd and he had his rifle and bayonet. 'Leave your bayonet and frog in my office,' said the SWO. 'It'll be safe enough here.' Matt said 'Thank you, sir.' Getting into and out of a vehicle with a bayonet and it's frog was difficult. It was also extremely uncomfortable to drive with that sort of appendage sticking into one's derrière. 'It'll be here when you get back,' said the SWO. 'Look sharp now.' Matt took his rifle and set off .

When he returned, the SWO had paraded the squadron who were waiting 'at ease' for the CO. 'Run down to your flight lad,' said the SWO. 'The CO is waiting to take the parade.' Matt ran and was directed to his place in the ranks. 'Shit,' thought Matt. My bayonet is in the SWO's office. 'I'm for it now.' They were bought to attention, the parade was put into open order and the command to 'Fix Bayonets' was given. Matt had no bayonet but he went through the motions as if he really did have one. The order to 'Present Arms' was given and the inspection started. As the CO and SWO approached each flight, the flight commander joined the entourage, followed by the flight sergeant. The foursome inspected the flight, with names being taken for extra duties by the flight sergeant when indicated by the SWO. It got to Matt's flight and as he stood there waiting for the 'Sword of Damocles' to descend onto him, Matt reflected on the injustice of it all. The inspection party filed past his front then passed his rear. There were a few muttered words at the end of the file then the CO and SWO marched back to the head of the parade. The CO handed over to the Adjutant who waited for the CO to leave, then dismissed the Officers. The rest of the parade waited as the flight sergeants were called over to the SWO's office. The sun was getting hot now as the men stood and waited.

Eventually, the flight sergeants came back and addressed their individual flights. Apparently, the CO thought that the bayonet drill needed smartening up. It was sloppy. So much so that each flight would practise bayonet drill until 10:00. After that time, normal duties would resume. Matt tried to excuse himself. He was after all, the squadron duty driver. 'Nobody will be excused,' said the flight sergeant, CO's orders.'

They marched out to a spare aircraft pan, its white concrete reflecting the blazing sun. The sun felt like an iron bar hitting their heads and soon their uniforms were dark with sweat. They were formed up into a hollow square while the corporals went about giving them lessons in bayonet drill. Each time they went through the routine a different person was called out to demonstrate the moves under the corporal's orders. It got to Matt's turn. 'Jenkins,' yelled the corporal, and Matt marched gloomily to his fate. 'Squad will fix bayonets. By numbers, Fix,' bellowed the corporal. Matt bent his knees slightly, moved the butt of his rifle to between his feet and supported the rest of his rifle with his knees. He then placed his left hand around his back as if to draw his bayonet. 'Bayonets,' screamed the corporal. Matt whipped his hand back and pretended to fix an imaginary bayonet to his rifle. 'Where's your bayonet?' screamed the corporal, 'You're supposed to bring it out and fix it to your rifle on the executive word of command. Let's see if we can get it right shall we.' Matt informed the corporal that he didn't have a bayonet. The corporal who was rapidly losing it, gave the order to 'Ground Arms'. They were then told to fall out for a smoke break. The men gratefully placed their rifles onto the hot concrete and moved off onto the grass. They crowded round Matt and lit up. 'How'd you get away with that Jenks?' they asked. 'I don't know,' said Matt. 'The SWO locked my bayonet and frog up in his office when he sent me off on a detail just before parade. When I got back I was sent directly to my place with no chance to retrieve my bayonet. I guess the SWO just forgot he had it. 'Yes but how did you get away with the whole parade without a bayonet?' they asked. 'There was nothing I could do about it,' Matt said. 'I just went through the motions as if I had one and nobody seemed to notice.' Listening to the group from outside the circle were four of the flight corporals. 'Okay Jenkins, you got lucky that time. Let's write it off to experience shall we?' 'Yes, corp,' said Matt, 'thanks.' They took a final drag from their cigarettes and 'fell in' once more. Another ten minutes worth of drill saw off the remaining time, then they were marched back to the squadron.

After collecting his bayonet, Matt took it and his rifle to the armoury and handed them in. It was time to crack on with being the squadron duty driver. Lunchtime came and went and by the time afternoon had turned into evening Matt had caught up. He took the evening meals and the mail around to the guns. He collected the empty meal boxes and made his way back to the command post.

His route took him across the end of the active runway. He had to be careful here and check for aircraft on approach before crossing. It was starting to get dark and the runway lights were on. He looked up into the approach path and sure enough, Matt could see the landing lights of an an aircraft just turning onto 'finals'. He noted with interest that the aircraft was a Vulcan. We don't get too many of those here, thought Matt. His glance turned idly to the runway and there, with horror, Matt could see a steel scaffolding pole shining against the black of the runway. It was lying right in between the touch-down tyre marks. There was no time to warn anybody. The aircraft was getting close and there was going to be a terrible accident if a wheel touched the pipe. Matt got out of the vehicle reasoning that if he was going to do anything about the situation, he didn't want to make it worse by stalling his Land Rover on the runway: besides, there wasn't enough time to drive onto the runway, stop, get out, pick up the pole, throw it in the back, get back in, then drive off. With his heart in his mouth Matt sprinted across and grabbed the end of the pole. Dragging the pole behind him, Matt carried on running. He got it to the other side and dived into the dirt. With a tremendous roar, the wing tip went over his head as the aircraft passed him by. He realised that the danger was past. He remembered now that civilian contractors had been working on the airfield that day and guessed that the pole had probably fallen off the back of their truck. Standing up and brushing the dirt off, he took the pole back to his Land Rover and threw it in the back. Heart still thumping from the adrenalin, Matt decided not to say anything unless specifically questioned. It could get me into a lot of trouble, Matt thought, running out like that in front of a Vulcan on finals. What if I had forced it to go around when it was low on fuel? No, thought Matt, best left alone that one. He checked in at the command post to collect 'any other duties'. The SWO was orderly officer that evening and looked at Matt with a quizzical eye. 'You seem to have been rolling in the dirt, Jenkins,' said the SWO. 'Sir,' said Matt, 'I had a flat.' 'Okay,' said the SWO, 'get yourself back to the billet and wait for any call out from your room.' Thankfully, Matt left. He was bushed. Back in the billet, a shower and bed left Matt to sleep until a call at 05:30 woke him for the handover.

One afternoon, some of the Matt's friends were lounging on their beds under the fan. They'd all had a shower and were clad only in towels, which were hung around their waists in the manner of Sarongs. 'What shall we do tonight?' asked Dimetrius. 'Dunno,' said Bill. 'Borin,' said Tone. 'Why don't we hire a car and go out for a meal?' suggested Matt. Great idea, enthused the lads. Where shall we go? 'I know,' said Bill, 'let's go to Alor Star.' 'Gordon Bennett,' said Matt, 'that's nearly seventy miles away.' 'No worries,' said Tone, 'we'll set off early, find a Chinese restaurant, have a meal and come back. We should be back in time to catch a few hours kip before the morning.' The four of them caught a taxi outside the camp gates, hired a car and set off for Alor Star. Dimetrius was driving and seemed intent on scaring them all out of their wits. Overtaking towards large log lorries and cutting in at the last second seemed to be his thing. He's playing chicken with us, thought Matt. He cast secret glances at Bill and Tone and could see the fear in their faces. After an unthinkably tense two hour trip they arrived at the bright city lights and started to look for a Chinese restaurant. The first thing that struck them was that this town was definitely not on the main tourist route. Cymbals were crashing from a nearby open air Chinese opera, adding to the cacophony of sounds that car hooters and revving engines were making to flood the streets. Pulling into the side of the road, they chose an eating house and realised that all the restaurants were Chinese. As they went in Matt noticed that there were no windows. Just window-shaped, large holes in the walls. It was just as loud inside as it was outside. The tiled walls didn't help either. They were shown to a metal table without a cloth and given menus. After a short while they all came to the conclusion that they were unable to read Chinese and so, called the waitress. She couldn't speak English. Several mimes and imitations later, much to the amusement of the other diners, they made it understood that they wanted chicken. They sat back under the slowly revolving fans and bright neon lights and waited. 'This had better be good after the journey here,' said Matt. 'Where the hell did you learn to drive like that?' asked Bill. 'Why, what's wrong with my driving?' asked Dimetrius. 'Call it driving, I've seen better drivers put in jail for trying the stunts you managed to get away with,' said Bill. 'Well, if you don't like it, one of youse can drive back,' sniffed Dimetrius. 'Alleluia,' said Matt.

The chopsticks arrived, and all three of them realised they were in trouble. The chicken was bought to the table and everyone was provided with a bowl of boiled rice. The bird had been roasted and placed on the plate breast-side down. It's feet were splayed out behind it whilst its neck lay in a straight line in the other direction. 'It's still got it's bleedin' head on,' observed Bill. 'It looks like it's been deep fried,' said Matt, 'ah well, at least it's got its eyes shut.

Who wants the head?' Abortive attempts to pick at the chicken were made with the chopsticks. They eventually resorted to tearing it apart with their hands. Trouble was, it was 'roasting' hot. Tasted okay though. It seemed as though they were the most entertaining act the place had had in a long time. Everywhere they looked, people were laughing at their attempts to eat this chicken and rice with their fingers. After all, every self- respecting Chinese had learnt to use chopsticks at an early age. After wiping their hands on paper napkins, they paid the bill and left. None of them wanted to linger longer than necessary in that loud, smelly, brightly lit, embarrassing cafe situated in a town in the middle of nowhere. They set off back; with Bill driving.

One cool day when the monsoon was due, the lads on the flight were comparing notes about how they spent their off-duty hours. Matt listened to stories about those who had gone to donate blood in the afternoon. 'Do you know, they give you three cans of Tiger afterwards?' said one of the lads. 'Gerraway,' said Matt. 'Nah, it's true,' said one of the others. 'I got so pissed on three cans after giving blood that I went the next day and gave some more.' Hmm, thought Matt, that sounds a bit dangerous to me. I think I'll take a rain check on that game.

The rain came down in sheets and the trees bent to the force of the wind, and Matt felt cool for the first time since leaving 'Blighty'. Between showers they made their way to lunch and thence, from the mess hall to their billets. 'What are you doing this afternoon Matt?' asked Tone. 'I need to go down to Radio Butterworth and do some prep for the show tonight,' said Matt. 'But you're not on tonight, are you?' asked Tone. 'Yes,' said Matt, 'I'm standing in for one of the married blokes who lives on Penang Island. He can't make it in tonight.'

After a shower and a change, Matt made his way down to the radio station and signed in. Some time later whilst in the record library,

Matt was called to the 'phone by Mildred, the secretary. He took the call which was from a young lad wanting a request for his friends and teacher at his school. Matt took down the details and realised from the conversation that the lad was from the Blind School on Penang island. His name was Albert and he wanted a classical piece playing. Not the normal type of request on Matt's show he noted but still, this wasn't his show, was it? The evening passed and the show seemed to go smoothly enough. Matt made his way back to the billet thinking about the blind school. He resolved to find out where it was and decided to help out if he could.

One day he phoned the school and made himself known to one of the teachers. He was invited along and shown round. There were approximately 50 pupils who immediately wanted to become his pal and couldn't ask enough questions about his life, past and present. He used to get along there two or three times a week after work and would play games or just chat with the children. It was run along the lines of a boarding school because that's what it was. The children tried to teach him Braille but his fingertips were not sensitive enough to pick out the individual letters. He played 'Blind Mans Bluff', running silently between the rooms and grounds, but always lost. He tried to ensure that he used up what little extra spare time he had by visiting the school. Just thirty minutes or an hour as and when he could, gave them a diversion from normal life at school. He would play the guitar and they would all sing the latest songs they'd heard. The kids were much better than Matt at memorising the words and melodies of any new song that came along. He was hard pressed to keep up.

Matts' off-duty hours were starting to fill up. He was a member of the camera club and went to Ju-Jitsu classes once a week. There was the radio station and the odd evening out in the island bars, laughing and drinking with his friends. A couple of times a week, late at night, he sat with one or two of his mates on the veranda outside his room in the cool of the evening, devouring the hottest curry ever bought anywhere in the world and of course, there was the swimming pool with its young mums, its bar and its steak sarnies.

The daily routine continued. Two days on Ops, two days on normal duties humping those back-breaking accumulators, and two days off. One day there was a commotion on the main road outside the main gate. The civilian workers, who had jobs on the camp, had gone on strike. They were picketing the main camp gates and generally causing an uproar. The local police, it seemed, were content to do nothing and were happy to let what was becoming 'civil unrest' continue. There were placards being held up proclaiming to anybody interested in reading them, "Support our strike" and 'Help us fill our rice bowls". When the heat of the day had died down, there were usually about 30 or so men. Sometimes a few more, sometimes a few less. The Australian airmen who were bussed to and from the island were complaining that their coach had eggs thrown at it on more than one occasion. Things were building to a head and something had to be done. There was only one bunch of soldiers based at the camp, apart from Treble One Battery of the Royal Australian Artillery, and that was number One Squadron of the Royal Air Force Regiment. The Australian camp commandant chose the 'Pommies' to go and face the music and so it was that Matt and his mates found themselves detailed for 'Riot Drill'.

They watched films and attended lectures about how crowd control was exercised and this, Matt discovered, was how it worked.

It would seem that order was achieved first, by identifying the ringleader, usually male, who leapt up and down shouting and yelling at the top of his voice. He was quite easy to spot on the training film. A white line of tape was then placed on the ground, while six rifle- men knelt in a line facing the crowd. The officer in charge then went behind each rifleman in turn and loaded the rifle with either a blank or a real bullet. The rifleman was not supposed to know whether he had a blank or the bullet. A banner was then displayed to the crowd and a bugle was blown to attract the crowds attention. Assuming that someone in the crowd had a sufficient knowledge of English, they would know that it proclaimed, *'Anybody crossing this line will be shot'*. The 'Ringleader' who was supposed to be exciting the crowd with his rhetoric was, of course, the target. The riflemen were given the order to *'Take Aim'*, then *'Fire'*. The *'baddie'* then fell down dead protesting that he hadn't crossed the line and the supposedly, by now, silent crowd went home leaving the stretcher party to cart the body off. The riot squad marched off for tea and buns and all was at peace with the world once more.

Considering what Matt went through some years later in Londonderry during the riots of the early '70s, the drill as taught then was hopelessly out of date.

They practised with water being sprayed on them, bricks, cans and rotten fruit being thrown and the liberal use of Tear Gas, or CS as it was known. They could not use gas masks or respirators as there were not enough to go around, so they had to suffer without them. And suffer they did. Every day for a week, in a line with batons and shields and nowhere to go but to suffer what was thrown at them in the heat and humidity. They all wanted to be *'riflemen'* but it would seem there were none for this type of rehearsal. Matt volunteered to be the *'bugler'* but was told to get back in line. After they'd rioted and practised their drills in view of the strikers outside the camp gates it all somehow, miraculously seemed to go away.

Perhaps the use of the CS gas upwind of the gates had something to do with it or maybe the sight of the line of shields and batons made the point. Whatever it was, the problem of the picket line, like the baker in The Hunting of the Snark, *'softly and suddenly vanished away'*. The next day it was 'business as usual', with the trouble-makers absent and the placards gathering dust as they lay face down in the dirt.

That should have been the end of it but, after everything had died down, the Australians being bussed over to the island still complained about having raw eggs thrown at them.

Matt and his mates made sure of that - as they stood six stories up on the roof of the ferry OP whilst the buses passed below to board the ferry. They felt justified because of the number of times they had been sent to the back of the lunch queue, by the rotund little corpuscle, simply because they were Pommies.

When they had finished their basic Regiment training at Catterick, they had passed out in the rank of Leading Aircraftman. After a year, if they passed the required exams, they would be promoted to Senior Aircraftman. This not only meant a rise in seniority but more pay as well. For a couple of hours each afternoon, Matt and his mates attended lessons and lectures in preparation for a series of exams and practical tests. They all passed and were eventually awarded the promotion. Not the biggest jump in the world but it was a start, Matt mused.

On one of his days off, Matt had driven around to the northern side of Penang . He had a favourite hotel there with a superb swimming pool. There were sun beds going free and an ocean view to die for. The management were happy for Matt to use the facilities for free because he brought trade to the hotel in the form of mates who drank and ate there. The pool sported a 10 metre high diving board and to be truthful, the first time Matt looked down from the top board he thought the pool had suddenly shrunk to the size of a postage stamp. He had been going to the the hotel for some weeks when, one day, he realised that the pool was crowded. If that wasn't unusual enough, most of the crowd were teenage Canadian girls. He got chatting to a seventeen year old girl who was obviously after his body but when her friends arrived on scene Matt thought he'd died and gone to heaven. One of the more voluptuous older girls introduced herself. She was one of the teachers, her name was Penny, and these other people were children and staff from a missionary school which had been displaced from Thailand due to flooding. They were going to move into new premises in some place called the Cameron Highlands. Had he heard of it? Matt knew the Cameron Highlands well, including the hotel they were taking over. There was also a Military convalescent home for service men who were sent there to take the 'airs' and recuperate after a spell in hospital for injury or illness. He had been there a few times to visit mates who were recovering from various ailments. It was about six to eight hours drive from Butterworth on the motorbike and was situated up in the hills, past the tea plantations, at about 6000 feet above sea level and the heat of Malaysia. It was cool enough to warrant an open fire in the winter and blankets on the beds at night. What luxury to escape the sticky, fetid heat of the lowlands at sea level. Over the next few weeks, Matt got quite friendly with the staff and pupils of the school. The day of their move got close and Matt was invited to come and see them any time he could make it. Matt made the trip a few times over the next few months and he became a familiar face there during his two days off. Kids used to look out for him when they knew he was due.

 One day, Matt was talking to Charlie, the squadron clerk. Apparently, he was never seen around camp on his days off. 'Too true,' said Matt, 'there's to much to do and see, without wasting the experience of being over here for a couple of years. I, for one, will not be zipped to my pit reading the same cowboy adventure for the twentieth time like some around here,' said Matt. He told Charlie about Tanah Rata and his time away from camp. Charlie asked Matt if he could come and get away for a couple of days. 'Sure, no problem. You'll need to get yourself a crash helmet though. Otherwise it's not on,' Matt said.' 'No sweat,' said Charlie, 'I'll get one this afternoon.' 'Bring the bare minimums with you for an overnighter,' said Matt, 'we'll need to keep the weight down.' Matt arranged for them to leave at six on Saturday morning as it was his next off-duty, slot. Sure enough, Charlie was there as breakfast started and having eaten they set off. It was a nice day with light traffic and they made Ipoh in three-and-a-half hours. Stopping for a coffee at one of the many stalls at the side of the road, Matt explained that they would not be stopping again until they got to Tanah Rata.

 The road was narrow, with hairpin bends and steep slopes to one side. It was slippery in places where water ran continuously down the mountain side. It was unlikely that they would see any traffic on the road but they might see a tiger. They had frequently been spotted up at the convalescent home. Indeed, one drunken Jock had chased a tiger across the lawn one night while brandishing an empty bottle of Tiger beer! They made their way steadily upwards. Past the tea plantations and on to the the Hotel complex at the top. Thick jungle surrounded the area where the hotel was set amongst large lawns. They were ambushed by the kids on arrival as Charlie was introduced to the shouting, screaming mob. Matt introduced Penny and her husband John and they, in turn, introduced him to the Principal, Jack. They ate that night in the large dining hall, along with the rest of the school. When dessert was served, John asked Matt if he would like any 'vanilla sauce' with his cake. Matt smiled when he realised that John was referring to a large jug of custard. 'We seem to get this stuff served with every desert,' said John, 'I don't care for it much myself.' Matt enlightened the assembled Canadian company about the English and their custard habits and gleefully helped himself to more. Charlie helped out too. Conversation turned to where they'd come from and how long they all expected to be here. John and Penny announced excitedly that they'd be moving to Phnom Penn in Cambodia in a couple of months to join another school there. Matt thought nothing about it at the time. Everybody moved about so much all the time that it was no big thing. Sad to see them go but there you are.

In the morning, Matt decided to show Charlie around the local area. One of the hotel lads came along as the local guide. Matt wanted to see and photograph Robinson Falls; a pathway led down from the hotel complex, through the jungle and on to the falls. The guide told them to be careful and not to stumble into the stream below the falls. They looked at the fast flowing water as it rushed downhill away from the falls. They were informed that roughly a quarter of a mile further on, the stream disappeared into a hole in the rocks and didn't reappear until it came out at the bottom of the mountain.

A couple of sightseers had slipped into the stream a few months ago and their bodies were recovered at the bottom of the mountain some days later. As the mountain was about 6000 feet high, it was an horrific thought as to what had happened to the two guys, who must have suffered badly until unconsciousness, then death, bought them blessed relief. The thought of the bashing from the rocks on the way down that they would surely have suffered during that awful journey through the mountain was too awful to contemplate.

They arrived at the falls bathed in sunshine. Matt took a few photographs but decided that he needed something to give the falls perspective. He shouted across to Charlie. 'Move to your left a bit to give me something to contrast against the falls.' Charlie gave Matt a thumbs up. The roar from the falling water was deafening. Looking through the viewfinder at Charlie, Matt moved across the stream and put his foot on a rock that was covered in wet, green moss. He was wearing crepe-soled chukka boots and didn't stand a chance. His foot slipped and he fell headlong into the raging torrent, head facing downstream and feet towards the falls.

Matt was a good swimmer. He had learnt to swim at an early age and over the years, had trained himself to be able to stay underwater longer than anybody. He had watched people at the local baths and had learnt the tricks of hyperventilation. He had almost drowned as a child in the the river Witham, near his home at Swinderby, and only his ability to hold his breath had saved him then.

As he was falling towards the water he took the deepest breath he had ever taken and held it. The shock of the cold nearly drove it from him: The buffeting against the rocks nearly drove it from him. It was impossible to grab anything. The rocks were so slippery and he seemed to be moving past everything at a 100 miles an hour. The surface was a silvery gleam about two feet beyond his outstretched hands and Matt knew that he was moving fast and had travelled a fair way in a short while. Trying all the time to grab something, the strain was using up his precious air and his breath was starting to give out. His lungs were struggling and trying to make him breath. Panic was beginning to set in. The current was so strong and the movement so swift that there was no way that he could even see anything to grab, to halt his inexorable movement towards the rock hole. He struggled not to breath as panic tried to take over his bodily reflexes. He clamped his mouth shut and screwed up his nostrils against the urge to breath. He started to see red - the last stage, he knew, before blackout and oblivion. He opened his eyes and to his amazement saw the face of Christ. He felt something which brushed against his left hand and he instantly snapped back into consciousness. He grabbed what felt like a tree root and gripping as only a drowning man can, Matt held on. Now the problems really started. Up until now Matt had been moving along with the current. Because he had grabbed the root, he had the whole force of the current trying to pull him away. His lungs were at breaking point. He was about to give up when he got his free hand around and over a rock, his head lifted up out of the water for a second. Enough for the briefest of breaths. As he went under again he prayed for the root to hold. Against all odds he managed to use his other hand to lift his head again. With a strength and desperation only given to a superbly fit, drowning man, Matt pulled himself up over the rock and into a quiet-water pool at the side of the fast flowing stream. He got onto his hands and knees, crawled up to the track and sucked air as hard as he'd ever breathed in his life. His surroundings now came back into focus. The silence was replaced with the noise of the mountain stream, someone running down the hill beside the stream shouting his name, and his heavy breathing. 'Here,' he yelled. 'Matt, for fucks sake,' yelled Charlie, 'I thought you were a goner.' 'Believe me,' said Matt, 'so did I.'

Matt lay for ten minutes or so on his back on the track. He gratefully smoked a cigarette that Charlie had given him. He focussed on the trees above him and watched the birds fluttering from branch to branch. He listened to the roaring of the water and wondered about Christ. His camera was still around his neck and dripping water but he didn't care.

He wondered about himself and how he was still alive. How had he got out of that one? He shivered. Not because it was cold but because shock was setting in. He stood up and leaned heavily on Charlie. 'I need to get out into some sunshine mate,' said Matt, 'It's a wee bit too chilly here for me.' Matt and Charlie started to walk slowly back up the hill towards the hotel. Matt noticed with surprise that he was still shivering. Back in the lobby, they met a crowd of surprised faces. The hotel guide had seen Matt fall in and assumed the worst as he disappeared downhill. So convinced was he about the outcome, he had run back to the hotel and initiated the call for an ambulance to meet a search party at the bottom of the mountain to recover the body. To see a bedraggled Matt walking back into the hotel was unbelievable. Matt looked at the concerned faces around him and answered questions for a couple of minutes. After giving assurances that he was none the worse for his adventure, he made his excuses and went off for a long, hot shower.

As he drove back to Butterworth that afternoon his senses seemed to be heightened . Sounds were clearer, colours were brighter and he savoured every second of what seemed to be a new life. Against all odds, he had survived falling into that stream. Time seemed to pass slowly and every second of the eight hours drive back to camp was sheer pleasure. Dropping Charlie off outside his billet, Matt parked up his bike and made his way to his room to get his kit ready for the morning. OPs tomorrow, he thought. Set the alarm for 0430 and lets have an early night.

One day, during mail call, Matt had a parcel. It was the smallest parcel he'd ever seen, measuring about one, by two, by one-and-a-half inches. When he opened it up he discovered a piece of wedding cake with a note from his father. Some ribald fun was poked at Matt over that but, eventually, over a week things died down. His parents had been divorced for years now and the thought of his father remarrying didn't phase him out any more. A couple of weeks later he had another small parcel. This time from his mother. The contents were identical. With his father and mother getting married within a month of each other, the lads concluded that Matt must have been born out of wedlock. They could now call him a bastard with impunity, which they did whenever an excuse arose. Matt was now becoming an experienced hand and started to look out for things to stretch himself. Squadron Routine Orders, one morning, showed that volunteers were required to become parachutists. If successful, the applicants would need to pass a medical and undergo physical training for some months before being selected to go to the parachute training school. The school was based at Changi in Singapore and Matt and his mates fancied a trip down to the bright lights once more. They applied, but were dismayed to discover that the six places available were subscribed three times over. There would be some lively competition if they all got through the medicals. A couple of men failed because they were too tall; six foot was the maximum height allowed. When he was measured, Matt slumped slightly so that his six foot one-and-a-half inches came out at six foot exactly. A couple of men failed because they were colour blind, though what difference that would make Matt hadn't a clue. Each day started with their early morning PT, followed by the pool. Some failed because they couldn't go off the top board. It wasn't the height, they said, but the deep water. They couldn't swim. One by one, the 'sick, lame and lazy' fell out of the running until, eventually, there were eight of the original 18 left. A run-off was arranged to see who wanted it badly enough. Only the first six would get through. The problem was, the CO had come to some sort of arrangement with the CO of the Royal Artillery Battery. It was going to be a race, Aussies against the Pommies. Each man was allowed two pints of water in regulation bottles and donning their Jungle Greens and carrying rifles and webbing, they were taken out in two trucks. They were dropped off 10 miles out, in two squads, and began the race back. The temperature was at least 100 degrees in the shade and the humidity was 90 percent. They prayed for rain on the way back but no such luck. Eventually Matt and his mates settled into a rhythm and began to stretch the opposition. At the end, it was no contest. It was easy to see who had taken the training seriously and who had not. Matt and five others earned their tickets down to Singapore that morning and felt really good about beating the rest, by a fair margin. They came in through the gates that morning to a hero's welcome - cheering from the Brits and booing from the Aussies. It was all good natured stuff as the sweat rolled off them and dripped onto the floor. They were stood down for the rest of the day. Thankfully they handed over their kit and made their way to the billets and cool showers. Later that morning, they joined the lunch queue. They were early and for once in their lives had managed to join at the head. They were at the door when the little rotund man came out from inside to inspect their hands and fingernails. As they had not long been out of the shower Matt had '*no worries mate*' but he had reckoned wrong. 'Back to the end and wash your hands,' said the corpusle. 'Shit,' Matt muttered under his breath as he moved from first in the queue to thirtieth.

One morning, as they were given their tasks for the day, Matt and his pals realised they would be working late that night. They had to report to the squadron compound in Jungle Greens, with shirt sleeves rolled down, at 18:00 that evening. They would meet up with a couple of Land Rovers and drivers. Five corporals would accompany them to ensure they stayed out of mischief. They were going to the railhead to collect four brand new, three-ton trucks and drive them back. The work detail timings were governed by the train times. They assembled that evening and loaded spare jacks, wheel spanners, fuel and assorted spare parts and bits which were supposed to make any reluctant truck go. As they set off, Matt noticed that there were no mechanics amongst the party. This could be fun, Matt mused.

Arriving at the goods yard, they found the vehicles parked up and locked. There was nobody about and by that time, all sensible railway workers had finished for the day and gone home.

A confusion of corporals now scratched their heads and asked each other as to 'who had bought the spare keys'. Nobody, it would seem, had any sort of responsibility for bringing any sort of spare keys. Matt sighed and slowly shook his head. He wandered over to one of the trucks and climbed up to the roof of the cab. Getting into the vehicles was no problem. They had been fitted with a machine-gun ring to the roof of the cab. This consisted of a large reinforced hole, concealed with a canvas cover. It was the work of a second to remove it and drop down into the cab. Starting these things was just as easy. Whilst Matt was at St Athens on his driving course, he had made a point of spending time in the servicing hanger with the mechanics. One day, one of them said to Matt, 'If you're ever in a fix because you've forgotten your keys, this is how you start these trucks.' The mechanic had started the truck and showed Matt the trick to get the ignition working. Now he put his knowledge to use and removing one of the fuses from the passenger side fuse box, he clipped it between the two fuse holders. The ignition lights came on and he pressed the starter. The engine fired. The effect on the corporals' huddle was electric. In the midst of their discussion, which had become quite heated, they froze and in slow motion, turned to face the sound of the vehicle engine. Jerry, the MT corporal, came over and enquired as to where Matt had found the keys. Matt told him there were no keys and showed him how to start the trucks. Soon they were all on their way and half-an-hour later they were parked up back at the squadron. Removing the fuses stopped the engines and as the lads made their way back to their billet they were grinning like 'Cheshire cats'. It had been funny to see the panic that the disorganised shambles had bestowed upon the five illustrious leaders. It had been funny to see the looks of amazement that the first truck starting up had instilled. The way the 'blame game' had stopped as they slowly turned in disbelief to stare at the truck ticking over behind them were memories Matt stored away, to occasionally bring out and smile at in later years. 'Let's go and get showered and changed,' someone suggested. 'There's still time to get a couple of beers in before the NAAFI bar closes.' The next morning the squadron had a visit from the Royal Military Police or Red Caps. Apparently, someone had got into the railway yard last night and nicked some trucks belonging to the Royal Green Jackets. Four to be precise. When the railway workers arrived at work that morning they had discovered the loss and being the injured party, they had reported it. The Red Caps wandered about and looked at the vehicles. They asked to inspect the paperwork and so discovered their missing vehicles. Jerry was called over to the SWO's office, where lots of yelling and shouting was to be heard. Eventually, the other four corporals were called for and a repeat performance ensued. Jerry developed a severely red face because he was responsible for removing the vehicles, albeit in good faith; with no covering paper work and no signed receipts. If anybody drove a service vehicle without current and valid authorisation, that vehicle was uninsured. They had all broken the law.

Chapter 9 - Going for a Jump

Detachment orders came through the following week. Matt and five others were to travel down to Singapore by train and report to the General Office at RAF Changi. They would receive further instructions then. The journey would take two days on the train and they would be able to use the NAAFI club situated on the platform at Kuala Lumpa railway station for breakfast. Matt and his mates packed their kit and included civilian clothes for the evenings. They were transported down to the railway station in the afternoon and given their train tickets and pay books. They were travelling in uniform so there was no need to get their civilian cloths dirty. They piled into a wooden-seated carriage and stowed their luggage.

The big adventure had begun. As the train whooshed and puffed out of Butterworth station, Matt noticed they were on a single track line. They seemed to be going through a thick forest or jungle as there was nothing to see outside but a wall of green. The carriage had bare, wooden seats and was not the latest thing in comfort. Matt discovered, later, when he went to use the toilet that it consisted of a hole in the floor. The sleepers could be seen rushing past a couple of feet underneath the carriage and warm air funnelled up through the hole. Izal slippery toilet paper on a roll was provided, along with a bucket of water. There was a stainless steel sink screwed to the wall, it had no taps although there was a drain-hole directed towards the hole in the floor. Matt hoped that the bucket of water was intended only for use in the bowl.

They discovered that their carriage was carrying a load of Gurkha soldiers, also bound for Singapore. Some, they discovered, were going on a parachute course. The lads soon made themselves known. The Gurkhas couldn't speak English and the Brits couldn't speak 'Gurkhanese' or Gurkhalhi. What the hell, they reasoned. These guys fight with the British Army in every theatre they are asked to go to, therefore they're our comrades and mates. The lads

87

sat amongst them and they all had great fun making mistakes whilst 'bastardising' each other's language. The afternoon turned into night as the train rolled on. The greenery outside turned grey and then black. The seats got harder and the lads started yearning for the comforts of their billet in Butterworth. After a long, uncomfortable night the morning dawn showed grey and they rose, as one, to get to the toilet before anybody else. A shower was out of the question but, using the water bottles from their green webbing belts, a cold water shave, a brush of teeth and a swig of clean water were a godsend.

At seven in the morning they came to a steam-shrouded stop at a small platform, in a siding, at Kuala Lumpa station. They were told by the guard that the engine needed to take on water and coal. They also needed to carry out essential maintenance to the running gear. It would take an hour. The train would then depart for Singapore. Looking around him, Matt thought he'd been dropped straight into the Victorian age. The old style of the platform and associated 'Wrought Iron' work was genuine, old style colonial, Victorian English.

They left the platform and walked through the station out onto the street. The NAAFI entrance was next to the station entrance and they went inside.

The heat and the smell that hit them immediately made their eyes water and caused them to catch their breath. The servery was laid out with steaming great bowls of curry and rice. Each of the Gurkhas was sat with a mound of curry and rice heaped onto a plate and a pint bottle of Anchor beer. Matt could see by the empties that some were on their second bottle. It was incredible, Matt thought, that these little men could put away so much food and beer. Let alone at seven in the morning.

They were invited to help themselves to breakfast and so, Matt and his mates found themselves sitting down at a little after seven a.m. in a Gurkha NAAFI, in a railway siding, in the capital city of

Malaysia. They dined on what they discovered was curry at the temperature of molten lava and between hiccups, they washed it down with pints of frothing bubbly beer. The Gurkhas thought there was nothing extraordinary in this fare but Matt and his mates thought they had done something *'above and beyond the normal call of duty'* as they sat red faced, bloated, belching and smiling. They thanked their hosts politely and made their way outside. They went back to the shade of the platform and wandered idly up and down 'people watching' until it was time to board the train again. That evening, at six, they chugged and puffed into the station at Jahore Baru. They arrived with a great sigh in a cloud of steam at the last station before the Singapore causeway and the end of the line for 'Puffing Billy'.

They wearily climbed down, gratefully giving up their wooden seats for the pleasure of standing up and walking. They made their way outside to the car park and towards an RAF coach which was waiting in the shade. The driver confirmed that they were expected and they climbed aboard. They were dropped off outside the 'good old' Transit Block at RAF Changi and were met by an orderly who issued them with pillows, sheets and instructions for the morning. They made their way gratefully to their allocated rooms and remembering their last visit, hit the showers before making their way down to the 'Makan' stalls, curry huts and bazaars of Changi village. Nothing had changed. It was just as noisy. The same menus, with the same mistakes, adorned the same walls. It was like coming home and Matt grinned at the thought.

Next morning they reported to the Sergeant in charge of the General Office and were directed to wait for transport. Ten minutes later, they were taken across the main road onto the airfield and dropped off outside the No1 Parachute Training School of the Far East Air Force. They were met by another Sergeant who was one of the Parachute Jump Instructors, or PJIs as they were known. They were escorted across to the training hanger and introduced to the staff. They were shown the equipment they would be working with and then stood down for the rest of the day. The prospect of actually jumping out of a perfectly serviceable aeroplane had been in the back of Matt's mind but he hadn't really dwelled on it. Until now, that is. Having the equipment shown to them sort of bought it home. They knew now that what had seemed like a bit of an adventure, with all the kudos that went with it amongst their peers back at Butterworth, was about to become a reality. They were told to be ready to get onto the transport at 06:30 dressed in green, long trousers with boots and putties. They had to wear a green vest under their shirts, a jungle hat and their webbing belt with two containers full of fresh, drinkable water. Arriving back at the billet, they met Freddy once more and agreed that he could look after them. Being a little wiser now, they negotiated a rate of ten dollars a week instead of two dollars a day. They hit the sack and those with travel alarms set them to go off at a quarter to six.

They were awake before the new dawn broke and went for breakfast early. They were waiting for the transport well before it arrived. On it were an assortment of people all going across to the other side of the airfield. They were dropped off outside the school hanger and made their way inside. A quick roll call completed the formalities. There was no muster parade or any of that rubbish: here they were treated like adults. Their course consisted of a Naval Surgeon Commander, a couple of Army dispatchers, six RAF Regiment gunners and ten Ghurkas. They were shown the landing roll and started practising it. 'Side right, forward right and rear right. Side left, forward left and rear left.' They practised for two days, on coconut matting, gradually working up to jumping from higher and higher platforms. Next came the 'Fan'. This consisted of a parachute harness attached to a cable. The cable was wound around a drum and the end of the drum was attached to a fan's blades. The resistance of the fan blades whilst spinning through the air governed the rate at which the person strapped into the harness fell. The rate of fall approximated to the rate of fall you'd get from a real parachute. The equipment platform was situated about 20 feet, or two floors, up. It seems like a long way down, thought Matt the first time he tried it, but before long he had got used to the height and started to enjoy the training.

 When they had learnt to fall and roll without breaking anything they moved on to the next piece of equipment. The exit trainer. This consisted of an aircraft fuselage complete with seats, static line cables and door. Outside, there was a cable running down the length of the fuselage and sloping down to the ground. A 'death slide'. Here, you learnt to exit the aircraft in 'Clean Fatigue' and 'Dirty Fatigue'. Clean Fatigue meant that you exited wearing only your parachute and its reserve. Dirty Fatigue meant that you exited wearing both parachutes and carrying a Personal Weapons Container, or PWC, as well. They were taught the aircraft drills and were practised all day, every day until they became so automated they could carry them out in their sleep. The first jump was set for the coming Friday. They would be jumping, in clean fatigue, from a 'Twin Pioneer' over the airfield of Semberwang. The day before, they visited the parachute packing section and drew their parachutes. They adjusted the straps so that they fitted properly and stowed them in numbered containers, then they made their way back to the hangers. When they arrived, one of the PJIs said, 'You're making your first jumps tomorrow. In about five minutes, the Royal New Zealand Air Force will be carrying out an equipment drop over the airfield. You might be interested to watch and get some confidence in seeing how reliable parachutes are at opening.' The course stood and watched. Sure enough the loads were dropped. Out of the 10 loads dropped, six piled into the airfield and crashed in great clouds of dirt and dust; as their parachutes failed. The students watched open-mouthed, stunned and silent. The only ones not affected were the Gurkhas who, Matt guessed, couldn't care less whether they had parachutes or not!

The next morning they were bussed over to Semberwang with their equipment. They were briefed that they would be jumping in two-man sticks from the 'Twin Pioneer'. A PJI would drop first, as a drifter, to work out the wind strength and direction. This would enable the pilot to make any corrections necessary to the aircraft heading or drop point. 'Don't forget your immediate action drills once you are out of the aircraft, check your canopy before you do anything else. Don't forget your in flight drills on the way down. Keep your knees and ankles together as you've been taught and you'll be okay.' The PJI drifter, Tone and Matt climbed on board. Tone was to be first out, and Matt second. They took off and the aircraft circled the airfield while making its way up to 1000 feet, then they turned and ran into the aerodrome. The PJI stood up and hooked on his static line. He fitted the safety pin and turned for the dispatcher to check the ties at the rear of his parachute. All okay, he turned and faced the door. 'RED ON, GREEN ON, GO,' yelled the dispatcher. The PJI glanced at them, grinned and ran out of the door with a loud whoosh. Matt knew he was wearing a parachute but it still seemed to be the most unnatural thing he'd ever seen. The dispatcher was shouting at them now, 'STAND UP, HOOK ON.' They stood and hooked their static lines onto the cable running the length of the cabin. They made sure their safety pins were inserted. 'CHECK EQUIPMENT,' came the call. They checked their own from the top downwards. Satisfied, Matt then checked the rear of his mate's chute. He then slapped Tone on the right shoulder and turned around. Tone checked Matt's rear and slapped his right shoulder. They turned back and faced the rear door of the aircraft. 'TELL OFF FOR EQUIPMENT CHECK,' yelled the dispatcher. 'TWO OK,' yelled Matt. 'ONE OK, PORT STICK OK,' yelled Tone. 'STAND IN THE DOOR,' yelled the dispatcher. They did what's known as the para shuffle down towards the door. Tone turned to face the door. 'RED ON,' they waited, 'GREEN ON, GO'. The dispatcher slapped Tone on the back and he was gone. Time stood still for Matt. Tone had disappeared and Matt was stood in the door. He looked down at the airfield 1000 feet below and his life flashed before him. This was the moment of truth for him. Did he have the bottle to go through with this? 'GO,' yelled the dispatcher. Matt leapt as hard as he could: it was an automatic reaction to the command. He saw the tailplane pass over him and dwindle up the sky. He realised now just how noisy it had been in the aircraft as he watched his canopy deploy in silence. All this seemed to be happening in slow motion but in reality, the sequence of events took about three seconds from start to finish. He checked his canopy again. His heart went into his mouth as he watched it close. Then it opened again, all fine there thought Matt as he remembered that the canopy breathed when it first opened. He checked all around him, all okay there. He assessed his drift and adopted the correct posture. Feet and knees together, knees slightly bent. Looking past his bent knees at the edge of his toecaps, he could make out a pair of gulls flying leisurely between him and the ground. He was being addressed by the course commander on the ground through a megaphone. 'Okay number two, good canopy, drift okay, good position, prepare yourself for your landing,' the disembodied voice drifted up. He experimented with pulling down on his lift webs to steer his canopy. The ground started to get close. The slow, floating flight had quickly turned into a frightening acceleration as the the ground rushed towards him. It's like being strapped to the front of an express train hurtling towards a brick wall, Matt thought later. At the moment though, Matt had his landing to concentrate on. He held his position. Elbows in, feet and knees tight together, knees slightly bent as he piled into the ground like a sack of potatoes. He lay and waited for the hurts to start. He sat up. He dragged in the lower shroud lines of his canopy to collapse it and released his harness. He stood up. He was okay. Eureka, he thought. He rolled up his parachute and slinging it over his shoulder, he walked off the 'Drop

Zone' (DZ) to the waiting vehicles. Handing in his parachute, he wandered over to the line of troops waiting to jump and nonchalantly lit a cigarette hoping that nobody would notice his shaking hands. He noted that a strange phenomena had occurred amongst the waiting troops. Those who were usually noisy or loud waited quietly and said nothing, whereas the normally quiet ones had suddenly become loud and talkative.

Back at camp that evening they couldn't stop talking about the experience. They were on a high. They went out to celebrate but limited themselves to a couple of beers and an early night. They were jumping again the next day.

That was the first and last time any of them jumped from the 'Twin Pin'. The next jump was from a Hastings. Again, clean fatigue but now in sticks of six. They took off from Changi this time, fully kitted up, and went through the 'stand up hook on' drills during the short hop to Sembawang. Matt was number one this time and as he stood in the door on the left or port side of the aircraft, his right hand was across his reserve whilst his left gripped the edge of the door lightly. Looking to the rear, he seriously wondered whether he had to lift his feet on exiting, or duck, because he tailplane was below and to the rear of the door. 'RED ON – GREEN ON – GO'. Matt leapt as hard as he could. The tailplane went over his head. Phew. The drop was a carbon copy of the first jump the day before, including the express train part. Once more, he got up amazed that he was still in one piece. Handing his 'chute in, he lit a cigarette and watched the third stick exiting the aircraft. One of them had pulled his reserve chute. It had opened awkwardly and the unfortunate owner must have somersaulted through the lift webs. The rear lift webs were behind his knees and he was coming down in the sitting position, buttocks first, under two parachutes. God, that's going to hurt, thought Matt. He threw away his cigarette and started to run towards the hapless parachutist. He could see now that it was the

Surgeon Commander. As he hit the ground, he had the presence of mind to lift his buttocks. His landing was rather like a judo break-fall. It took a while for him to recover his breath, so winded was he. Matt collapsed both of his chutes and released his harness. The directing staff arrived at the scene now and took over. A few minutes later, the Commander got up and walked painfully towards the waiting coach. He stood all the way back to Changi!

During the ground training, it had been drummed into them that they were to keep a good lookout for other parachutes near them. They were to steer away if they looked like colliding. If it was too late to steer away and it looked like you were going to penetrate the other person's shroud lines you had to spread-eagle your arms and legs to try and stop yourself going through. If you went through and got tangled then the lower chute would take the air from the chute above. The owner would free-fall until the canopy filled once more. It would then become the lower canopy. The new lowest canopy would steal the air from the one above and so it would continue until impact with the ground occurred during one of the free-falling moments. Nobody with any sort of imagination wanted to get tangled up with someone else's 'chute.

The next jumps were to be 'dirty fatigue': one in the morning and one in the afternoon. They would be jumping from the Blackburn Beverly next. A huge great lumbering giant of an aircraft, it had a fuselage interior large enough to fit a small church into. You could also climb a ladder up the inside into the tail boom, where more seats were fitted. There was another hatch up there to drop through if the simultaneous release of three sticks of paras was required.

Dirty fatigue meant that they now carried a PWC. This was a pack designed to hold their rifle and equipment during the drop. The training PWCs were ballasted at 60 pounds to give them some weight. There was a 15 foot length of rope which attached to the waist. A pair of quick release clips, one for the waist and one for the leg about knee height, were provided. You had to remember to pull the lower leg release clip before the waist clip. If you got it wrong the PWC would be hanging off your bent leg and nothing you could do would release it. Under those circumstances you were guaranteed a broken leg on landing. You also had to remember to secure the end of the rope to your waist belt. The DZ could get quite exciting if 60 pound packs started hurtling down from 1,000 feet. It would, at the very least, spoil your day thought Matt if one of those things hit you.

They donned their parachutes and carried their PWCs on board. The PWCs were now attached to belt, legs and waist and each owner sat with it held between his legs. They sat on red canvas, open-webbed seats facing the other stick. Steel helmets on, parachutes on, reserves on, PWCs on and strapped in. In the heat of a normal Singapore day in an aircraft that lived outside in the burning sun, they were soaked through with sweat before they sat down. They all sat in their private worlds of misery knowing full well that if something caused a fire during the engine start they didn't stand a chance of getting out in time. In great clouds of belching smoke each of the four engines started, and they began to taxi. As they roared down the runway, Matt gave silent thanks that the earth was curved. It could only be because of that, that the lumbering giant got airborne. As they climbed, the routine started. They stood up, hooked on and completed their checks. Matt was number seven of the starboard, nine-man stick. They shuffled down to the door and Matt, with the weight he was carrying, seriously doubted his ability to get through the door. They got the green light and started to exit as fast as they could. They all got out in good order and Matt turned sharply right as the slipstream hit him and he went down the slide. It was fascinating watching the parachutes open ahead and below him. He realised that his should be doing something by now. He looked up and behind and watched his canopy deploy. All okay. Check all round. All okay. Check below.

All okay. Release knee clip, okay now release waist clips. The PWC shot away and was pulled up short on its 15 feet of rope. Check canopy again. No tears or splits, it looks like a 'goodun'. Assessing his drift showed very little wind, which was born out by the red smoke 83 grenade marking the DZ. Keeping a good lookout for anybody getting near him, Matt floated down. Here comes the express train bit thought Matt and just then the PWC hit. His rate of descent seemed to stop, then continue at express speed once more. Of course, he'd lost 60 pounds of weight. He landed a split second later. The landing was not his best but he was okay. They handed in their equipment and climbed onto the bus. There was another jump that afternoon and Matt had a cunning plan. First though, lunch.

Matt wanted to take some highly illegal air-to-air photographs during the drop. He had a small, 'half frame', fully automatic camera called an 'Olympus Penn EE'. This had a smooth steel strap and if hung around his neck under his smock, it was undetectable once his smock had been zipped up. Over lunch, Matt told his mates about his plan. He told them to keep a safe distance because he wouldn't have much time to take pictures and he didn't want to spend what little time he had taking avoiding action by playing aerial starfish. Okay, that was the plan then. They finished lunch and made their way out to wait for the transport.

The afternoon took much the same format as the morning except, this time, they would be jumping from the Armstrong Whitworth Argosy. The Argosy was a much more modern machine than the Beverly. It was quieter and smoother, too. It had four prop jets and whilst there was more than enough room inside it was not as spacious as the Beverly. Standing up and hooking on, they completed their checks once more. They stood in the door and were dispatched. As soon as Matt hit the slipstream, he realised something was wrong. He was disorientated. He must have tumbled. He tried to check his canopy but his neck was being pressed by the rear lift webs. Shit, I've got 'Twists', thought Matt. His hand flew down and released the knee clip. He flipped the waist clips and felt the PWC jerk on the rope. He started kicking as hard as he could. He could see the horizon spinning as he kicked. Suddenly the pressure on his neck ceased. At the same time, Matt felt his PWC hit the ground. He went in again like a sack of spuds, only this time it hurt. His buttocks were numb and his feet were both smarting. He lay there thankful for his deliverance. He might be hurting but at least he was in one piece. Sounds came now and Matt realised that up to that point everything had been totally silent. People had run across the field. 'Jenkins,' one of the PJIs said, 'Are you okay?' 'I think so,' said Matt. He got up and released his harness. 'You had a fine set of 'twists' there,' said the PJI. Matt limped across to his parachute and rolled it up. His backside hurt like hell but he was moving, so no harm done. He was dammed if he was going to be medevac'd at this point of the course. They got on the transport and Matt offered a silent prayer of thanks that it was Friday. There was a whole weekend to recover. He was the second course member to stand all the way back on the coach and that night, after he'd slowly and carefully got to bed, he slept on his stomach but woke, frequently, with the pain during the night. The weekend was spent mainly at the pool. Swimming was good non-impact exercise and on the Monday morning, whilst still feeling a bit tender and sporting a huge bruise, he was ready for action. Over the next week, they jumped again from the Hastings, Beverly and Argosy. Each time they jumped from the Argosy, Matt had 'twists'. He never had a bad landing, certainly not like that one he'd had the first time he had the 'twists'. He was ready for them, and usually kicked and spun out quite quickly. They were briefed for a night descent. It would be 'dirty fatigue' in a ten man stick. They jumped over Sembawang once more, at eight in the evening, from a Hastings. The Hastings was now Matt's favourite aircraft. He never had 'twists' exiting the Hastings and the night jump was no exception. It was a strange feeling floating down without being able to see the ground. He just held the para position as briefed and kept his elbows in as he steered towards the 'A' marker on the DZ. He made the best landing of his life. He watched the rest of the jumpers from the DZ and thought it strange that the darker Khaki-coloured canopies stood out against the dark sky whereas the white canopies were almost invisible. He would have thought it the other way round but here was the proof.

And then the course was over. They paraded on the Monday and were presented with their parachutists' badges. The course had consisted of eight jumps, night and day, clean and dirty fatigue. They had practised drills for landing in trees, water and on land and on the whole, they had enjoyed it immensely. That afternoon, they flew back to Butterworth courtesy of a Royal New Zealand Air Force's Bristol Vibration box. The squadron now had its para team. It would be their job to jump in should their services be needed in the event of an aeroplane crash in inhospitable country which could not be reached by road and when choppers were not available. Part of the team would be made up from the medical branch and the rest would be them, the cover or guard.

The best part was that they now qualified for para pay at a rate of one shilling and six pence per day or ten and six a week. As long as they carried out their eight qualifying jumps each year, they would continue to receive para pay.

Chapter 10 – China Rock

Reporting back to the flight the next morning, they resumed their normal duties. They were told that the squadron would be going 'on detachment' in two weeks, to a place called 'China Rock' situated to the south of Singapore. They would be travelling on the land convoy. The guns and generators would be towed by the trucks down to Singapore and then taken by landing craft to the Rock itself. They would be there for two weeks, and the guns would be firing live ammunition against a 'sleeve' target towed behind a Meteor jet.

The guns were Bofors 'Forty Seventy' cannons. They were called 'Forty Seventies' because the calibre was 40 millimetres and the barrel length was 70 times its calibre, or 2.8 metres long. They fired a one-pound projectile of semi-armour piercing, high explosive at a rate of four rounds per second. The projectiles travelled at just under 1000 metres per second. The projectile itself would self-destruct at between 13 and 15 kilometres if it had not struck anything beforehand.

The gun itself weighed four-and-three-quarter tons. Removable wheels were fitted but, in an emergency, the gun could be fired whilst still on its wheels. It could be fired under power, which meant that the 'Gun No.3', or 'layer' as he was known, could aim and fire the cannon by means of a control bar or Bow. A thumb-switch was provided for firing. The bow was gripped with both the layer' hands and his arm movements, left or right, up or down, were followed faithfully by the gun. It could also be fired by hand or without power but other crew members were necessary for that activity.

The power was provided by a 27.5 KVA Meadows Generator. This consisted of a gigantic diesel engine mounted on a wheeled platform coupled to a generator. A couple of these could power any large UK hospital; indeed, one of them could easily power a village. It was capable of much more than its official electrical power rating and was only de-rated, on paper, to ensure that the military operator did not require a 'Plant' licence. Needless to say, the generator provided more than enough electrical power for the gun and so was used for kettles, cookers, lights, private radios and so on.

One gun detachment with all its equipment and Meadows generator trailer needed two Bedford trucks to move it.

The convoy to China Rock would consist of four guns, while four more guns would be left behind to supplement the Royal Australian Artillery's airfield defence solution. The squadron headquarters would use another Bedford truck and Matt's flight yet another. The ammunition would be carried by a Matador truck. With all this hardware and explosives moving 500 miles by road, they would all be armed and live ammunition would be carried. Matt was detailed as a Bedford truck driver towing a large, truck-sized radio communications caravan. All in all, the convoy would consist of 21 vehicles either towing or being towed. There would also be two 'Dispatch Rider' motorcyclists.

It was decided to have a rehearsal or practice convoy. It was set up so that drivers could get used to driving in convoy. The great day dawned and the convoy set out from the camp gates and headed towards Butterworth town. The MT corporal was riding one of the motorcycles, weaving in and out of the moving trucks with great panache. But, one time, as he cut across the front of Matt's truck, he over-cooked it. His recovery caused him to wobble, then leave the road. His bike hit a large stone and somersaulted, throwing him over the handlebars and into the monsoon drain that ran beside the road. Matt stopped beside the cloud of dust, as the front half of the convoy disappeared into the distance. The rest of the convoy was now stationary, as the angry Flight Sergeant made his way to Matt's vehicle. Matt was out of the cab and in the monsoon drain helping the hapless MT corporal attend to his many cuts and grazes. 'What the fuck's happening here?' the Flight Sergeant demanded. 'The MT corporal's fallen off his bike and got himself a 'Honda Rash',' said Matt. 'What happened?' asked the Flight Sergeant. 'The front wheel seized up,' said Jerry. Hmm, thought Matt, he doesn't want to admit he got it wrong and lost control. Scottie was taken away to the medical centre, while Matt and his co-driver heaved what was left of the motorcycle onto the back of the truck. 'Hope he fills out an accident report,' said Matt, to no-one in particular. 'Form FMT-3, I believe it's called. I'd have been roasted for pulling that stunt.' They all remounted and set off in pursuit of the rest of the convoy. They navigated around a large loop of local roads which eventually took them back to the camp. They didn't see the the rest of the convoy until, finally, they arrived back at the compound. The air was blue. Matt sat back and smiled to himself. Couldn't organise a piss up in a brewery this lot, he thought. It'll be better when they leave us alone to get on with it.

 The next two weeks were spent cleaning, painting and packing the equipment they were going to take down to the rock. The last days were used to load the vehicles until, one morning, they had their final brief. They drew weapons, and signed for and were issued with live ammunition. They set off. The monsoon had started by now and most of the morning was spent driving through torrential rain. They stopped mid-morning to refuel just north of Ipoh at Tampenies Junction. The turn-off at the Junction went up to Tana Ratah, which was high in the Cameron Highlands nestling among the tea plantations. Matt knew the area well having travelled there on his motor bike and spent many weekends there. After refuelling, they carried on to Kuala Lumpa. Reaching the capital that night, they slept in the back of their vehicles while parked up on an airfield owned by the Malaysian military. The next day was another marathon drive, down to Singapore. They made Changi that night and parked up in the compound of the resident No. 27 squadron

RAF Regiment unit. The vehicles were secured and after a couple of beers in the squadron club, it was suggested they all go downtown to 'Bugis' street. 'What's Boogy street?' asked Matt. 'It's where it's all at,' said one of the Jordies. 'Lets get doon an have a laugh, mon.' They wandered up to the gate and having negotiated a price with the local taxi drivers, headed off to Singapore's Bugis street. They arrived and were ushered to tables by touts. Matt and the lads from Butterworth had never seen anything like it. They were seated at metal tables placed in the middle of a blocked-off street. The lights were bright neon. The noise was typical of Singapore, loud and foreign. All along the street were bars and Makan stalls. Hawkers walked up and down selling everything from watches to sisters. Matt was warned by the lads not to go off with any good-looking girls. They weren't girls! In fact, it was safer here not to try for anything. Being out in the Far East, one could catch something quite exotic without trying too hard. 'You wan 'jig a jig' Johnny?' this male voice whispered in Matt's ear. He turned, startled, to find himself nose-to-nose with the most beautiful girl. She had a body that most women would die for but the voice just didn't match. 'Er, no thanks,' said Matt, blushing. His mates were wetting themselves with glee. 'Eh, fuck off kytie,' shouted someone else. Without a word, the girl-boy sniffed and walked off - but not before blowing a kiss in Matt's direction. They drank a couple of beers and then, after 'egging' each other on, decided to explore. Careful to stay within the brightly lit main avenue and not stray down any dark side streets, Matt caught the eye of a street hawker selling cheap jewellery and fake 'look alike' watches. Matt had pawned his watch a couple of weeks ago for some beer money and was looking for a replacement. After some spirited haggling, Matt paid four-dollars-fifty and considering that there were 11 dollars to the guinea at that time, he thought he'd 'done good'. At about two in the morning they realised they had to be 'up and at em' in the morning so, negotiating once more with a hard bargaining taxi driver, they made their way back to camp and bed. The taxi had cost them dearly because the driver realised that without his services to get them back to camp they were 'stuffed'. It was too far to walk and no-one wanted to move away from the bright lights of Bugis street and risk venturing off into the dark in the hope of finding a cheaper taxi. They arrived back at their billet and went to bed. 'What time is it?' asked one of the lads. Matt glanced at his watch: it had stopped. 'Fuck it!' he said and hit the sack. They were bushed.

The next morning saw them trundling down to the docks in the bright sunlight and steaming heat, both of which seared into their hangovers as they prepared their vehicles for loading into the landing craft.

Eventually, they were loaded and pulled away from the docks. As they moved further and further away, a breeze steadily blew up and the Singapore smell was left behind. They threaded their way through shipping anchored away from the port and steamed south around Palau Bulan island. There were so many little islands around that area it was like threading a needle, thought Matt. The journey took five hours; Matt found some shade and slept soundly for two of them. The landing craft slowed down and it was the vibration of the reversing propeller that woke him. He looked around and could see they were heading towards a beach of white sand. The water was clear and blue and it looked like a tropical island from a travel brochure, which, of course, is exactly what it was. About 100 yards back from the beach, sand dunes rose up. Matt estimated them to be about 20 to 30 feet high, and behind them stood mature poplar trees extending for the length of the beach. The beach looked about 600-800 yards long and gently sloped towards the sea. A grove of palm trees sat on the left-hand edge, and they had peppered the beach with fallen fronds and coconuts. The bow doors opened and one of the crew stood at the edge of the lowered ramp with a pole to test the depth. The landing craft shuddered slightly as it touched the sandy bottom. The drivers started up and engaged four-wheel-drive. They moved off in file through the water towards the waiting line of troops on the beach. They were directed towards one of the gaps in the dunes and driving through, they came across a clearing which doubled as a vehicle park. Switching off and dismounting, they grabbed their kit and made their way to the tent lines. Looking out for their flight, Matt spotted familiar faces putting up tents near the rear of the camp-site. 'Hello Jenkins,' said one of the corporals, 'You're over there with those lads. You can go and help get your tent up before you eat.' Matt wandered across and joined a group stood by an unpacked tent. They erected it making sure that it was in line with with the rest of the tentage. They made sure that the tent pegs were in line with the rest of the tents pegs so that anyone walking at night could keep to the line between the tents and not trip on a guy rope. They erected their camp beds, made their beds and broke out their tin plates, mugs and 'eating irons'. Matt wondered out loud as to what might be waiting for them at the mess tent - but one thing *was* for sure. There would be no Australian corporal waiting at the door to send them to the back of the queue. 'It looks like 'Compo', said one of the lads. Compo, or composite rations, was the tinned food they ate whenever fresh could not be obtained. Individual meals could be made up into separate 24-ration packs and stowed in backpacks to sustain individuals who were away from camp. 'Corr,' said Luke, 'babbies heads.' 'My favourite,' said Matt as they queued for individual steak and kidney puddings, mashed potatoes and tinned peas. This was eaten at bare tables. The temperature was in the hundreds and the roar of conversation was deafening. They washed their plates, grabbed their mugs of tea and went outside. It was cool there, as the sun was setting. They sat on the dunes and watched the sun set, while quietly enjoying a cigarette after their meal. A couple of miles out to sea they could see another island. It arose from the water with sheer cliffs. 'That's China Rock over there,' said one of the lads. 'It's only used as a bombing and strafing target.' 'What time is it?' asked Luke. 'Don't take the piss,' said Matt, still annoyed with his four-dollar-fifty watch purchase. They made their way back to their tent lines.

 Fall in outside the Flight HQ, they were told when they got back. They dutifully made their way across to the HQ tent and were detailed off for that night's camp guard. Each flight would be responsible, in turn, for a night's guarding. So, a broken night's sleep would occur only on every fourth night. Their time passed peacefully enough and after a 'Full English', they were detailed off for their daily jobs. As a flight, they had to mount OPs to warn of anything approaching. This could be from land sea or air, so the OP's would be in contact with the HQ by radio and telephone. The land-line cables needed to be laid and the batteries charged. The guns would be firing the next day so, for the lads of Control and Reporting flight, there was not much to do that day. Time to grab some 'ZZZs' thought Matt. That afternoon Matt and the lads wandered down to the beach. The guns had been set out with their equipment and the gun crews were busy cleaning the guns and getting everything for the morning. It was a hive of industry. They helped out where they could but, not knowing much about the guns' internal mechanisms, their tasks were confined to bore - checking and inspecting ammunition. These were tasks which took up valuable time so the detachments were grateful for any help; it freed up the crews for the more important work. During the firing they would be manning the OPs and observing and reporting on the 'Fall of Shot'. What that meant was that the observer stood directly behind the barrel of the gun, moving as necessary to remain in line behind it. The gun's tracer stream relative to the target was observed, called out and recorded. A '*Plus*' meant that the rounds were passing and disappearing behind the target, whereas a '*Minus*' meant that they were passing between the target and the gun. A high was a high and a low was a low. A hit was, of course, a hit and usually bought the target down.

The next day started early. Safety-arc markers were checked so that the correct bearings would be used. The gun-firing safety mechanisms, known as *'Taboos'*, were checked. The Taboos stopped the gun from firing when outside the firing arc and needed to be checked against the safety-arc markers to ensure they were set correctly. A firing circuit interrupter switch was checked for correct operation. This was used to allow the No.3 to fire when the *'Safety Officer'* was satisfied that he was laying the gun on the designated target. The spare barrels were laid out ready for use and the ammunition was loaded into the gun racks. They were ready.

The target-towing aircraft flew from the centre of the down-range area over the centre of the firing line of guns. The CO, or Director of Practice as he was known, was happy with the sleeve target and announced over the tannoy the next run as a Firing Run. The aircraft passed overhead once more and the Safety Officers raised their interrupter switches and called 'Safe to Shoot'. Single shots only were fired on the first run. The idea was to give the 'layers' some experience of the noise and vibration when the gun was fired. The first gun to fire startled the birds; great clouds of them leapt from the trees and swept away from the firing point. BOOM, BOOM, BOOM: blue-black smoke hung over the firing point as empty shell cases were ejected from the front of each gun. 'High, Plus, Minus, Minus, Plus,' sang the observers. The next run will be at auto, came the command over the tannoy. The gun 'number ones' and the 'safety officers' raised their hands to signify that they'd heard the order. 'Firing run, firing run' came from the tannoy. The aircraft flew overhead, the safety officers pressed their dead-man's switches and called *'Safe to shoot'*. Now the guns were fired at automatic. The noise was incredible as four guns, in close proximity, started firing four rounds a second down the range towards the sleeve target. It passed overhead with impunity, and the whole choreographed dance began once more as the aircraft towed the sleeve around for another run. The run started again as the observers called their mantra of

'High, High, Minus, Minus, Plus'. Matt was just wondering how the sleeve could survive all that flak in such close proximity when it gracefully described an arc down towards the beach. Each 'No.1' was claiming the downed target as theirs. 'Ceasefire' was ordered and they stopped firing.

The target aircraft had to return to base at this point to get a new sleeve fitted, so the 'D of P' decided to call lunchtime. The afternoon followed much the same pattern as the morning except that the target escaped unscathed. The range was closed at 17:00, when gun cleaning and preparation for the next morning commenced.

After tea there was a flight muster parade. Everybody shrugged at the minor inconvenience and arrived on time and 'got fell in'. The flight commander came out to address the men. This was unusual in itself but what he had to say was even more unusual. He addressed the flight. 'There is an unfortunate case of crabs in the camp,' said the flight commander. Some wag muttered from the back, 'Well don't let 'em out then.' 'SILENCE,' shouted the flight sergeant. 'Is he trying to tell us something?' muttered someone else. The flight commander looked at the flight sergeant uncomfortably once again, and a steely-eyed look from the flight sergeant stopped the chuckles within the ranks. All the men tried to keep a straight face. 'As a result of the infestation, you will all need to undergo a medical inspection to ascertain as to whether or not you are carriers.' 'Fuckin' 'ell,' said Tone. 'Do they think we've got it or summit? Whoever it is, they got it from a prossie and passed it on to 'is missus, pure and simple.'

'I understand your concerns,' said the flight commander 'but this is a direct order from the squadron commander. Your names will be posted on the notice board and the medic will cross you off his list when you have been inspected.' They were dismissed. That evening the notice was posted and Matt saw that he was going to be inspected at 14:00 the next day. The hour came and saw Matt queued up outside the medic's tent. His turn eventually arrived and the first thing he noticed was that it was almost dark in the tent. The medic was sitting on a stool with a torch in his hand. 'Okay,' said the medic, 'this won't hurt a bit. Just drop your pants and let's have a look.' Matt dropped his pants. The medic shone his torch and inspected Matt's pubic hairs, minutely, from close quarters. 'No problem there,' said the medic and crossed Matt's name off the list. Matt left the tent and walked past the line of men waiting. 'I feel sorry for you lot,' said Matt. 'NEXT,' came the call from inside the tent. Matt chuckled all the way back to his tent. He'd actually caught a dose of the crabs from a married woman at the last party and hadn't quite got rid of them yet. That medic needed glasses or, maybe, he was just distracted! Apart from the 'Short Arm' inspection, the week at the firing camp passed pleasantly enough and eventually the landing craft arrived off the beach once more.

They were taken back to Singapore and landed at the dock just as it was getting dark. They were unloaded and sat on the dockside, in their vehicles, throughout the night: they were not allowed to drive back to Changi as a convoy because that had not been organised. Why they could not go back as single vehicles Matt had no idea - sometimes the military planners even had the enemy scratching their heads!

Chapter 11 – Goodbye Butterworth

A week later, the convoy arrived safely back at Butterworth. There were a couple of incidents along the way. At one junction a truck following a towed gun got too close. It couldn't stop in time and the gun barrel went through the radiator. That held things up for a while. The ammunition carrying Matador caught fire and 'Ginger', the driver, stopped in a cloud of smoke, leaped out and extinguished the fire with the judicious pumping of a hand - held extinguisher. Fortunately, he forgot to turn off the engine. It was an electrical fire and didn't affect the diesel engine so he made it back but without lights.

A couple of days later, they were taught to use the '*A510 radio set*'. This radio set came from the 2nd World War. It was an 'HF' radio. It had two boxes which were worn on the chest in place of bullet pouches on the webbing. One box was the transmitter receiver and the other was the battery pack. They were connected by an 'umbilical' cable. A headset was provided with an old fashioned 'horn' mouthpiece to speak into. It could be used with a 'whip antenna' or a long wire antenna thrown up a tree. The lads preferred the 'A510' to the 'A41 Larkspur' purely because it was much lighter and easier to carry.

It was about this time that three Australians went missing. They took a boat out from the Australian Boat Club for a fishing trip and had not returned by the next day. After three days, a large search operation was under way. After a week, the large scale search was called off and a body search instituted. Matt and the lads from C & R Flight were divided into six man teams. Two teams were dropped off 12 miles apart on the beach where they were to search whilst walking towards each other. This would be repeated during the hours of daylight for the next two to three days. The radios were checked, water bottles filled up, and fresh batteries, maps, compasses, compo rations, ponchos, para cord and a change of clothes were packed in their backpacks. They drew rifles and ammunition and clambered aboard the waiting three-tonners. They were dropped off about 50 miles north of camp and having established communications with the mobile command post, they set off. It was quite pleasant walking along the beach in the shade. The sea breeze came from offshore and was cool. They headed towards the other group some 12 miles away. Matt tried to contact the group but nothing was heard. Strange, he thought, I've also lost contact with the CP as well. They stopped and tried the long wire antenna, still with no result. They decided to keep on walking. They would meet the other group eventually, anyway. A couple of hours passed. No washed up bodies were seen but a group of men could be seen walking towards them in the distance. Matt tried the radio again. Surely I should get them at this range, thought Matt. Still nothing. I wonder if they have changed frequencies, thought Matt. He changed channel. All of a sudden American voices filled the ether. They were American helicopter pilots going into a drop zone in Vietnam. Bloody typical, thought Matt, I can't talk to people at a range of half-a-mile but I can talk over 600 miles. They met up with the other group and moved to the pre-arranged RV. The truck was waiting in a clearing, so they set about feeding themselves in preparation for the afternoon. Their combined efforts drew a blank and after three days of fruitless searches, they returned to camp. Over the coming weeks, three bodies were eventually discovered by fishermen. They were unrecognisable after the time they had spent in the water but they were flown home to Australia anyway.

Occasionally they were called upon to carry out special duties - duties that were outside the normal working routine. On one such occasion, Matt found himself laying on and in soaking wet, swampy ground. Already, Matt knew that there would be plenty of leeches on his body to get rid of when they moved back to base camp.

It had been raining heavily since they left their bivouac area. They had moved off well before dawn and were dropped by the side of a road before moving off, initially, along a track through a rubber plantation. At the far end of the plantation, the track petered out and they moved into secondary jungle. Here, the canopy covered the day 100 feet or so above them and down in the murk, the patrol lay in ambush. The gun group covered their left flank and they had used the natural cover available between them and the nominated killing zone of their ambush site. Their wrists were tied together with cord so no words were necessary: any man could jerk the cord and instantly alert the man next to him. As each person was alerted, so it was passed on. They were waiting for Communist Terrorists, or Cts, who had been terrorising local plantation owners. Any enemy moving towards them would get a nasty surprise. The rain eased off a little and Matt noticed a movement out of the corner of his eye. It was only an ant climbing up the tree trunk next to his face. It was his nineteenth birthday and there he was, lying on the ground in the pissing wet rain in some stinking jungle over 6000 miles from home, getting eaten alive by creepy crawlies, with a fair chance of getting hurt, or even worse, that day. The shadows lengthened and in the distance, the sudden rat-a-tat of automatic weapons firing grabbed their attention. It sounded like someone else had sprung an ambush. Everyone was in a heightened state of alert as the adrenalin started to pump. The discomfort was now forgotten as they waited to see if any of the CTs would come their way. The cord tugged his arm and he looked across. The rest of the section was standing up. Matt got up and gave a tug to his left and the next man looked across. They moved out, spaced apart at 10 to 15 yards between them. The point man took it at a reasonable pace, which meant to Matt that he was confident about the way ahead, as they made their way back to the main road.

 Before they set off they had been numbered off so that orders could be addressed to odd or even numbers only. At the road, they were told that odd numbers could relax and de-leech.

They learnt from the radio man that it was going to be half-an-hour before the pick up so Matt, being an odd number, took out his cigarettes and matches from the polythene bag they had been packed in and lit up. Boy that tasted good. All of the odd numbers on the section lit up, smokers and non-smokers alike. The best way to get rid of leeches was to burn them off with cigarette ends and Matt and his mates wasted no time in purging themselves. It was incredible how big those things got when they were gorged on blood, compared to their size beforehand.

Later, at the debrief, it transpired that two men carrying rifles had been challenged by another section. They had run away, shooting as they went. and then, they had fallen into a deliberate ambush which, quite happily ruined their day. They were identified by the police as part of a group of known terrorists who had committed atrocities in the past. All in all, then, a good result for a warm, wet, hungry day. Happy Birthday, Matt. Back at camp life continued as normal, two days on OPs, two days on flight duties and two days off.

There were flight and squadron exercises 'up country' with the occasional aircraft crash guards thrown in. There were visits to Penang on days off.

What with the Camera club, Radio Butterworth, Ju-jitsu club, Cameron Highlands, Penang Blind school and general touring around the local area, life was great but it was lived at a breakneck speed.

Then, one day in October 1966, Number One Squadron, Royal Air Force Regiment was given a warning order. They would be returning to the UK in December of that year. Matt and others who had only been 'In Theatre' for eighteen months would be travelling down to join various units in Singapore for a year or so. They would remain behind for a couple of weeks after the squadron had left to carry out a care and preservation program on the guns or to put them into 'mothballs'. Then they would clean up and hand over buildings and accommodation. It was a busy three months. At last the great day came and the men returning to the UK assembled on the aircraft pan. The families had already left for the Married Quarters of RAF Bicester back in the UK. The men climbed aboard a Bristol Britannia of Eagle Airways. It started with the whine of its Proteus turbines spooling up and some twenty minutes later, took off. The captain circled the airfield once before rolling out to the North and disappearing as a speck in the distance. As the Britannia made its circuit, Matt stood in the squadron compound quietly watching. Just then, Ismael rode up on his bicycle and recognising Matt he stopped beside him. It was a Thursday and that would normally be a pay day, the day everybody settled their bills with Ismael. 'Where is everybody?' Ismael asked. Matt pointed up at the aircraft. Ismael pulled out a pad of IOUs. 'Where is Tug?' he asked. 'Up there,' replied Matt, pointing up at the Britannia. 'And Sailor?' 'Up there,' said Matt. 'What about Mac?' 'Up there,' said Matt. This continued until Ismael began to realise that he wasn't going to get paid that week. 'Where is it going?' asked Ismael. 'To Blighty,' said Matt. Ismael had been ripping people off for years and for once he had been ripped off himself. Mind you, thought Matt, what goes around comes around. Ismael had been owed hundreds of dollars by a bunch of rogues who had managed not only to keep the greatest secret of all time from him but had been able to rack up their credit by buying extra cartons of cigarettes in preparation to going back to Blighty. As Ismael charged 15% per item for credit he was looking forward to a particularly good payout that day. Instead, he rode off on his bicycle – empty handed and incandescent.

They worked for two weeks straight. Everyday they were in a shed with a gun. They stripped it, cleaned it and took off old paintwork. They repainted everything in its specification colours. Then they greased everything in sight and commenced the wrapping process. They wrapped the gun in clear, thick, industrial grade polythene. They cut individual bits and sealed them together like a giant '3D' jigsaw using a heat sealing machine. Just before the final seal, they shovelled a barrow load of desiccant into the gun then used an industrial vacuum pump to extract as much of the air as possible. The final seal was made and the gun was cocooned; forever if need be.

When the gun work was finished, they were given a couple of days off. On his last day, Matt went over to the island to say his goodbyes. First the Blind School, heartbreaking. Next was Kam Hok Hoe's Ju-jitsu school, then the various bars and clubs. Matt hoped for a few shags for old time's sake, but nothing was forthcoming apart from a married woman in one of the bars. Matt had met her before and she had been his cause for concern down at China Rock. She was hot for him but he was not hot for her, so he went to the toilet and disappeared out of the window. Jumping on his bike he made his way to the ferry and then back to camp. He parked up outside the billet and sat quietly on the veranda savouring the last molten '*Keema*' and '*Chapaties*' before his trip down to Singapore.

The next morning, Matt made his way to the Aircraft Pan where a Blackburn Beverly was loading. He had a word with the Air Load Master and was given permission to take his motorbike on board. Great, thought Matt. He was prepared to drive down to Singapore if he couldn't take his bike on the aircraft but that was not to be. He was posted to 15 Field Squadron, Royal Air Force Regiment, based at RAF Seleter and the aircraft was due to land there, so Matt was set. He came off the ramp at Seleter and drove around to the domestic side of the airfield to fill his empty tank with petrol. Having got directions from the garage, he made his way to the billet. There were, of course, many old pals there from Butterworth but, even better, there were people he hadn't seen since 'Basics'. You're on 'A' flight, he was told. 'Stick with us in the morning and we'll get you sorted out. Tonight though we'll introduce you to the

WRAFs and get pissed in the NAAFI.' After the showers, shaves, liberal applications of 'After Shave' and 'Under Arm' smellies they made their way to the NAAFI. 'Hello,' thought the girls as the boys walked in, 'Hmm, fresh meat,' and coyly they smiled as they were introduced. The night soon got very loud, very bawdy and very drunk. He remembered being helped back by some new found friends, but the morning came all to quickly. Ouch! The sun streamed in and punched his closed eyes with its brightness. He groaned and rolled out of bed. Grabbing his towel he hit the showers, then dressed ready for work. The rest of the lads were still asleep. Waking up the nearest, Matt was asked what the fuck did he think he was doing. It's Sunday, he was informed. 'Oh shit,' said Matt, 'sorry'. He felt bad, stupid and knackered. It was quite a session last night. As he undressed and got back into bed, he kept getting flashbacks from the night before. 'Oh no,' he groaned, as he remembered getting engaged to the 'Big One'. Oh well, he thought, I'll have to keep a low profile for a while. No wonder he felt so sore.

Chapter 12 - Singapore

On the Monday, at 0645, Matt and his mates made their way down to the squadron. Their accommodation block was situated on a hill next door to the Malcom Club. Their Flight Sergeant and Sergeant were the same ones they had had at Butterworth. These senior NCOs had moved down to Singapore when 1 Squadron flew out of Butterworth. The role of this squadron was different from the last one. This was a Field squadron as opposed to a Light Ack- Ack squadron. A Field squadron was, in essence, an infantry unit. It comprised three flights of Riflemen, a Support Weapons flight and an HQ flight. The Support Weapons flight were equipped with the 81 millimetre Mortor. Each 'Field' flight comprised 32 riflemen who were subdivided into sections of eight each. Each section was broken down further into six riflemen plus a 'Gun Group' who were equipped with a Bren Gun. In a fairly standard infantry breakdown, each flight also fielded a General Purpose Machine Gun and four 84 millimetre Carl-Gustaf anti-tank weapons.

Matt knocked on the office door. 'Come in,' shouted a voice from inside. Matt went in. The Flight Sergeant sat behind a desk facing the door. 'Hello Jenkins,' said the Flight. The sergeant nodded at Matt. 'Glad you made it okay. Go and report to the SWO after muster parade,' said the flight sergeant, 'then report back to me.' 'Dismiss,' said the sergeant. Matt about turned and left the office. After the mornings work had been detailed Matt reported to the SWO who, Matt learned later, had been one of the British Prisoners of War incarcerated in the infamous Changi jail during the Second World War. Matt wondered how he felt about being out in Singapore once more some nineteen years later. After a short interview with the CO, he was dismissed and went to rejoin his flight.

The   AOC's annual inspection was due and all hands were employed cleaning and painting. The rules were: If it moves, salute it; if it doesn't move, carry it away; and if you can't carry it away, paint it. Everybody involved in getting their hands dirty in this annual event wondered why such a monumental waste of time was allowed year in, year out. Matt spent the next week underneath a Land Rover with a diesel soaked rag cleaning embedded dirt off right down to the black underseal. Then he started on the engine compartment. He thanked his lucky stars he had been given a Land Rover to look after and not a three-ton truck.

The great day arrived, the rehearsals were over and it was time for the real thing. As they went to move off towards the parade ground, the flight HQ Land Rover refused to start. Pressing the start button elicited nothing. Not a peep. They push-started it and moved off to take up their positions on the parade ground. Vehicle bonnets were raised to display gleaming engines. When everything was lined up, the vehicles and weapons were checked and shuffled minutely backwards and forwards by the corporals, sergeants, flight sergeants and flight commanders in turn. Half-an-hour later they were ready. The Air Officer Commanding the Far East Air Force arrived, the band played and the inspection commenced. When the entourage reached 'A Flight' the AOC stopped in front of Ginger. 'Start your vehicle, airman,' he said. 'Yes sir,' gulped Ginger. The flight sergeant stared straight ahead. Ginger got in, turned the key and pressed the button. The whole flight exhaled as one, as the recalcitrant Land Rover burst into life. Un-fucking-believeable, thought Matt, stifling a grin as the AOC moved on. Even the flight sergeants moustache was twitching as, with eyes twinkling, he mulled over his good fortune. When the parade was over and they started to move back to the squadron that same Land Rover had to be push-started to get it going.

One morning, during break, Matt noticed a pall of black smoke rising from the aircraft pan. 'Look, there's a fire,' he shouted and pointed. The fire took hold in a second or two. 'My God, that's an aircraft going up there,' he shouted. They started to run towards the smoke. It transpired that an aircraft being refuelled had caught fire. They saw the RAF Fire Service arrive and start pumping foam at a high rate in an attempt to smother the fire. The fire was eventually bought under control but not before the aircraft and the fuel bowser were destroyed. Two men were killed and another three were injured that morning. The normally rowdy, echoing dining hall was unnaturally quiet that lunchtime. Everyone was affected by what had happened so quickly, so close and so tragically.

Matt started to take an interest in folk music. There were various clubs around Singapore. In fact each base boasted one. This was the era of 'Peter, Paul and Mary', 'The Seekers', 'The Kingston Trio', 'Pete Seager' and others of the swinging 60's. He got in with the 'Folk' crowd and spent at least four nights a week doing the rounds. He got to hear about the British Military Hospital, or BMH. They had a club which opened on Thursday nights. The next Thursday he drove up on his bike, with his guitar slung over his shoulder, and found the entrance. There were a couple of off-duty nurses taking money at the door: one dark- haired Scottish lass and one English rose. He became tongue-tied and felt awkward. He hadn't had a British girl speak to him for over eighteen months and listening to the feminine Scottish lilt was a rare treat. During the evening he kept catching her eye and when he did she smiled back. At half-time he went across to chat and he noticed her friend make excuses and leave. She hadn't returned by the end of the intermission so Matt took the now vacant seat beside the Scottish lass. He learned that her name was Bonny and before he got up to take his turn on the stage, he had a date for that Sunday. Bonny and Matt took time saying their goodbyes that evening with Matt promising to collect her from the nurses home at one in the afternoon.

In the meantime, Matt had been wheeling and dealing and had sold his motor bike. He was riding it for the last time that Thursday night. He had arranged to use the money to buy a secondhand car from a 'Chief Tech' who was 'Tourex' - returning to the UK. The payment for the bike and collection of the car were due that Saturday and both deals went through without a hitch. He had effectively swapped a Honda 250 Dream motor bike for a large 5.4 litre, automatic Packard passion wagon. It was christened 'The Yank Tank' and it seemed like there was enough room to throw a party in the back if he wanted to. So what, if it only did nine miles to the gallon? More important than the fuel consumption was the fact that it had bench seats, front and rear, and a working radio.

Apart from the folk clubs, he had also joined the Seletar Yacht club and he booked a table for Sunday lunch overlooking the Malacca Straits. All in all, things were set for a pleasant Sunday afternoon.

Matt rolled up at the appointed hour to find Bonny waiting in the shade. He glided up beside her and opened the door from the inside. 'Are you going my way?' he smiled. 'I could be,' she said, sliding in beside him. 'This is a bit posh,' she said. 'Is it yours?' 'Yes,' said Matt, 'I traded the bike in for it yesterday.' She shot him a disbelieving look. 'It's true,' he laughed. 'So, is it lucky you or lucky me?' smiled Bonny. At the boat club they both enjoyed lunch. The drinks flowed and afterwards, they took a stroll down towards the swimming pool and lingered awhile amongst the trees. They chatted, laughed and whiled away the afternoon and all to soon, it was time to go back. Over the next year, they became inseparable and shared many memorable moments.

Matt soon got to know the characters at the 'Boat Club' and as his social life expanded, so did his range of pursuits. He now spent weekends crewing in yacht races or water skiing or just puttering about. He didn't own a boat himself but that was no handicap as he was always in demand as crew. He teamed up with a pair of lads who owned a speed boat and weekends took on a routine.

On Friday afternoons, Matt would finish work and get showered and changed. He'd then set off in 'The Yank Tank' for the BMH Army hospital in downtown Singapore. After collecting the three 'dates' he made his way back to Seleter and the yacht club. Meanwhile, the other two lads had been busy preparing the boat and loading it with beer, fuel, barbecue kit and food. By the time the girls were also on board things were getting critical, the last person getting in would swamp the boat. The solution was simple. The last person would have to water ski, using a snatch start, and hope the boat didn't stop on the way to the island. When the boat got up onto the plane it only drew a couple of inches of water, the same for the skis. That meant they could take short cuts across fairly shallow water. One weekend, the great expedition set off and headed for the shallows directly in front of the yacht club veranda but, about half-a-mile out, they hit the mud. They had miscalculated and the tide had fallen more than usual. The boat was stuck fast, so Matt had to crawl using the skis on his hands and knees to get to the boat. What to do, they thought. The girls refused adamantly to push them out of the mud so they decided to wait for the tide to come in and float them off. Matt, mindful of sea snakes, reminded the lads that the water ski return journey would be someone else's turn and they would have to swim ... at which he was invited to 'ski off and multiply'. 'You are still Officer in charge of skis,' he was told. Making the best of a bad job, they opened some beer and set up the barbecue kit on the mud. They learnt later that with two inches of water covering the mud, the barbecue appeared to be floating on the water. The sun set and as the evening turned to darkness, their warning beacon to shipping burned red. They could see the yacht club veranda quite clearly as it was lit up. They watched as they were toasted and the assembled members made ribald comments about dirty weekends. Their voices drifted across the water, eventually turning to singing as the alcohol took its course. Naturally, back on the boat, the beer began to make demands as well and nature eventually commanded their attention. It was fine for the lads. Men are built to cope with such situations, naturally. Girls, on the other hand are not. The girls, each in turn, clambered on to the side of the boat in the vain attempt to keep clean, retain their dignity and pee at the same time. The boys, of course, turned their backs and waited for the splash. Each girl, in turn, failed to complete their task successfully and all went overboard into the stinking mud, at about the same point that the boys had relieved themselves earlier. Now, everyone was black and stinking. As the mud dried and stiffened it helped, at least, to keep the cold out. And it was getting surprisingly cold. They spent the night huddling together. Sleep was impossible. There was sitting room only for five people. The sixth had to stand so the boys took it in turns throughout the long night. Eventually, the half light of dawn relieved the darkness, along with the realisation they were floating once again with just an inch of freeboard. 'It's a good job I got rid of so much beer last night,' said Matt. The yacht club had disappeared and they realised that they had drifted some miles and needed to get back. Matt gingerly jumped back into the water to ski as they made their way back to civilisation once more. The water was like glass and every few hundred yards the head of a sea snake could be seen breaking the surface. Do not hit one and do not fall off, Matt reminded himself.

Unsurprisingly, the girls, apart from Bonny, declined further dates with the boys from the Seleter yacht club, preferring, instead, to be wined and dined in the bars, clubs and hotels of downtown Singapore by gay young blades who were definitely not of the Seleter yacht club set.

Chapter 13 – Hong Kong

It was the morning muster parade. The time of the day when the daily work or tasks were given out to the airmen. Matt and five of his mates were detailed off to get back to the billets and pack for a three month detachment. The squadron was going to Hong Kong. Matt and his chums were not travelling with the squadron. Instead they were going by sea. Ten days in a 4,500 ton vessel stopping in at Borneo and the Philippines on the way. It sounded like a holiday cruise until they saw the ship. They made their way down to the docks the next afternoon with four Land Rovers and trailers complete with all their weapons, equipment and squadron supplies. Pulling up on the dock beside the ship they could see that it was listing at about 20 degrees. Leaving their Land Rovers and going up the gangplank, they were told that the captain would not be aboard until the morning. Also, the list was only because the bilges were being pumped out and the 'old gal' would straighten up later in the morning before they set off. Their confidence hit a low at this news and they wondered if the list was the reason for the captain sleeping ashore that night.

They unloaded all the equipment and packs from the Land Rovers and mindful of the fact that they were in a harbour in Singapore, they removed the rotor arms from the vehicle ignition systems so that they couldn't be pinched. They unloaded and carried the moveable equipment onto the ship, which seemed to take forever in that sticky heat. They were soaked in perspiration after a minute and by the time they were finished they could wring out their clothes. A corporal had been put in charge of their party, which bought them up to almost section strength. They were shown their cabin and the 'heads' then left them to their own devices. They dumped their kit on the bunks and headed off to the showers. The evening meal was excellent. The Chinese cook knew his stuff. It was compo but it was good. After dinner it was too hot to explore the ship, so they smoked cigarettes on the deck whilst trying to catch any breeze they could. They were allowed to buy two cans of Tiger each, which they sipped. Along with the usual yarns and the stories they watched life on the docks go by in the darkness, until tiredness told them it was time to go below and hit the sack. They woke early and showered. In the early morning cool they breakfasted in the mess. The plates were still trying to slide off the tables as the the ship continued to lean. Perhaps not so much now, they thought. Gradually, during the morning, the list became less and they commenced loading. The vehicles were reversed in through the bow, which opened like a clamshell. There was a ramp from the vehicle deck onto the quayside. They parked where directed, switched off and commenced lashing the vehicles with chains and turn-buckles. They sailed that afternoon. It couldn't be soon enough for the lads, they knew that when they got under way there would be a breeze. It had turned into an extremely hot and sultry day, more so than usual, and a breeze was the most wonderful release. Suddenly, the breeze turned cool then cold. Matt stood against the rail and watched the rain squall heading towards them. He moved to one of the hatches and got ready to leap inside. Too late, the rain was upon them with the fierceness of the monsoon tropical downpour that it was and in an instant, Matt was soaked. By the time it had passed, they had cleared the harbour area and were moving past the ships riding their anchors waiting to go in. The bows headed towards the breeze now, as the wind appeared to freshen. That evening, with their two beers, they made their way up onto the deck. The stars showed them they were heading in a north-easterly direction, with Indonesia to their south and Malaysia to their south-west. Their heading changed during the night to easterly and the next morning saw them at sea: they had lost the muddy coloured waters of Singapore and Malaysia. These had been replaced with a clear blue sea and clean, white topped waves. The sun shone and with nothing to do, it was like a holiday. On the second day, they pulled into Kuching Borneo.

They stood alongside a wooden pier and offloaded ammunition to a waiting shore party. After taking on some cargo, the ship slowly pulled away and the captain set course for Manila. Six days into the voyage they made port again, in Manila, but were not allowed ashore. It was probably a wise move by the captain as he wanted all of his cargo to arrive intact in Hong Kong. Leaving Manila they headed north on their final leg to Hong Kong, about four days steaming across the South China Sea. The waves now began to worsen and things were definitely starting to get rough. They learnt that they were running before typhoon Carla and Matt found out that they were trying to get to Hong Kong before the typhoon. By the time they were nine days into the 'voyage of a lifetime' the water was coming green over the bows and they were getting green in the face. There was little sleep to be had at night as they clung miserably to their bunks. The roll of the ship threatened to pitch them out onto the deck at any moment. Come morning the movement had eased, with the seas a lot calmer. Looking out they could see they were in a bay with lights on shore showing a large city. It must be Hong Kong, they thought. They showered, dressed in uniform and went to breakfast. 'Why the fancy dress?' asked the cook. 'What do you mean?' asked Matt. 'We've put in to Macau, not Hong Kong,' said the cook. They all ran and changed into civvies. Matt and the troops would have started an international incident if they had been spotted from the shore in Her Majesty's uniform. They made a point of staying out of eyesight, whilst waiting for the typhoon to die off. They could see no point in advertising their presence. After three days the typhoon had abated enough for the ship to set to sea once more and a couple of hours later, they set into Hong Kong harbour.

When the ship tied up alongside, Matt was surprised to see the Commanding Officer and the Deputy Commanding Officer standing on the docks. What a welcoming committee, thought Matt. They made their way down into the hold to unchain the vehicles and waited for the bow doors to open. Eventually, after a lot of clanking and groaning, the bows opened and the ramp went down. They drove off the ship and met the CO. 'Corporal Smith,' the CO said. 'Welcome to Hong Kong, Corporal Smith. Were there any problems?' 'No, none sir,' the corporal replied. 'Good, good,' said the CO. 'I'll just see the squadron ammunition off-loaded before I head back,' said the CO. 'Go and check on progress will you corporal.' 'Yes, sir,' said the corporal as he ran up the gangplank. Spying the Boson, corporal Smith breathlessly enquired about the unloading. 'That's it for you lot,' said the Boson, 'you've got it all on the quay'. 'There must be more stuff than that,' said the now worried corporal. 'What about the ammo?' 'What ammo?' said the Boson. 'You've got everything you brought with you'. Corporal Smith gulped, ran back down the gangplank and started rummaging through the assorted cargo that had been unloaded. 'Er, it's here somewhere, Sir,' said Corporal Smith, replying to the CO's now very irate enquiry. 'Are you telling me that you've sailed all the way from Singapore without the squadron ammunition?' said the CO. 'Sir, we had it when we set off,' said Corporal Smith, unconvincingly. 'I signed for it,' he said, unhappily. 'Yes, I know you did, so where is it?' said the CO. 'Sir, it appears not to be here,' said Corporal Smith, even more unhappily. 'Not to be here,' the CO roared, 'that's the under-bloody-statement of the year!' And with that, he spun on his heel and stormed off towards his Land Rover. He left in a cloud of dust, and to Matt's satisfaction he saw, for the first time in his life, a corporal looking distinctly unhappy and lost for words. The ammunition, of course, had been unloaded in Borneo and an Army unit was now enjoying their unexpected bonanza.

Matt's first impression of Hong Kong was the noise and the smell. It was much noisier than Singapore and the stink came from the locals who lived in boats. These aquatic homes were moored five deep and the local incumbents burned all their rubbish, including chicken bones, in their 'on board' braziers. Anything not burned was dumped over the side and the water resembled, smelt and was in fact, a vast communal toilet.

On one side of the RAF camp was a main road and on the other a runway, separated by about a hundred yards of water. The runway had been built in the sea and from certain angles appeared to be floating. The runway served the RAF base and doubled up as the Hong Kong civil Airport. Any aircraft making an approach to the runway had to thread its way through the skyscrapers in one direction and approach over the sea in the other. All departures were over the sea, irrespective of wind direction.

The squadron had been detached to Hong Kong in a 'Peace Keeping' role. Local dissidents had been setting off bombs downtown and the fear was that trouble could escalate towards military installations. RAF Kai-Tak and the civil airport were prime targets but more vulnerable was the radar installation on the top of the Tai Mo Shan mountain. Sited at about 6,000 feet above sea level, its one access road ensured that the radar site was situated in splendid isolation. If the road were blown up, it would be a simple task to destroy the radars at leisure. To this end a static guard was required, as was an ability to reinforce that guard with troops from the air using the resident helicopter squadron. It was decided that it would be a good idea to practise roping drills from a hovering helicopter and so it was, the next day, that Matt and his mates found themselves on a patch of grass outside the chopper squadron awaiting the arrival of one of the Whirlwind helicopters.

With a great clattering whopping sound, the chopper announced its arrival. Hovering overhead, the winch man let down a steel cable. He gestured to the lads on the ground to grab the cable and was rewarded by the sight of a leaping gunner shaking his fist. The lad on the ground had just received the biggest electric shock of his life when he had grabbed the cable as directed. The winch man knew this would happen as, inevitably, static electricity built up from the

127

rotor blades whilst rotating through the air. It was normal to ground the cable before touching it but he simply couldn't resist having a laugh at the gunner's expense. The cable was winched in once more and the helicopter landed and the pilot cut the motor. There followed an extensive brief on roping drills before climbing on board to try it for real. After the morning's roping, they were detailed to report after lunch dressed in 'Light Fighting Order' (LFO) and carrying rifles. They were going out to the radar station on Tai Mo Shan, a mountain, 6,000 ft high, situated within the New Territories. They would be roping down out on the slopes near the top road. They self- briefed their drills and worked out the procedures they would follow in various scenarios. They were aware that acting as an 'Immediate Reaction Force' in the future, it would be unlikely for them to be called out for a 'bit of fun'. This would be their one rehearsal.

 They reported back at the appointed time and climbed on board. Taking off, they were surprised at how cool the air became as they climbed. It was an unexpected luxury. It took about fifteen minutes to reach their operating area, which they overflew and inspected. It was clear so they roped down. Once the helicopter had cleared away, they got up and moved off to the narrow road, checking both sides for any signs of interference. There were no signs and the drainage ditches were clear. The chopper, which had been standing off, now came back and they jumped on board ready to carry out the same activity in another area. By now the aircrew were getting bored and they suggested a variation to Matt and the patrol. This time, after clearing a stretch of road, they were to conceal themselves. If the chopper crew came back and saw them, they would have to walk back to base! As there were no options they reluctantly nodded assent and roped down once more. The grassy hillside was bare. Not a tree nor a bush was to be seen. The only place to offer concealment was a culvert, or drain pipe, which ran under the road. They crawled in and waited. They heard the chopper come back and fly around, then the sound got fainter until it disappeared altogether. Crawling out, the lads soon realised that they'd been had. If the helicopter crew couldn't find them, how could they take them back. They were now faced with the prospect of walking back some twenty miles, the last ten through the Kowloon side of town and its markets - whilst armed with rifles. Not the sort of 'Winning the Hearts and Minds' profile they were meant to adopt, they thought. The answer to their transport problem lay within the radar site and the communications equipment it possessed, so they turned uphill towards the radar domes and started walking. After a conversation with the squadron WO they were told to stay put and transport would be arranged for their return and sure enough, after an hour, the chopper returned. The sheepish aircrew gave the excuse of leaving them out on the mountain because they had to go back to refuel but Matt suspected that they'd just had an 'interview without tea and biscuits' - what was known in the Air Force as a one-sided conversation - with the boss. They flew back in silence.

The next day, six of them were sent back up to Tai Mo Shan in a minibus. Live ammunition had been issued and they would be up there for twenty-four hours. Arriving at the site, they were briefed on their duties. They had to provide the static guard and a roving guard. The static guard was for two hours in the gate guard post. There then followed two hours mobile, when they were expected to patrol outside the wire and wander through the radar domes. Because these domes contained working radars, they were briefed by a chief technician as to where they could walk and where they could not. Matt paid particular attention. After the two hours on roving patrol they had two hours off, which was to be spent in the canteen. In the case of an alarm being given, they were to make their way to the scene of the trouble and assist until the Immediate Reaction Force (IRS) was choppered up from Kai-Tak. Matt started with the roving patrol, outside the wire. The path was as wide as his foot and dropped steeply away. He could only see two or three yards ahead as the cloud base had come down. The mountain top was covered with a dense white, sound absorbent, fog in which it would be easy to slip and disappear. Matt was by himself and so he took great care walking around the outside. I can see this will be fun when it gets dark, thought Matt. Arriving back on site, he started on the radomes. In the second dome he spotted a bright green snake. About four feet long, it escaped down the steel grating when he chased it with a handy broom. Later, during his two hours off in the canteen, Matt noticed a poster on the wall: it was an information poster on snakes. He soon found his bright green friend from the radome and discovered that it was a Bamboo snake. Quite venomous and not at all shy. He made a mental note to find an excuse for someone else to go into that particular radome the next time. The duty dragged on and the cloud eventually lifted. By the time the sun had broken through, mid morning on the second day, it was time to hand over to the relief guard who were making their way up the narrow road in the minibus.

 Driving down the mountain, the lads tried to ignore 'Baz, the knob'. He was in the back trying to stir up trouble with his mate. When that didn't work he tried it on with each one of them in turn until they all became heartily fed up. 'Why don't you give it a rest,' said Mac. 'We're all tired and fed up with your big mouth,' he added. Baz was always moaning. He thought the world owed him a favour but the lads knew better. Instead of quieting down, the reproach had the opposite effect. 'If you don't button your lip,' said Mac, 'you're gonna walk home.' This elicited a furious response from the troublemaker who, in turn, was jumped on. They took his rifle and took his clothes. After a short discussion they replaced his unlaced boots on his feet. They were just passing through a busy market. 'STOP,' yelled Matt and the driver hit the brakes. As smart as you like, Mac opened the back doors to the minibus and they bundled the troublemaker out. 'DRIVE ON,' yelled Mac and the minibus set off. As naked as the day he was born, except for his boots, Baz chased after the minibus yelling for them to stop. There was pandemonium in the market as the local Chinese laughed and pointed whilst children ran alongside the swinging dick. Traffic came to a standstill and Baz caught them up. 'Let me in,' he shouted as he hammered on the locked minibus door. The lads were doubled up with laughter. The arse had got his 'come uppance' and not before time either. They reluctantly let him back on board but not before extracting promises and threatening a repeat performance at the camp gates should he slip back into his old ways. In short, he was told in no uncertain terms what everybody thought of him. Baz was strangely thoughtful for the rest of the journey, which passed in peaceful bliss. Arriving back on base, they handed in their arms and ammo and headed for some food before hitting the sack.

On one of their days off, Matt and some mates headed off to look around. They jumped in a taxi and negotiated a price for the Star Ferry Terminus. Walking around the ferry terminus, they came across an ultra modern shopping mall. Matt and his mates had never seen anything like it before. Certainly nothing in England had existed like this when they were last there. The whole mall was air-conditioned and deliciously cool as they came in from the heat, humidity and din of the outside world. They walked around like kids in a sweet shop as they looked through windows filled with duty-free goods. They noted some very high class shops with prices to match and Matt made a mental note to come back after they'd seen Hong Kong island itself. The ferry was very much like the Penang ferry; they looked the same and the crossing times were similar. Getting off on the island they set off to explore. A couple of hours later found them back at the ferry waiting to return. They all preferred the Kowloon side of town and Hong Kong island held nothing special for them.

Having cooled off once more in the shopping mall, they set off in a taxi to look at downtown Kowloon. They stopped, as far as they could tell, in about the middle of the town. There were numerous hotels, all with air conditioning, so they dived into the nearest one and asked for the bar. They were directed down a 'Grand Staircase' into a very upmarket 'Gilt and Mirrors' bar. Large potted plants graced the walls and a pianist, in evening dress, played a Grand Piano in the corner. Sitting at the deserted bar they ordered beers, lit cigarettes and silently soaked up the ambience. Walking in off the street and finding this was like entering another world. Needless to say, they required little persuasion to stay awhile.

Eventually it was time to head back to camp. So they made their reluctant way back out on to the street and into the night. They walked along the pavement towards a set of traffic lights they could see in the distance. It had been raining and the lights reflected off the road. Matt was the first to notice. 'Would you look at that,' said Matt. 'What are we supposed to be looking at?' said one of the lads. 'Exactly,' said Matt, 'there's nothing to see, is there. There's no cars and no people in the middle of Kowloon at eight o'clock at night.' Something was about to go down and the lads found themselves on a deserted eight-lane highway that should have been teeming with people and cars. They ran back into the hotel and back down to the bar. They didn't want to hang about in the hotel lobby in case a bomb went off. The risk of flying glass up there was too great. An almighty boom echoed around the empty streets, followed by the sirens of the police and other emergency services. They walked back up and through the hotel where they found a rear entrance. They made their exit and walked around the corner. This road was full of people and noisy, honking taxis. Great, they thought, as they mingled with the crowds and flagged a passing taxi. They breathed a sigh of relief as they sank into the leather seats and watched the city lights flash past on their way back to base.

One day merged into another. They continued the support of the radar station with both the 24 hour guards and the IRS standby. Off duty, they went sightseeing and shopping, with one memorable trip to the 'San Mig' breweries in the 'New Territories'.

The detachment came to an end, with Matt and his mates detailed to fly back to Singapore the next morning. They packed that night and went to bed early. It was going to be an early start. They awoke the next morning to a very loud boom as two of the shutters at the other end of the billet flew across the room. There was smoke everywhere as sunlight streamed in through the holes left behind. The shutters were normally closed because they faced the main road running past the camp and it was deemed an easy target for anyone driving past to throw a grenade. Indeed, that's precisely what had happened. Matt and his mates stumbled out of the doors on the camp side of the billet and stood in a state of shock at their abrupt awakening. As they smoked to calm their nerves, they watched the camp slowly come to life as the men of the duty Fire Piquet ran around to discover the reason or source of the bang. As the Fire Piquet ran past the lads waved and motioned them towards them. The Fire Piquet waved back and carried on running. They trooped back inside their billet, gathered up and handed in their bedding, had the necessary wash and shave, then made their way to dump their kit with the handling party and go to breakfast. At breakfast, word had obviously got out. The CO was there, along with the Squadron WO. Naturally, they wanted to know what had happened. There wasn't much anybody could add to the story, the obvious damage spoke for itself. Eventually they were left to eat their breakfast, in peace.

They reported to the HQ flight and were driven across to the airport where a Beverly was waiting to take them home. 'Oh shit,' said Matt, 'this is gonna take weeks.' Climbing aboard, the loadie directed them upstairs into the rear boom. That's a first, thought Matt. He'd often jumped from Beverlys but had never travelled in the rear boom. They took off and the pilot set course. The noise made it impossible to talk but the seats were comfortable enough. For the next five hours they dozed or looked out of the circular windows at the unending sea, swung the lamp or walked up and down. It was terminal boredom. Then the engine note changed. A quick look through the hatch down into the carnivorous hold showed the loadie gesturing that a landing was going to occur. Interesting, Matt thought. We're nowhere near Singapore so why the hell are we landing? Looking out of the window they saw the sea turn to light blue, then land. They crossed over some barbed wire and hit a runway. As they looked outside they saw the terminal building flash past. A huge sign above it pronounced that they were in Saigon, Vietnam. The Beverly taxied to its parking slot and the boom incumbents gratefully climbed down. 'We'll be here for a little while to refuel,' said the loadie cheerfully. 'Make your way to the airport building and I'll come and get you when we're ready to shove off.' Drenched in sweat, the lads made their way across the superheated aircraft pan towards the airport building. Reaching the cool interior, they stood under the fans for a moment and clocked the buildings interior layout for the bar. A loud conversational buzz through the door to their left gave them the clue they were looking for, so they entered a vast room and surveyed the assembled throng. Pushing their way through the throng to the bar they realised two things. The first was that the men they were pushing their way through were Americans and much bigger than them. The second was that there was no beer. There was no alcohol at all. Only soft drinks. They stopped pushing. Soon their accents drew attention to the fact that they were not American boys and they became minor celebrities. Ice-cold Cokes were thrust into their hands as they were interrogated by the throng. Matt excused himself and headed back out towards the entrance hall. Crossing over towards the 'Gents' sign he'd clocked earlier, he went to relieve five hours' worth of liquid. As he stood in the queue, he noticed that an old woman dressed in a black pyjama suit stood behind each man relieving himself. When he'd finished and was just shaking things off she moved in with a 'sandcastle' sized pail of water and sluiced everything down. The urinals flushing mechanism had broken down and this was the Vietnamese way of dealing with it. What a job, thought Matt, spending the day looking at 'dicks' and sluicing down after them. Must be rather like being in our mob.

Their loadie had managed to get to the bar by that point and was gathering half a dozen ice-cold Cokes. He caught their eye and motioned with his head to get out. They all bought six iced Cokes and made their way back out towards the aircraft. Three Cokes were drunk as they were taxiing out and the rest they donated to the aircrew. Climbing back out of Saigon brought the cool air once more and there were no complaints as they flew through the Monsoon laden, afternoon sky - back to Seleter and home.

Singapore was almost cool after Saigon, and Matt and the lads luxuriated in the showers before stepping out for the evening. A few beers, then down to the village to the curry shop. They served freshly baked French loaves with their curry. It made them drool just to think about it. Ah, heaven with the door shut.

Chapter 14 – Back in Singers

Work took on a familiar pattern and it seemed like they had never been away. Start at 07:00, NAAFI break at 10:00 and knock off at 13:00. One afternoon, after lunch, as they were taking their turns in the showers, they were called back to the squadron headquarters. Come as you are was the message. This was an unusual situation they thought as they made their way to the flight office. They milled about on the veranda outside until the flight sergeant came out of the flight commander's office. 'Gather round chaps, I've got some bad news,' said the flight sergeant. 'This morning Sergeant Sandy Waters and Senior Aircraftsman Charlie Wilson were killed. They were on their way back from Tengah in a Land Rover and were involved in a head-on collision with a logging truck. By all accounts they were killed instantly. Some of you will be detailed for the funeral, which will be in about a week. That's all for now. If there are any more details, I'll let you know. Dismissed,' said the flight sergeant. They made their way back to the accommodation block, stunned. The two people killed were the squadron MT guys. Sandy was on his second tour in Singapore. On his first tour his wife had been killed in a road traffic accident and now it had happened to him. A couple of days later the wrecked Land Rover was bought back to the squadron compound and Matt, along with a few others, wandered over to have a look. The first and most obvious damage was to the engine compartment: it was squashed flat. The seating area or cab was almost intact. The top of the windscreen was broken and distorted and they bore chips of skull and flecks of blood. It was obvious they had not been wearing their seat belts. Matt couldn't help thinking that, if only they had worn them, they might have survived. He resolved never to drive anything in future without a belt properly fastened.

Matt was one of the men detailed for the burial party. The funeral was to be in the Military Cemetery, with Charlie being cremated in the morning and Sandy being buried in the afternoon. They paraded on the day in their best uniforms with bulled boots, peaked hats and white webbing. Matt was detailed to drive the truck carrying the rest of the party to the cemetery. Bloody typical, he thought. Why couldn't I drive a Land Rover instead of this dirty truck. I expect I'll get a rocket for getting oil on my uniform when I'm inspected. Arriving at the cemetery, they were inspected and sized off. They paraded outside the chapel and lined up either side of the path. They were ready and would file in after Charlie and the mourners had passed. All went to plan and Charlie was cremated on a bright, sunny morning - six and a half thousand miles from home.

The monsoon rain clouds were gathering and huge cumulus nimbus boiled up in the sky to wait in readiness for the afternoon's events. At the grave of Sandy Waters, the minister read his sermon whilst Sandy's widow sobbed into her hankie. A contingent of Buffalo members from Sandy's lodge were there and as they filed past the open grave, they placed an ivy leaf on the coffin which was waiting to be lowered. The heavens suddenly opened up and the fiercest downpour of rain that Matt had ever experienced came down like a continuous bucket of water being poured. It rained so hard that he couldn't see further than the edge of the peak on his hat. Within a minute or two the grave had filled with water and a decision was made to carry out the burial at a later date, when the grave had drained sufficiently to allow the internment to take place. Matt and the lads were dismissed and told to make their way back to the squadron. He was glad he was driving a truck and not a Land Rover now. The water on the main roads was flooding and was above his axle. Matt took it steady and recovered back to Seleter. Some of the Land Rovers were unable to get started, Matt found out later, with only a foot of roof visible above the water. They looked incongruous sitting in the flood waters, in the bright sunshine.

One morning, Matt along with the other parachutists on the

squadron were sent to see the officer in charge of the squadron team. They had kept up with their continuation training and so, couldn't think of a reason as to why they might be called. The team boss was a young flying officer and they formed a semi circle around him to hear what he had to say. He handed each of them a set of paratroop wings and told them that they were now authorised to wear them in place of the Light Bulb: up until now, they had worn a badge which didn't have wings and was known as the 'Light Bulb'. The Light Bulb was worn by those who had completed the para course but were not engaged or called upon to carry out proper soldierly duties. Those who wore the Light Bulb were usually members of search and rescue teams and indeed, that's what Matt and his mates had been doing up at Butterworth. Now they were on an operational Field Squadron, they were jumping regularly with Four Two Marine Commando and the Gurkhas. On one jump, at Batu Pahat, they jumped just as night was turning into morning. It was too dark to see the ground on the DZ but could just make out the glim lamps, set out in an 'A' shape, marking the landing spot. That jump was from 600 feet in dirty fatigue and so, there wouldn't have been enough time to deploy the reserve parachute even if it had been needed. Indeed, one member of the section had badly broken his ankle on that one and had had to be casevac'd. Besides, Matt reasoned, they had done six months of pre-para PT in the heat of Malaysia, completed the full paratrooping course and had been doing the job for nearly two years by this stage, earning full para pay which formed a useful supplement to their meagre salary, so why shouldn't they wear the wings?

There was the usual joking and piss-taking when they got back to the flight but, that afternoon, Matt and his mates unpicked the stitching around the now redundant Light Bulbs and proudly replaced them with 'Badges Para With Wings'.

The latter part of the swinging 60's in Singapore was nothing like

London at the time. Indeed, the only concession Singapore seemed to have was the clothes. On the Bases ex-pats listened to the latest tunes from the UK, America and Australia. 'A Whiter Shade of Pale' came out and took the ex-pats by storm, becoming the most popular song for a while. 'Downtown' was another, whilst 'Puff the Magic Dragon' continued to frolic in the autumn mists. 'Yellow Submarine' caused such a stir that a group of lads painted their car yellow and fitted a conning tower, complete with dustbin lid, to the roof – which apparition caused a few accidents as local drivers watched them pass in disbelief instead of watching the road ahead.

There were many more accidents when it rained on the Singapore roads but they were caused for quite different reasons.

During the Japanese occupation, a programme of improvements to Singapore island was initiated by the Japanese. One of these projects was to build a road across the approximate centre of the island to connect various, key points. The Japanese located a civil engineer who was one of their 'British Prisoners of War' and forced him into supervising road building and repair. If he refused, his comrades would be killed in front of him and he would be the last to die. Torture until death, he was told. He thought about how he could get this road built, safeguard the lives of his fellow Prisoners of War and yet, still sabotage or make the road useless. His solution lay in Palm fronds. The trees grew all over the Far East and so, as the road was built, palm leaves were added in copious amounts to the underlying surface of tarmac. The result was that the palm oil leeched up into the top surface of the road and caused it to become lethal in places when it rained. As it rained rather a lot in Singapore, it wasn't long before the repaired roads started to claim their Japanese victims. That was in the 1940's but, in early 1967, they nearly claimed Matt. It was just before he bought his 'Yank Tank'. He was driving back to Seleter from Changi one night, on his bike, in the rain. Matt knew the reputation the roads had in the wet and was taking it slowly. Indeed, he had both his feet out almost touching the road. The bike suddenly went out from under him. He stepped off just in time but then slipped over himself. It was like walking on oil. He picked up the bike and slowly walked it towards the crossroads where he knew the surface would improve. He should have taken the round about route, he knew, but youth and arrogance had prevailed over common sense. From behind him, a shout from a small boy called out in the night. Matt just wasn't in the mood to buy anything, including sisters, and he shouted for him to 'Fuck off'. The lad kept shouting 'Johnny' and came up to Matt holding out a watch. Matt looked down at his wrist and realised that the watch being proffered was his own. He immediately felt guilt at his behaviour and thanked the lad for his honesty. Matt got away with it that night but he knew it was more through luck than judgement.

One Wednesday afternoon they were paraded after lunch. This was normal as each Wednesday they were detailed off for various sports activities. Matt wanted to get his name down for sailing. An afternoon crewing a yacht with a few cold beers on board was much more appealing than sweating it out on a rugby pitch. 'Listen in you lot', said the sergeant. 'I've got a nice little job for you this afternoon'. Oh shit, thought Matt, as thoughts of sailing disappeared in a puff of smoke. 'We'll be going across to the 'Burning Pan' on the other side of the airfield where we'll populate a crashed aircraft as passengers'. 'We'll be simulating as realistic a crash as we can, so we'll be using an old Hastings and setting fire to it'. 'We'll then call out the Crash Crew to deal with the incident'. 'Any questions'? Before anybody could say anything a Bedford three ton truck pulled up and they were dismissed. Climbing on board, Matt was thinking hard. He could see many flaws in this plan. The thought of the Crash Fire Engine not reaching the scene quick enough didn't bear thinking about. No, he thought, this is just not right. It doesn't feel right and too much can go wrong. They arrived at the burning pan and milled around looking up at the fuselage of the aircraft. 'Okay, on you get', shouted the corporals. They made their way towards the rear of the aircraft so that they could climb on board and Matt slipped away under the wing. Nobody saw him go and nobody missed him. I'm not going to be stuck in that burning hulk with no fire engine, thought Matt. Forty five gallon drums of kerosene were distributed around the aircraft and Matt watched as he lay on the ground to one side of the aircraft 'footprint'. The fuel was set alight and a radio call was made. Then the wind changed and the smoke and flames were blown directly towards the crash.

Meanwhile, the crash crew thought this to be another routine exercise call out and had not realised that human beings were involved. As they happily bimbled along keeping to the speed limits and generally being courteous to other traffic they gradually realised something was seriously amiss as the calls got more and more urgent. They arrived about five minutes later and by this time the aircraft was blazing away. A huge black cloud had formed and visibility on the ground was reduced to zero. The first engine started to pump foam and then the second. Matt instantly became invisible as he was covered in the smelly stuff. The foam, made from dried animal blood stank. Matt got to his hands and knees to breathe as a fireman ran over his back towards the rear door and pushed him back down. He scrambled to his knees once more and saw to his relief that the fuselage was by now covered in the foul smelling stuff and a pathway had been cleared to the rear door. 'Let me out, let me out', someone was screaming. Men piled out of the rear door, vacating what had become a nightmare. Matt moved towards the rear door in case he needed to provide help. The fire was extinguished and they all moved away to a safe distance. Many shaking hands lit cigarettes as soothing tobacco smoke replaced the stink of the foam. Their clothes were black and sweat poured off them in the heat and humidity of the Singapore afternoon. A few minutes later, they clambered aboard the truck and made their way back to the squadron. There were a few empty seats on the way back, where some had been taken away in an ambulance for treatment at the station medical centre. All in all it had turned out to be a different sort of 'sports afternoon' when some higher ranking clown 'volunteered them' to be 'casualties'.

The squadron was tasked by the Far East Command to deploy to an area near Kota Bahru, on the east coast of Malaysia. It was decided that before the deployment could take place, a route reconnaissance would be required. A single Land Rover with a trailer and communications equipment would set off, with two signaller drivers and an Officer in charge, to check that the proposed routes to and from Kota Bahru would allow trucks as well as light vehicles to navigate safely. The outward journey would utilise the road that ran up through the centre of the country and the return would be down the East coast and involve river crossings on ferries. Matt was one of the signaller drivers detailed and Dusty Miller, the other. In all, they were expected to be away for a week and a half. They took amongst other things, rations, rifles and ammunition. On reflection, it was a risky trip going by themselves up the central highway through the jungles of Malaysia. Apart from a chance encounter with terrorists, they would have to be totally self-sufficient. The baby officer, who was fresh off his course at R.A.F. Catterick in the UK, wouldn't be much help if any trouble started, thought Matt. Fingers crossed then.

They were given the weekend off and early on the Monday they crossed the Singapore causeway into Jahore Baru to set off northwards. About three hours later the road had lost its tarmac surface and had turned into loose shale. This, in turn, changed into a brown-red dirt which billowed up and behind them as dust. There was no wind and the dust became so bad that they had to stop and roll down the Land Rover canvas sides and rear, tying them off as tightly as they could to stop the dust from permeating. Although this helped, it didn't stop all the dust and they travelled along the dirt road advertising their progress with a plume of rust coloured dust. They travelled through the day with their face veils over their mouths trying not to breath in the dust. As evening fell, they arrived in Kuantan.

The next leg of the recce was northwards on the coast road. They motored throughout the day stopping only to change drivers and refuel from the jerrycans they carried. They arrived that evening and stopped in the centre of town. The room was basic, but it could be secured so the routine was much the same as the previous night. The town of Kota Bahru was the most primitive place they had yet come across during their Far East tour. God knows what the 'Baby Officer' thought of it, fresh out from UK, so to speak. They ate from a metal topped table set up on the dirt road, in the heat of a night where the breeze was non-existent. Moths and mosquitoes were attracted by the bright 'Tilley' lamps. The food was good though and the cool beer helped.

It was agreed to push off back the next morning after looking at the proposed squadron harbour area and that's exactly what they did. That night found them back in Kuantan and the boss decided to stay two nights with the next day given to 'Rest & Recuperation'. Two rooms were booked in a hotel on the beach. A bit upmarket for the lads but good enough for an officer, they decided. On the beach that evening, Matt and Dusty came across another hotel guest. She wore a little flowing black number that the wind painted against her shapely curves. They chatted and learnt that she was Swiss, a doctor and on holiday. They arranged to meet later in the bar, after the evening meal. That night they dined on a veranda looking out at the sea. The cool breezes kept the flying insects away and the whole set up was a million miles removed from the conditions of Kota Bahru.

Walking into the bar, Matt and Dusty noticed their new found friend from the beach. She motioned the lads over and introduced them to her friend. 'Boy', as they had christened the 'Baby Officer', came in and sat at the bar. He failed, at first, to notice the lads in the subdued lighting but, eventually, he recognised them and came over. The lads introduced him to the girls, a waiter bought up a seat and the lads thought 'Oh shit.' They had a few drinks, chatted and laughed, told jokes and waited for the Boy to get the hint. He didn't. They had learnt by now that Yvette and Ursula were old friends travelling together around the world. It was obvious that Ursula fancied the pants off of Dusty, whilst Yvette was being coy with Matt but smiling at lot at the Boy. Ursula leaned over and whispered in Dusty's ear. After a while she got up, said goodnight to everybody and headed off. Twenty minutes later Dusty had also disappeared. The three of them chatted for a while and it became obvious to Matt that nothing was going to happen with him and Yvette. The truth was, it had been a long day's drive and Matt was knackered. There was nothing for it but to leave the Boy and Yvette chatting together like old school chums, so Matt made his excuses and headed off to the room. Opening the door softly in case he disturbed any tender moments, Matt crept inside. There was no sign of Dusty. Lucky bastard, thought Matt, as he got into bed and fell asleep in an instant.

The sun streaming through the blinds woke Matt at seven and he looked around. Dusty had returned during the night and was snoring loudly. Matt got up, had a shower, got dressed and went for breakfast. The hotel setting was idyllic. The dining room veranda ended on the beach and was set in a palm grove. The breeze off the sea was cool as Matt sat and ate fresh pineapple and sipped freshly squeezed orange juice. He ordered pancakes and bacon and settled down to wait. Presently Yvette came along, smiled and sat next to him. Then Ursula arrived and sat on the other side. As they chatted across him Matt thought he noticed something unusual. No, he thought, it couldn't be. Oh yes it bloody well was. Well, fuck my old boots, thought Matt, they've both got Adam's-apples. He glanced again to make sure and it was fucking well true. Well I never, he thought. The idea of Dusty and the Boy finding out at the 'moment critique' that 'all that glitters is not gold' caused a moment of deep, sadistic satisfaction tinged with relief that he had been spared. He mentally thanked the gods who had spared his blushes the night before and chatted to the 'girls" over breakfast. He shook his head in wonderment. Their boobs alone would have done any girl proud. It was only the poor light yesterday evening that stopped him noticing before. Well, well, well. How deliciously funny. Just wait until the journey home, he thought.

The next morning, fully refreshed, they loaded up the Land Rover and trailer and set off south along the coast road. It was a pleasant drive punctuated by river crossings on antiquated ferries which were occasionally interesting.

After half-an-hour's worth of quiet driving Matt opened up the batting by asking Dusty, innocently, 'What time did you eventually get back to the room the other night then?' 'About half-an-hour after you, I guess,' said Dusty. 'So did you get off with Ursula then?' asked Matt. 'Certainly not,' replied Dusty. 'We just went for a walk and chatted. She went off to her room and I came back,' he said. 'Why do you ask?' 'Oh, no reason,' said Matt. 'How about you, sir?' said Matt. 'Did you get anywhere with Yvette?' 'Oh, perish the thought,' said Boy. 'Officers don't go chasing any bit of skirt that happens by them. Officers behave like gentlemen,' he added. Matt burst out laughing. He was helpless. He had to stop and pull over. He got out and was doubled over with laughter until tears ran down his face. His sides ached as the other two sat and smiled, uncomfortably, embarrassed even, saying nothing. Every time Matt looked at their expressions he was reminded of their smug looks at the table and he laughed again. They knew, he knew and nothing more needed to be said. By the time they made Singapore it was dark and Matt was still chuckling. Both Dusty and the Boy knew that their reputations hung by a thread and keeping Matt sweet would also keep his silence, maybe, mused Matt, as wicked thoughts went through his head! They rolled through the gates of RAF Seleter and home. Time for a shower and change. Matt was heading off to the BMH folk club in downtown Singapore, where men were men and women were female nurses! He had a date and it wasn't with a bloke.

 The squadron deployed with Matt driving a truck up the central dirt road towards Kuantan. The dust was choking. They were about third or fourth in the convoy. With everything shut in vain attempt to keep the dust out, it was unbearably hot in the cab. Matt knew what this road was like and could not believe that Boy had recommended the route. Eventually, at nightfall, they made their harbour area and set up camp for the night. Not quite like the hotel thought Matt, smiling at the memory. 'Oi Jenkins,' the corporal's voice interrupted his reverie. 'Get over here and get fell in for guard duty.' 'Can't corp,' said Matt. 'I've been driving all day and I'm driving again tomorrow.' The corporal was put out that Matt had answered back, doubly so because the excuse was watertight. Before he could say anything else, he was called away by the flight sergeant. Matt made himself scarce and disappeared behind the truck for a smoke. He set up his camp bed and 'mossie' net in the back of the truck and that night was rewarded by the sound of rain hitting the canvas roof. He smiled and rolled over, dry unlike some poor sods out there. They breakfasted the next morning on cold compo before setting off on the next and hopefully, final leg of their journey. Evening found them at their destination and camp was set up in a clearing. The trucks were parked up and Matt found himself detailed to drive a Land Rover on a local familiarisation jaunt. He took another driver and a couple of sergeants and followed directions. They found that smooth patches of sand were to be avoided at all costs. The sand was like talcum powder and they sank up to their axles. Having dug out twice, they didn't want to repeat the exercise. It was best to drive around these clearings over the bushes which populated the edges; they gave the firm ground. They spent the morning driving around then returned for lunch. That afternoon they were detailed off for various tasks around the camp and told to report in the morning in Light Fighting Order for patrol duties. They would be going out into the jungle and Matt, being a signaller, would be carrying the A41 radio.

The next morning, they set off into their patrol area. They were exercising against the Ghurkas. Setting off along a jungle path they settled down to a rhythm. The patrol consisted of the front man, or scout. It was his job to see snipers, booby traps or anything else considered dangerous to the patrol. The patrol was sandwiched between the scout and the 'tail-end charlie'. He protected and kept watch to the rear. The patrol leader was somewhere in the middle and wore no rank badges, whilst the second in command stayed near his machine gun or gun group. They all carried blank ammunition to simulate gunfire. One man in the patrol carried blanks and a 20-round magazine of real ammunition in case they were attacked by wild animals or terrorists. The magazine with the real bullets was painted white so that there could be no mistakes. All observed total silence and used sign language to communicate. Approximately an hour into the patrol, the tail-end charlie signalled that they were being followed. Automatically, they went immediately into their ambush drills and peeled off to one side of the track. Jumping over the long grass, they moved silently into the bush at the side of the track ensuring no foot prints were left. Moving silently, they ran parallel to the track, then took up hasty fire positions to one side of it. The gun group moved forward to cover the track as a stopper to cover any 'leakers', then they waited. The ambush was set. The gun group would fire down the track whilst Matt and his mates would fire across the track. The signal to open fire would be signalled by the gun group starting its own rapid fire. No orders were necessary. By now, these drill were second nature. After the Jungle Warfare school at Khota Tinggi a year ago, they had practised these drills every time they had been in the jungle since then. The enemy moved into their field of view and they could see that they were about to bounce a Gurkha patrol. Excellent.

The Bren started to hammer out its song of destruction. The Gurkhas on the track froze for a moment, then turned as one to run at them. The section opened fire at the Gurkhas and as they ran through the section line three were tripped up and sat upon. Prisoners, Matt thought with glee. Matt had already given a 'contact report' over the radio and now followed it up with an 'after action' report. The Ghurkas walked back to their position, led by a young English officer who spoke Ghurkali. They all moved off to a clearing for a debrief and it was reluctantly agreed that in view of the effectiveness of the ambush and the fact that the Gurkhas had blundered into it totally unaware, that they could have a choice. They could all be declared 'exercise' dead or become prisoners. The young officer chose the latter, then talked to his troops in Gurkhali. Matt passed the message about the number of prisoners taken and requested reinforcements to look after them. The Gurkhas sat on the ground, smoking cigarettes and looking innocent. The patrol adopted all-round defence and waited for the reinforcements. All was quiet until the young Gurkha officer chose his moment and in one movement stood up, yelled something in Gurkhali and ran up the track away from the ambush site. As one, the Gurkhas got up and ran. They had foolishly been allowed to keep their rifles as this was only an exercise. Matt, carrying that heavy radio, gave chase and immediately radioed a 'sitrep' through to the command post. Matt caught up the 'tail-end charlie' and dived for his legs. Both came down in a heap and Matt saw the Gurkha go for his Khukuri. Matt knew that if a Gurkuha drew his Khukuri he would not replace it until it had drawn blood. Matt leapt off the Gurkha and moved back. The Gurkha cut his own finger, replaced the Khukuri and ran off. Matt stood to one side, bent double, hands on his knees and panting as the section ran past him. Good luck lads if you catch them, thought Matt. He hoisted the heavy radio to the ground, sat down and unscrewed the top of his water bottle.

That afternoon, back at the headquarters camp site, Matt and another driver, Chalkie, were detailed to take another new Baby Officer, or 'BO', on a familiarisation of the local area. They reported to the young Pilot Officer who, festooned with maps, pencils and compass, got into the front passenger seat of the Land Rover. This looks like we could be heading for a whole load of trouble, thought Matt. 'Err, which way, sir?' Matt ventured. 'Just drive on and I'll follow you on the map,' said the BO. 'Yes, sir, but which way?' 'Err, take that track over there and we'll get up to speed on the way.' Matt did as bid and they soon left the camp behind. After a while, Matt saw a Papaya tree laden with fruit. He stopped under the overhanging branches in the shade and jumping out, he grabbed his machette and climbed up onto the Land Rover bonnet. 'What are you doing?' enquired the BO, looking up from his map. 'Just getting us some fresh fruit, sir,' replied Matt. 'Get down at once!' said the BO, 'Someone might own that tree. You can't just cut fruit down, willy nilly.' Matt looked around him at the uncultivated jungle trying to encroach the track sides. They were miles from anywhere and the chances of anybody owning that tree were zilch. Apart from the government, he thought. Matt reluctantly stowed the machette and got back in. The BO map read them further into the wilderness and Matt started to get uncomfortable. 'Shouldn't we turn round, sir?' said Matt, 'And start heading back?' 'No,' was the reply. 'I know exactly where we are. Turn left onto this track.' Matt obediently turned onto the new track, which soon petered out. In front of them lay an expanse of what appeared to be smooth sand surrounded by bushes. Matt stopped. 'Why have we stopped?' enquired the BO. Drive on across the clearing,' he said, as Matt leapt out with the machette. 'Where are you going?' demanded the BO. 'For some wood, sir, to put under the wheels for traction. We'll need it once we've dug the vehicle out enough to get going again.' The sun was starting to get low on the horizon as Matt started cutting bushes. He came across a wooden sign lying on the ground and added it to the pile. Dragging it back to the vehicle he noticed they still had a long way to go with the digging. The sign fell to the ground and Chalkie said, 'What's that?' 'Dunno,' said Matt, 'I don't recognise the writing.' They stared at the strange writing then Chalkie broke the spell. 'If I didn't know any better, I'd say that sign's written in Thai.' 'You could be right,' said Matt. 'Impossible,' said the BO. Matt had had enough. 'Can you show me where we are on the map, sir,' said Matt. 'Of course,' said the BO, 'just here.' 'Sir,' said Matt, 'we have crossed over the Thai border and are in Thailand. We couldn't be where you say we are and if we don't get this Land Rover out and get back sharpish, there's going to be an international incident. Give us a hand sir, and let's get out of here.' The BO put the maps back into the Land Rover, took off his beret and grabbed some wood. Two hours of dirty, hot, back breaking digging, cursing and cutting more wood saw them moved sufficiently to regain the firmer ground around the edges of the sand hole. It was now dark, and Chalkie managed to get through on the radio to inform the command post that they were on their way back. They arrived at ten that night. The CO was waiting outside the command post. As they drove up the BO got out complete with his maps. 'Well done lads,' said the CO to Matt and Chalkie. 'Go and grab something to eat before you put the vehicle to bed.' 'Yes, sir,' they replied. 'Come with me,' said the CO to the unhappy looking BO. 'I'll be talking to these two later,' he continued. Matt and Chalkie took the hint and left. 'Serves him right,' said Chalkie later. 'Stuck up Baby Officer who knows nothing that one. God help his men when he gets his own Flight, they'll be hard pressed to keep him out of trouble.' Little did they know!

The exercise lasted for two weeks, followed by two, long, days to recover back to Singapore. But the coast route was a much better, more interesting route than the central dust road and the two days passed quickly enough.

The first morning back at work bought its own little surprise. During the morning muster parade they were stood to attention for a short address by the Flight commander. With him was the BO. The Flight commander expressed his regret that he was leaving. He was going back to the UK on Tourex and he'd be handing the Flight over to the capable hands of Pilot Officer Ryall. Matt kept his head to the front and moved his eyes across to Charlie who was looking back. Keeping a poker faced expression, Matt looked to the front again. Eventually they were 'Fallen Out' to their duties and a disbelieving Matt said to Charlie, 'Why us? What did we do?' 'What's the matter with you two?' asked the Flight Sergeant. 'Err, nothing, Flight,' they replied. 'Well, shove off and do something useful for a change,' he said. 'Come to think of it, when was the last time you two cleaned out the Elsan toilet buckets?' They hurried off to their Land Rovers to wash and clean them inside and out before NAAFI break. Charlie and Matt both agreed that the Flight Sergeant and the new Flight Commander deserved each other. What they didn't know was that the CO had put the new Pilot Officer under the Flight Sergeant. He was on six months probation for almost causing an international incident by getting lost on the wrong side of the boarder and for getting the Land Rover stuck there against better advice. The BO was going to be no trouble for while.

One morning, Matt woke up feeling like he had gone 10 rounds with Muhammed Ali. He staggered out of bed and announced that he was going on sick parade. He reported to the the squadron and was transported to the Sick Quarters in a Land Rover. He was seen by the resident Medical Officer and was promptly diagnosed with Jaundice. There followed a week of drugs and bed rest, followed by another week when he was allowed up for a few hours at a time. He was discharged from the medical centre after two weeks but was not allowed to go to work for another week. When he got back to work, he found himself on light duties and excused exercises and deployments for another six weeks. The worst thing of all was a total ban on alcohol for six months. He was not allowed any, not a drop, not even a sniff. He'd had enough of Singers!

Chapter 15 – Tourex

A second detachment followed, to Hong Kong, in the September of 1967: flying out via Labuan in Borneo and back via Saigon, Vietnam in the November. Not much of note happened except for one of the usual troublemakers getting twenty-one days in the military prison on Stone Cutters island for GBH. Matt had to escort him back to the squadron at the end of his time but didn't think him much changed. Matt was now getting towards the end of his tour in the Far East. It was November in Singapore, and hot. Long, painful goodbyes were said at the BMH and Matt bought a suitcase.

The long awaited morning arrived and they were taken over to Paya Lebar, the civilian airport, in a Land Rover. They would be returning to the UK on a civilian flight. Formalities over, the suitcases were weighed and dumped on a conveyor belt. Matt and Bill headed towards the bar but, short as the distance was, they didn't make it. They were stopped by two, large, Red Caps blocking their way. 'Are you two Jenkins and Williams?' they were asked. Oh God, thought Matt, what now? Racking his brains for any misdemeanour's he might be guilty of, he drew a blank. Matt looked at Bill. It must have been him. Bill was looking at Matt thinking the same thing. The next instant they were both in cuffs, with a new face between them. The police had transferred their handcuffs to the lads, along with a prisoner. 'This man will be taken from you at London airport. Until then you have custody of him. Sign this live body receipt and make sure he gets to be handed over.' The Red Caps had spoken, so Matt and Bill signed. 'You'll have to stay on board the plane during any stops, okay?' 'Okay,' said Bill and Matt. 'Right, go over to that room and wait,' said the first policeman. 'You'll be called separately when it's time to board.' At that, Matt and Bill ensconced with the prisoner were watched as they entered their separate waiting room. 'Oi,' came a shout, 'you'll be needing these.' The keys for the handcuffs were slid across the floor and Matt grabbed them. The waiting room was small but at least it had air- conditioning. 'Why are you going back to Blighty like this?' Matt asked the prisoner. 'I'm being done in a UK court,' was the reply. 'What did you do?' asked Bill. 'I'm accused of murder,' came the reply. Fucking great, thought Matt as they smoked in silence and waited. There were no magazines to read and the door had no window. Boredom with fear chucked in, thought Matt.

Eventually they were called to the aircraft. They got up, walked outside and made their way to the steps, stopped and looked up. It was a Bristol Britannia, the same type as they came over to Singapore in, two and a half years ago. The hostesses had obviously had a good time during their stay in Singapore, Matt noted, as they waited looking hungover at the top of the steps. I hope to God the captain's feeling better than this lot look, thought Matt, as he, Bill and the prisoner crabbed their way up the steps and ducked through the front door into the body of the aircraft. They were shown to their seats, a row of three, in the sound box. The sound box was a compartment, almost opposite the door. It was close to the engines and had a bulkhead or wall immediately behind and in front of the of the seats. The idea was to stop the din from the engines' propellers reaching the rest of the cabin. Those seats were not normally occupied. The aircraft was full however, so the sound box seats were being used even though they were the most uncomfortable seats on the aircraft. It was into these seats that Matt, Bill and the prisoner were ushered. Oh great, thought Matt, almost twenty hours of this and the only thing to look forward to was getting off at the other end.

'Mr Jenkins?' an air hostess enquired. Matt looked up to see a vision of beauty, who was standing there with a large bouquet of flowers. 'Err, yes,' said Matt. Who the hell would be giving me flowers, he thought. The hostess reached up and laid the flowers in the overhead locker. She was obviously putting them there for somebody else. 'Would you come with me,' she said. 'I can't,' said Matt. 'I'm supposed to be escorting this chap back to the UK.' 'I don't think he'll be going anywhere now,' said the hostess, 'the doors are closed and the engines have started.' Matt undid his handcuff and handed the key to Bill. He got up and followed the hostess down towards the rear of the aircraft, the quiet end where the families were. She stopped by two girls and told Matt to take a seat. There was only one seat available and it was in between the two girls. Matt, like the 'Virgin Sturgeon who needed no urging', slid across, sat down and strapped in. The first thing he noticed was a warm thigh pressed against his own, from both sides. Smiling, he looked at the girls, who appeared to be twins. They smiled back and Matt noticed that they were both brunette, slim, good looking and identical. As they watched the hostesses cavorting to their carefully scripted safety brief, the aircraft taxied out and took off. Singapore disappeared in a brown haze behind them as they climbed out towards the clear air of cruising altitude. Blighty, here we come.

Matt couldn't believe his luck. Everything that had happened in the past few years involving himself and Bill had ended up with Bill getting the best of it. Everything, without exception. Now look at him - stuck with a prisoner for nearly twenty hours whilst Matt, for some reason he couldn't fathom, had been chosen to sit between two beautiful girls.

The route back was via Bombay and Karachi. The first leg would be in daylight, with a night descending soon afterwards. Matt opened the conversation and discovered that they were, indeed, twins; they were nineteen and returning from their father's rubber plantation in Malaysia. They had been on holiday with Mummy and Daddy and were returning for the last term at finishing school. Their names were Carol and Jennifer. They chatted the day away and somewhere over the Maldives, they all became firm friends.

155

The twins seemed to have a plan worked out. God knows they'd had long enough to plan something while stuck on Daddy's rubber plantation, and a good snog when darkness came was only part of the plan. Matt, of course, was the innocent in all this deceit and was led like a lamb to the slaughter as the girls smiled and plotted their way across the afternoon sky towards India. The girls had thought up some very naughty games and all of them included Matt. He, in his sublime ignorance, knew nothing about any of this and it came as quite a surprise when Carol decided to get her way somewhere over the Gulf of Oman. Jennifer followed suit over the Mediterranean. The hostesses saw nothing. They were down the back of the aircraft sleeping off their hangovers. Matt and the girls were just part of the silent movement of those few passengers who 'enjoyed' the on-board facilities during the quiet hours. Years later, Matt flew in a Boeing 737 and wondered at just how small the lavatories had become!

They landed at Heathrow at 'oh crack sparrows' on a brisk November morning and waited on the aircraft until all the passengers had left. Two Red Caps came on board and escorted the trio off the aircraft. Once they had reached the main terminal building they were ushered into a room where they were relieved of the prisoner. Clad in short-sleeved shirts with matching suntans, Matt and Bill were freezing. Once they had grabbed their luggage, they wasted no time in unpacking and searching for something to put on. Transport was provided into London and as Matt was dropped off at Kings Cross St Pancreas, they wished each other 'Bon Voyage' and went their separate ways. Matt had been posted back to Catterick to Training Support Flight, or TSF, but had no idea what it would be about. First though, there was a spot of leave to get through. Two weeks' disembarkation after two-and-a-half years in the Far East was due, plus two weeks annual accrued leave. That amounted to a nice long holiday.

Matt found his train and climbed on. It was a corridor train and there was a compartment right opposite the door. Good, he thought, grab that. He opened the sliding glass door, stowed his cases above his head, sat down and lit a cigarette. Looking about, two girls smiled back at him. They were twins and they were good looking brunettes on their way to finishing school. They'd just flown all the way from Singapore. Could you believe it! It was as if he'd never been away. He got off the train at Huntingdon with a large smile on his face and caught a bus to R.A.F. Wyton. He smiled all the way. Jumping off the bus outside the camp he made his way to the married quarters and found the house he was looking for. He stood back and rang the bell. The door opened. Matt said 'Hello, Mum. Sorry I didn't write' and stepped in.

Chapter 16 – A New Start

Matt's parents had been separated since he was ten and divorced since he was fifteen or so. Both parents had remarried since. His mother married a Flight Lieutenant in the Supply Branch and his father had married a lady called Sue. Matt's father was currently serving a tour at Takoradi in Ghana. He was seconded to the Ghanaian Air Force and was teaching them or converting them to fly Caribous. A twin-engined transport aircraft. Dad being away made Matt's choice of who to see when he came home a lot easier. 'You'd better come in,' said his mother. 'How long are you intending to stay?' 'Oh just a week or so,' said Matt. 'I've got to get back to R.A.F. Catterick and report in.' When his stepfather came home they had a chat. It transpired that he had been posted to R.A.F. Seleter. They would be travelling out in about six months' time. He was looking to sell his car. The amount he wanted would use up all Matt's savings but it was still a good deal. The next morning saw Matt at the R.A.F. Station Post Office drawing out his savings. He became the proud owner of a Triumph Herald, but couldn't use it until his mother and step father flew out in about six months' time.

The week passed and Matt left. He went down to see some old friends in Maidenhead, just one of the places where he had lived in the past. Walking along Kings Street, he made his way towards the Greyhound pub. Coming the other way, also making for the same pub, was his father. They met at the door. 'Stranger things have happened at sea,' exclaimed Matt as his father got closer. 'What on earth are you doing here? I thought you were in Ghana.' 'Hello son,' said his dad. 'Lets go in and chat over a pint. This will be my first drink for six months and I'm gasping. I caught jaundice and had to go on the wagon. I'm tourex and as you know Sue comes from round here, so here I am. What about you?

Two pints of Worthington please,' said his father to the barmaid.

'I can't believe the coincidence,' said Matt.' 'This is also my first drink for six months, I've also had jaundice and I'm on disembarkation leave, tourex from Singapore.' 'Well, well, well, the world's a strange place,' said his father. They caught up on family and service gossip and generally put the world to rights until closing time that afternoon. They went their separate ways again knowing that they could get in touch if needs be. They both went northwards, one to R.A.F. Topcliffe to take over the Beagle Basset Conversion Flight and the other to R.A.F. Catterick to be taken over by the Regiment once more.

The arrivals procedure on every R.A.F. base was a chore. It was more than that - it was a pain in the ass. At the general office one was issued with a blue 'arrivals' card. This contained an entry for every section on the camp and a signature was required from every section head before you could be construed as 'having arrived'. It took Matt two days to 'arrive' and finally he reported back to the general office, proudly displaying his completed card. He was about to be become a member of the Station. 'Report to Flying Officer Hill at building 159,' said the sergeant 'shiny' of the general office. 'Yes, Sarge,' said Matt and left. Building 159 was only a couple of minutes walk from the station headquarters but one could get into a lot of trouble along the way. Especially if you took a short cut across the grass. Matt was older and wiser now but there was a time in the past when he'd been seen walking on the grass and he was punished by God, or the station Warrant Officer who shared the same name. Arriving at building 159, Matt found the orderly and stated his business. After a short delay he was ushered into the Flying Officers office. Matt was still in civilian cloths. He explained that when he had unpacked his vacuum-wrapped blues last night they literally fell to pieces. He was left holding two pieces of cloth which turned to powder in his hands. Matt had had them packed when he first arrived at Butterworth but despite his best efforts at preserving his uniform the woolly bug had got to them. He was

159

welcomed, told to report that afternoon to the Training Support Flight (TSF) shed but, in the meantime, to get over to clothing stores and get his disintegrated rags exchanged for a uniform.

That afternoon Matt went down to the shed. It was large enough to house six trucks with eight Land Rovers. There was an office built into one corner with a crew room. One wall was devoted to shelves holding tables, folding chairs, Tilley lamps, tentage, cookers or stoves and other assorted camping equipment. The flight existed to support any training course that might be running. Whether it was support for shooting ranges or field exercises or just map reading, they were there to provide logistical support. They worked night and day, weekdays or weekends. They would get reasonable time off in lieu of days and nights worked but would be expected to use their intelligence and initiative when necessary. This was a new one, thought Matt. Since he had joined up, he had always been discouraged from uttering that 'initiative' word, let alone using it. Over the next few months, Matt began to enjoy his job immensely. He was treated like an adult by the directing staff and once given a set of instructions he was left alone to carry them out. Matt did some serious thinking about signing on for a longer term.

Matt's current engagement was for five years: he had already served three. His options were to sign on for nine years regular service and three years reserve or, for twelve years regular service with no reserve but a bounty of just over £400 at the end of it. Matt thought that the twelve years might be the best option. He didn't wish to be called up once he'd finished and a bounty sounded attractive. By this time, he'd already served a third of a twelve year engagement so off he went to the general office and had a word with the clerk. A few weeks later, with the paperwork sorted out, Matt reported to the officer in charge of the general office and signed on for a total engagement of twelve years. Now, with nine years ahead of him, Matt had decided to make a career in the Royal

Air Force Regiment. He started to take things more seriously and tried his best to be as smart as circumstances allowed. It was during this period of settling down that Matt got married and moved out of the billets and into married quarters, about 20 miles away at Middleton St George.

It was also about this time that news arrived about Bill. When he came back from the Far East, Bill was posted to an RAF Ground Defence Training Flight. They'd all been back about eighteen months by then. Bill was dead. He'd crashed his car one night on the way home from a dance. Four people died that night. Two nurses and their escorts. Matt knew Bill's dad. Bill was an only child and his mother had died many years earlier. They were very close. Matt and the other lads who knew Bill talked about what had happened and despite their shock and grief, all agreed that Bill's driving habits had made this an inevitable event. It was such a shame that other people had been killed and yet more were left to grieve.

One Thursday morning, some months later, the OC TSF, who was known to all as 'The Bully', paraded the flight and reminded them that one of the courses they supported was the Junior Officers Course. The trainees had to complete the 'Lyke Wake Walk' within twenty-four hours. If they couldn't, they failed the course and said goodbye to the Regiment. He didn't see why airmen should be able to witness these officers under training, suffering from the physical and mental strains exerted during this walk. Support airmen needed to experience the hardships endured first-hand and to this end, the support flight would be completing the walk commencing at 03:00 the next morning. The only people excused would be the support party consisting of junior NCOs or, in other words, the corporals.

The walk was from Osmotherly on the edge of the Cleveland hills to the sea at Robin Hoods Bay. As the crow flies it's a straight forty miles to Robin Hoods Bay. It's actually more than forty miles when you walk it because there's quite a bit of up and down and left and

161

right going on throughout the route. Half-past-three the next morning saw 'The Bully' along with the 'volunteered walkers' approaching Osmotherly. They went through the village up to a place called 'Chop Gate' and started walking. They had to go the wrong way to start with because the walk didn't officially start from the road: it began from a point about a mile off to one side of the road. Miserably, they trudged up the hill in the pre-dawn chill to the radio masts that marked the start of the walk. 'The Bully' addressed them before they walked back. 'Remember,' he said, 'a man is not a man until he's walked one step further than he's physically capable of.' They then turned around and like the Grand Old Duke of York, they marched back down again. They passed the vehicles, endured the derision of the occupants and set off, this time in the correct direction.

 The first eleven or twelve miles were hard going until they reached the plateau. The Cleveland Gliding Club was situated on the top of the moors on this plateau. It was luxury to walk the length of the airfield on solid level ground. At the end, the ground fell away and they scrambled down the rocks and boulders keeping to the path. A mist filled the valley they were heading into and they descended into its whiteness. At the bottom of the hill was a road. They followed it for a few hundred yards and made their way towards the waiting vehicles in the car park. Breakfast was tea and a wad. It was welcome. They drank the tea then ate the sandwich as they started their climb back up the other side of the road. It was a steep, difficult climb but eventually they came out at the top where the ground levelled out once more. They soon found themselves on a cinder track. It was a disused railway bed and according to the map, it ran in their chosen direction for another twelve miles. The cinder track was smooth and firm and it was easy going. Too easy, as Matt was about to find out. Eventually, they came off the track and made their way to the next rendezvous at Rosedale Cross, where Matt realised his feet were hurting. It felt like blisters. Sitting by the vehicle, Matt took off his boots and socks. He had a large blister on each foot. Right on the ball of each foot. 'Give up lad,' said one of the support NCOs. 'You'll never make it on those blisters. You've only gone half way. You've still got twenty miles or more to go.' Matt replaced his socks, this time putting the nylon socks on first then the woollen ones second. The idea was to stop his feet from slipping inside his boots every time he took a step. He tightened up the laces as tight as he could and stood up. It was bearable, just. Grabbing a sandwich and filling their cups with soup, Matt and Ginger set off behind the rest of the walkers. The next leg was the longest but it was over gently sloping moorland and the going was soft but dry. The radar domes at RAF Fylingdales stood out for miles and the visibility was so good that at one time they could see the radio masts at their start point and the large mast at the finish. The domes never seemed to come any closer. They walked for hours until they crossed a river using stepping stones, at a place called the Esklettes, and suddenly they were past the domes. They made the third RV and Matt didn't dare undo his boots to check his feet. They drank hot tea, ate another sandwich, filled their water bottles and set off. This last leg, from the main Scarborough road, was only about five miles but Matt felt every stone, pebble and grain of sand along the way. He crawled the last quarter of a mile to the finish and gratefully accepted a lift to the nearby cafe. Having signed the book, Matt glanced at his watch: they had been on the go for 14¾ hours. The vehicle dropped him off at home and he crawled across the front lawn and up the stairs. His wife ran the bath and Matt eased himself into the hot water. His socks eventually soaked off his feet and twenty minutes later, Matt was in his bed fast asleep. It was Friday night, so at least he had the weekend off. Despite his feet, which would take a while to heal fully, he was on parade on the Monday morning, qualified now, and willing to support the Junior Officers as they struggled to complete the Lyke Wake Walk. As for 'The Bully', he had walked it on his forty-fourth

163

birthday, and then turned round after a cup of tea at the cafe and walked back. Respect!

Matt was becoming quite adept at all aspects of the Regiment Gunners training. He went out and assisted with Basic Courses, SAC to Corporal or Further Training 1 courses, the Further Training 2 (FT2) courses, the Junior Officers courses, the Wireless Instructors courses and Senior Officers Study Periods. After a year of this varied and interesting work, Matt was told that he had been selected for the FT1 course. He had already passed the RAF education tests for promotion whilst at Seleter, so the course was a logical next step in his career progression. It also had a high failure rate. He would have to do well if he was to become a corporal. Nothing was guaranteed. Passing the course was only another tick in another box. For promotion to come, he had to get good annual assessments and good write-ups. Matt would be in direct competition with all the other SACs who passed the course and would have to prove that he was made of the 'right stuff'.

The course was six weeks long and amongst the many subjects covered were Methods of Instructional Technique, basic tactics, field craft, shooting coaching, and drill. It was a good course and they enjoyed learning along the way. Matt had covered a lot of the detail whilst on TSF and he was selected to give the pyrotechnic demonstration as his practical - a stroke of luck.

One sunny afternoon, the course was in the classroom listening to a boring lecture on tactics given by the course commander. Nobody was really listening and the course commander knew this. At one point during the lecture he slowly reached behind the lectern and suddenly came up with a Thunderflash. The fuse had been lit and God knows what effect it was going to have when it went off. 'GRENADE,' yelled the course commander. In one movement, they all hit the deck. Each man tried to burrow to the bottom of the heap as desks and chairs were flung aside in the melee. The adrenaline was flowing as Matt watched the fuse burn down. He placed his hands over his ears and pointed his backside at the Thunderflash. Phut; the fuse went out. There was no explosive inside. It had all been removed. Matt now noticed that the course commander was still leaning nonchalantly against the lectern, observing the mayhem in front of him. They stood up sheepishly and the course commander told them to have a ten minute break. They went outside and lit up. They realised now that they had been shown an 'attention getter' and resolved to be bright -eyed and bushy-tailed in the course commander's presence in future. They exercised at night and during the day. Map reading and navigation, before the days of the GPS, was a basic skill but a necessary one. They practised it until it became second nature. They shot on the ranges and and screamed at each other on the parade ground. They gave practical lessons on all the subjects that made up their military training and one morning, the great day arrived. They were all sat in the classroom early, quiet, still and attentive. The course commander came in, followed by the course NCOs. 'Officer present,' yelled the senior student of the day. 'Sit to attention.' They adopted the sitting position of attention as the course commander took up his position behind the lectern.

'The following have failed,' he said. 'When I read out your names, you are to stand up, and without speaking, leave the classroom and wait in the corridor outside my office.' He then proceeded to read out the names of the failures. One by one, students silently got up and left the classroom, disappointment etched on their faces. After about half the course had left, the course commander abruptly turned and walked out. There was a stunned silence. 'Congratulations,' said the senior NCO, 'for some strange reason you wasters have passed. Now get out of here and get your kit shifted from the billet. Those of you who are leaving the station, report to the general office first.'

Matt cleared his kit out from the billet and loaded it into his car. He made his way over to TSF to see what was going on. Making a cup of tea, he looked at the duties list for the following week. Nothing for him, great he thought, time for a spot of leave.

'Ah, Jenkins,' said the sergeant. Matt jumped and looked round. The sergeant was sitting at his desk. Matt hadn't seen him. 'We're a little short handed at the moment. I want you to nip home and get changed into greens and get back here before lunch. You'll be taking a Land Rover out to Gandale to help out with the basic course. Take your small kit as you'll be out for three days. Look lively now. Oh, and just before you go, how did you get on with the course? Passed did you? Knew you would anyhow. Off you go then. What are you still doing here then?'

It was a strange feeling going back to work knowing what he now knew. The staff treated him slightly differently to the other SACs as well. Most of his mates whom he'd joined up with, gone through training and the Far East with, hadn't been on the course yet. They didn't seem to want to know about it and indeed, were a little distant. Matt thought nothing of it. I've not changed, he thought.

One day at mail call, Matt received a letter. Not a strange event in itself but it bore a Malaysian stamp and the handwriting was unfamiliar. Wonder what this could be, thought Matt. He sat down, opened it and started to read. It was from Jack Lemon, the principal at the school in the Cameron Highlands. He wrote that Penny and her husband had moved to Phnom Penh in Cambodia. He went on to say that they'd been killed by the Khmer Rouge some six months after their arrival. Matt recalled their excitement at their impending move the last time he'd seen them back in the Cameron Highlands. Matt thought about them every time he was notified about a move and often wondered whether or not it was necessarily going to be a good thing.

One morning he had a message to report to the general office. Matt went along to see the sergeant in charge and was informed that he'd been posted to Germany. To 26 Squadron Light Ack Ack (LAA) based at RAF Gütersloh. He was also wanted by the SWO and had better get a move on. Matt gulped. Oh shit, he thought. What now. He ran down the flight of stairs to the ground floor and gingerly knocked on 'God's' door. 'Come in,' came a voice.

Matt opened the door, marched in smartly and stood to attention in front of the desk. 'SAC Jenkins, Sir,' said Matt. 'Jenkins,' the SWO said, his voice raised slightly. 'Gamekeeper turned Poacher I see. 'Sir?' said Matt inquisitively. 'You're improperly dressed,' said the SWO. 'You are not setting a good example. Your promotion was published yesterday, so get yourself over to stores and get your stripes up'. 'Yes, Sir,' said Matt grinning.

As luck would have it, the station tailor was in and Matt walked out sporting a new set of stripes on his arms. Back at TSF Matt learnt that he had two weeks to get ready for the move. His family couldn't accompany him at first but would have to join him later once he'd qualified for a married quarter. For now, they would be remaining at Middleton St George.

Chapter 17 – Germany the first time

Royal Air Force Gütersloh was home to 19 squadron and 92 squadron. They were both equipped with the English Electric Lightning mach 2 interceptor aircraft. Also resident was 18 squadron who were equipped with the Wessex helicopter and 26 squadron RAF Regiment, with the Bofors 40/70 Anti aircraft guns. The station was situated in the 'Nord Rheine West Falia" region of northern Germany and existed solely to intercept Russian aircraft as they approached the east-west border of Germany. In the event of the cold war ceasing and the real war starting with Russia, the life expectancy of the Lightning was about a day as only two intercept flights were thought to be possible before being shot down or running out of fuel. Twenty-Six squadron equipped with the Bofors were there, of course, to protect the airfield and to allow the Lightnings time to be refuelled and rearmed for their second and probably final mission.

Matt had the normal station arrival procedures to carry out and horror of horrors, he discovered that he even had to complete a mini arrivals procedure when he joined his new squadron. He was interviewed by the squadron WO then the CO. There were two new arrivals at the interview. The CO had decided to put Matt on the guns and the other chap on OPs or Control & Reporting Flight.

The thought of spending the next two-and-a-half years, cleaning and nursing four-and- three quarter tons of dirty, noisy and unwieldy metal canon did not fill Matt with enthusiasm. Needing to do some fast talking and adroit escapology, Matt successfully argued that he could serve the squadron better in C & R flight than the gun flights. He knew nothing about guns, he said, and would therefore require a period of training. On the other hand he was already a qualified signals instructor. He had completed a tour on C & R at Butterworth and therefore knew how C & R worked. Without any training he could be productive from the start. Matt got

168

his wish and was sent to report to the sergeant of C & R flight.

RAF Gütersloh still had a lot of wartime Germany about it. Matt's accommodation block still had rifle racks fitted along the corridor and one room retained the metal bars on the windows from its days as an ammunition store or magazine. During the war the airfield was flooded during the day. The Maas canal ran alongside the airfield and was used to provide the water. From the air, the airfield appeared to be a large lake and was drained only during the hours of darkness for the launching and recovery of aircraft. The underground pipework still existed and was tested from time to time. The officers mess had retained its 'Goring's beam': this was a wooden beam which had been loosened at one end by a group of young German pilots who were hell bent on playing a joke on the General. One night, In the middle of an impassioned speech, when Goring once again called on God to witness the truth of his statement or strike him down, the pranksters loosed the free end of the beam which fell until halted by a retaining rope. Metaphorically, it bought the house down. The urinals in the lavatories were also original. They had grab handles on the sides, the purpose of which was to stop the user falling in when being sick after imbibing to excess.

Matt had driven over from England in his Triumph Herald and so, at least, had the mobility to get out and about. As there was no chance of a married quarter for some months, Matt answered advertisements in the local papers offering housing for rent. One weekend he was at a loose end and decided to drive out to Hamm. He knew that it had taken a fair pasting during the war and was curious to see whether or not the city still bore any scars of the bombing. When he arrived, Matt discovered that it was just like any other town. There was nothing of note to see. He had come too far to just turn around and drive back so he looked about for something to do. He followed signs to Hamm Zoo and eventually found himself in a car park which was situated just outside the main gates. He paid his entrance fee and went in. It was the first time he'd been to a zoo and he found it an interesting experience. He was particularly struck by the Hertz Mountain Bears. He had no idea that wild animals still roamed the countryside, let alone something as dangerous as bears. Matt made a mental that should he ever find himself in the Hertz mountains, he would remember not to travel without an armed guide.

Later, Matt reported to the sergeant in charge of C & R flight - a charming, well-spoken gentleman who seemed to be out of place in the regiment. 'Ah, corporal Jenkins I presume,' came the greeting. Matt was taken aback, so strange was it to hear his name being preceded by the title of corporal. 'Yes sergeant,' he replied, 'I'm going to place you initially in the command post. I see you are a signals instructor. We have a problem with the OPs not being able to communicate one hundred percent with the command post and I'd like you to sort it out. I've already informed corporal Smith that he'll be handing over so go and have a chat with him.' 'Yes, sarge,' said Matt who, having found himself dismissed, smartly turned about and marched out of the office. His meeting with the old hand ex-command post leader was less than inspiring. 'So, ye're the new man sent to show us how to dae things roond here are ye?' 'Well, I wouldn't put it quite like that,' said Matt. 'Weel,' he said in his broad Scottish accent, 'I dinna give a shite, cause I ken ye'll nay be able tae get comms wi all the OPs. So ann ye go and try.' Matt could see that this guy had had his noise put out of joint and was seriously upset. Still, his first brief was to establish communications and that is what he was going to do despite corporal Smith.

The next day found him dropping and dismantling the command post aerials. They were dipoles; well made but suffering the effects of weather and neglect. They would need stripping and rebuilding. Matt spent three days remaking the aerials, then hoisted them back up on to their masts and checked the radio communications. The comms were perfect. Corporal Smith was predictably miffed that Matt had fixed the problem but he held his tongue and waited to pounce. He was looking for the chance to discredit Matt in front of the, by now, interested following. The opportunity would surely arise soon and it did. A regular weekly communications check of all the guns and OPs was held and it was up to Matt to carry out the next check. He did and used the 'collective call' terminology detailed in the 'Voice Procedure Pamphlet WO70711'. He received no replies. Not one signaller on the squadron understood the voice procedure Matt had used. Matt had a phone call from his irate sergeant and was told to report back to the flight immediately. Corporal Smith was there with the sergeant and the rest of the corporals. Some of the SACs were also there and were listening with interest. Corporal Smith had obviously been making quite an issue of Matt's voice procedure. As Matt walked in, corporal Smith launched into the attack. 'What the hell do ye call that abortion of a comms check the morning then?' he said. 'The signallers on this squadron need some refresher training on 'collective calls' it would seem,' said Matt. At that, corporal Smith exploded. He told Matt in front of everybody that he had forgotten more about voice procedure than Matt had ever learnt. When Matt pointed out that he had followed the detail laid down in the 70711, corporal Smith demanded that Matt show it to him. Normally, Matt would have told him to find it for himself but he realised that this was a test. He had been put on the spot and there could be only one winner. Matt knew he was right and that there was no need for any of this. He produced the pamphlet and opened it. He turned to the relevant page and read it out. It transpired that Matt was quite correct in his handling of the comms check that morning and that corporal Smith had unknowingly given out the wrong information to squadron signallers in the past. So, the squadron signallers now required that refresher training, which impacted on their normal training schedules. Matt had made his point and instead of being discredited as corporal Smith had intended, he was vindicated to the point of being of being detailed to conduct the new signals training to all, himself. Moreover, it was important to carry out this training as soon as possible because the squadron was due to deploy and communicate with army units in the near future. Matt's experiences of working with the army in the past had demonstrated to him their adherence to the publication WO70711. Twenty Six squadron was not going to get egg on its face if he could help it.

Every year the station was be subjected to a 'No Notice' three-day exercise known as a Taceval. The station personnel would be called out during the night to test the response of a 'Call to Arms'. It was supposed to be a surprise. The judges of the station's performance, i.e. its ability to survive during a war, were a team drawn from various nations comprising the membership of NATO. Answerable to the Supreme Allied Commander Europe, the Taceval team awarded a mark to indicate the station's performance. To get a '1' would be the highest accolade a station could aspire to, but a '4' would bring the wrath of God down upon those unfortunate enough to be involved with the failure. The exercises were carried out simulating a ground war with chemical, biological and nuclear scenarios thrown in. Ground troops attacked and attempted to infiltrate and sabotage installations and equipment. Umpires started and monitored incidents. They injected information to check the speed, accuracy and response to that information. All in all, it was war games on a grand scale.

So that RAF stations would be ready for their annual Tacevals, Maxivals were held every six months. These were more intense than Tacevals and were staffed by officers and men from the RAF. It was intended that if a station could pass a Maxival then it could get top marks at a Taceval. In order that RAF Güttersloh would be ready for these war games a Minival was held every month. These

Minivals were staffed by the officers and men from the station. What with Tacevals, Maxivals and Minivals the only thing missing from station life was Intervals! But, there were also squadron exercises to teach and test necessary various skills so that the squadron would perform well during any evaluation. These squadron exercises were called Microvals!

It was into this scenario that Matt was thrust. He enjoyed the squadron life and was kept busy, but one day it all came to a temporary halt. The Harrier aircraft had by this time been introduced into RAF Germany and one of them had had a problem with its fuel computer. The pilot was forced to eject but the aircraft picked up after the ejection and headed towards the East-West German border. Panic set in as it was realised that the Russians were about to have their border violated by an RAF Harrier. They would, of course, be able to shoot down the sitting duck and capitalise on the ensuing international incident whilst removing the wreckage of the aircraft back to Russia for evaluation and analysis. Two Lightnings were scrambled to intercept and shoot down the errant Harrier before it reached the border. The Harrier, being a patriotic sort of aircraft, decided to touch down before the border but it was a close-run thing. The fuel flow stopped, the engine followed suit shortly after and it joined terra-firma soon after that - all within sight of the guards manning the border. A crash guard was required and communications to the crash site needed to be set up. Matt got clearance from command to use selected frequencies and had the radios 'tweaked' by the technicians for maximum output at those frequencies. Three element aerials were constructed for those specific frequencies and whilst Matt manned the CP, five vehicles set out to provide a 'Remote Rebroadcast' link to the crash site. They were working ground-to-ground on VHF, at just under a 140 miles between each ground station. Not bad for a radio set with an advertised range of 20 to 25 miles! The crash guard lasted for two weeks and 26 Squadron provided the only communications between the crash site and Royal Air Force Germany.

One day, an RAF Police 'god' was posted in. He was a Warrant Officer policeman and soon made a name for himself as a bit of a character. Known as the Sheriff, he had his RAF bicycle painted red and black with 'RAF Police' written on the frame. It sported a blue light and was fitted with a radio. One channel on the radio was in case he wanted to cross the runway on his bike. He would communicate directly with Air Traffic Control and woe betide the pilot who might be on finals, short of fuel and with multiple system failures. If the Sheriff was waiting to cross then he would just have to go around again. The Sheriff took precedence. He could often be seen with his blue light going at the side of the road where he'd stopped some hapless motorist and was lecturing him or her on road manners. Between the guardroom and the station headquarters was a patch of grass known as 'Gods little green Acre'. It was hallowed turf and God help you (or otherwise) if one blade was trodden on. There could be no short cuts. One had to walk around the square. On the other side of the airfield was a Hawker Hunter. This airframe had been irreparably damaged by fire. It had been resprayed to look like new and it was used as an airfield decoy, being moved from time to time. One Christmas eve morning as the station personnel were going to work they couldn't fail to miss the Hunter. It was sitting on Gods little green Acre with a red figure in the cockpit. The portly figure sported a white beard and the top of a sack could just be seen. Father Christmas was duly arrested and removed to custody until those naughty elves replaced the Hunter from whence it came. It didn't happen. Finger prints were taken but the culprits were never identified. Eventually, the aircraft was dug out of the grass and towed back to the other side of the airfield to resume its duties. Gods little green acre was now rutted and marked. It never was quite as pristine after that and it was rumoured that the Sheriff himself had scattered grass seed over the scarred area whilst muttering and looking around him furtively. He was checking for anyone who might be looking around the corner of buildings smirking or gloating.

One of the memorable characters on C & R flight was a faired-haired wiry Glaswegian. He was nicknamed 'Minging Charlie'. Charlie 's fair hair stuck out horizontally from under his beret and no matter how smart he tried to be, he always looked unkempt. Married to a girl from the same tenement block they set up home in a private hiring. Their lifestyle did nothing to cement Anglo-German relationships. If a visitor were brave enough to visit the house, their nostrils would be assaulted by the amniotic smell of dirty babies nappies kept in a bucket near the front door. If the visitor were brave enough to accept the proffered hospitality, the 'Cocktail Cabinet' would be opened with a flourish and a choice of Heineken or Amstel beer would be offered. No glasses mind. Just the caps knocked off with one hand using the already splintered wood on the cabinet top as the opener. This cabinet was by way of a service issue, two-door oak sideboard that had been prettied up by a wooden trellis being nailed to the rear of the cabinet. Minging Charlie and Nellie lived in a blissful unawareness that their lifestyle could be viewed as anything less than normal. His car was not spared copious amounts of neglect either. It was never cleaned inside or out - ever. When the ashtray overflowed it was left for the ash to form a pile on the floor beneath the ash tray. The pile of ash grew larger and larger, before covering the inside of the car when a door was opened in the wind. And then the pile grew again. Charlie's propensity for Amstel was his undoing as one afternoon he was stopped and breathalysed. The reading was over the limit and he was charged, tried and found guilty of driving whilst over the limit. He was fined a month's wages and his wife Nellie was heard to berate him whilst following him into the football club that night. 'Fifty poond Charlie, fifty poond'. He was also disqualified from driving for a year which at least prevented the ash pile from growing any more for a while. Charlie indignantly protested his innocence throughout all these proceedings as the breath sample had been taken in the afternoon and he'd had nothing to drink since the previous evening.

Life on the station was hard work but morale was high and the duties were different from normal Regiment work. Keeping the main runway and taxi ways clear of snow was of paramount importance. The snow clearance machinery consisted of a Sickard which resembled a Combine Harvester and snow-blowing jet engines. These latter machines used an obsolete De Haviland Ghost or Goblin jet engine bolted to the front of a fuel bowser. They were very effective at blowing the snow away but once started, stopping was out of the question. The heat generated was so intense that the tarmac surface would melt if the vehicle stopped with the jet engine running. Runway snow duties were usually an all night duty but Matt didn't mind. It was different work and you knew you were making a significant contribution to the station's effectiveness. But there were also the boring squadron duties, which consisted of wandering around occasionally to check that all was secure and no fires had started. The boredom ceased one Sunday morning when Matt found himself as 26 Squadron orderly Corporal. Sitting with his feet up drinking a cup of tea, he realised that a Hercules aircraft was landing. Unusual for a Sunday, thought Matt. Then another, then another. Matt got up and looked out of the window towards the Visiting Aircraft Section, or VAS. There were Hercules taxiing in from the runway in a constant stream and the VAS was a hive of vehicles buzzing around the aircraft. He could see the aircraft being loaded up with equipment then starting up and taking off. This went on until well into the evening. In the midst of all this activity, Matt's phone was going mad with requests from people he'd never heard of wanting to know if certain types of equipment could be loaded into the aircraft, what was the maximum payload, what was the maximum size. God knows where they'd got his number from but he did his best to get the answers. Something major was happening and in his own small way, Matt was part of it. Operation Motorman, the reinforcement of troops and equipment to Northern Ireland had started. The security was so good that nobody outside the 'need to know group' had any idea that such a large air movement was going to take place - let alone that it would take place from RAF Güttersloh that weekend.

Matt eventually amassed sufficient points to reach the front of the Married Quarters queue and was allocated a flat in one of the local villages. He took some leave and returned to the UK to bring the family over. They moved into the village of Blankenhagen and Matt and the family settled down to enjoy the life out of camp in the local Anglo-German community.

Chapter 18 - Northern Ireland

In nineteen seventy two, Twenty Six Squadron Royal Air Force Regiment were warned for Northern Ireland duties. The squadron were to become a Company and be part of Two Two Regiment, Royal Artillery. They would be based in Londonderry for three months and would have control of the inner part of the walled city under the command of Two Two.

Meanwhile, back in 1689, King William of Orange fought the battle of the Boyne and won. He attempted to make Ireland a protestant country but didn't succeed. The Protestant part of Ireland became Northern Ireland some time later but during King Billys time, Derry lost it's Catholic name and became Londonderry. After the battle, Ireland became a divided land with both the Catholics and the Protestants hating each other with a mutual loathing. There were areas in Belfast where any Catholics would be killed on sight, women and children included. There were also Catholic communities where the same would happen to Protestants who entered the no go areas. Londonderry was the same and both the Catholic and the Protestant fanatics hated the British soldiers.

Northern Ireland in the early seventies was generally a 'lose lose' situation and a year after Bloody Sunday, Twenty Six squadron were about to find themselves living in a car park. On the other side of the city wall and looking down on them would be the Rossville flats.

Training now took on a serious note. PT was stepped up to every afternoon and was attended with a 'will do' attitude. Matt and selected others had a weeks Akido training with the Army. They would become part of the 'Snatch Team'. Their job would be to sit in the rear of an armoured car with see through shields protecting them. The vehicle would reverse into a rioting crowd. At a given signal, the snatch team would leap out of the vehicle, grab the wanted person, drag them back into the vehicle and 'sit on them' until they got to the police station to make a formal arrest. Apart from the Snatch team duties, Matt had to go on another course and learn how to operate a 'Gelignite Detector' or sniffer. This piece of equipment was carried on the back like a rucksack and had a hand held device which was used to sample anything suspicious. It would give an audio indication as to whether or not the sample contained explosives.

All of the squadron trained in riot control and Matt couldn't help thinking back to Butterworth and how simple it all seemed then.

One of the most intensive courses Matt had attended so far began. He had a team of four who would become the squadron Search Team. Matt would be the search team leader and they were trained by a mix of Royal Engineers and Royal Artillery Personnel. The first thing they learnt was that they would never go out on a 'shout' without the whole team. Similarly, they would never accept anyone from another search team as a temporary member of their team. They must never, never use an untrained person in a search and if one of the team were unable to attend a shout, the job would be handed to another team. In the future, they would rely on each other with their lives. Any single member of the team setting off a booby trap could kill them all. They all had to know their jobs and be trusted to do them properly.

The training started with a weeks classroom work where they learnt about different methods of building construction and different types of buildings. They would be searching for arms, ammunition, bombs and bomb making equipment in occupied and unoccupied buildings. They moved from the classroom on to search exercises where they not only looked for arms, ammo and bombs but also hidden rooms and booby traps. They worked with mine detectors and they were taught to use mirrors to look underneath things or around corners. They worked using the mark one eyeball, looking

179

for things out of the ordinary and they worked by feel alone in the dark. They learnt about light sensitive devices, pressure sensitive devices and trip switches. They saw how clothes pegs could be used as initiating devices and they learnt how to make bombs from easily available materials around the house. They needed to recognise what they were looking at when they examined potentially explosive devices. By the time the course had finished they were confident of their abilities and had built a mutual trust between themselves.

The squadron now moved to Sennelager training area where they practised various scenarios taken from real past events that had occurred. There were streets made up from actual street plans of Londonderry and Belfast. The buildings were made from corrugated iron but that did not detract from the realism felt in what was known as 'Tin Town'. They used and noted the effects of firing Rubber Bullets and Baton rounds. The rubber bullets were about five inches long and an inch and a half across. They were made from a hard compound rubber. The Baton round had the same dimensions but was made from plastic and was lethal. Matt was hit during a riot exercise by a rubber bullet. It hit him on the shoulder from the rear. It spun him round and the shock to his body rendered him unconscious for a few seconds. When he came to, he discovered that somehow, he'd managed to get into a doorway for shelter. That night he not only had a bruise the size of a football on his shoulder but he also discovered the rubber bullet lodged in the hood of his jacket.

They trained as a unit then trained as part of 22 Royal Artillery Regiment. The day finally arrived when Matt and about a dozen others found themselves boarding an aircraft heading West. They were the squadron Advance Party and were going out ten days before the squadron. Their job would be to get out onto the ground and familiarise themselves with the territory. When the main party arrived and started patrolling they would be able to do so with the by now, experienced members of the advance party.

They landed at Aldergrove in the evening and climbed onto a civilian coach for the journey to Londonderry. At about the halfway point, the driver stopped to buy some cigarettes. It was quite dark as he walked across the road and entered the shop. There was a loud bang as the large side window burst, then someone shouted grenade. In a split second as he was hitting the floor Matt realised simultaneously that this was for real and that this was going to hurt. He lay on the floor with his arms over his head and waited. The waiting seemed to take forever, then he realised that the explosion hadn't come. They all started to get up slowly when someone discovered the grenade. It wasn't a grenade at all. It was a rock. Perfectly oval in shape and about the size of a grenade, it weighed about the same. Adrenalin was still coursing through their veins as they moved off complete with shattered window. Off into the freezing night to their new home in a car park in Londonderry.

They arrived at a hutted camp made out of corrugated iron Nissen huts. Situated at the northern end of the inner city, it was next to the gate which separated Bishops Street Within, from Bishops Street Without. It was surrounded by a high wall where it was necessary and so was not overlooked. They had all the facilities needed there to live and it even had its own shop. The shop was owned and run by a pair of Indian gentlemen who lived there permanently. The only time one of them left was to obtain more supplies. The other remained behind to make sure they were not robbed.

Shown to their hut, they stowed their kit then reported for a briefing. The briefing covered their locale, the people in it and the general mood of the population. Over the last three months, the unit who were leaving had had their fair share of incidents. Matt got the impression that they were not sorry to be handing over. Briefing over they were taken to the cook house for a meal then shown around the camp.

The next morning after breakfast Matt was called to the command post where he was told that he would be taken around the local area visiting the various unit locations. He would be travelling in a one of a pair of semi armoured Land Rovers with three other persons. They would be using safe routes which Matt needed to memorise.

They loaded their weapons at the weapons pit situated by the entrance to the camp. They then got into the landrover and set off past the guard. About twenty yards down the road there came the crack crack crack crack of bullets going past. With rounds ricocheting off the walls about them Matt realised that they were being fired at by a Sub Machine Gun. Matt counted seven shots in all as they came screeching around in the road to return back into the camp. The gate guard had had what was known as a 'Negligent Discharge'. It was an automatic chargeable offence and the guard was relieved at once. Blimey, thought Matt. It's bad enough being here without being shot at by your own side.

They went out that afternoon and the vehicle mounted patrol passed without incident. They were back in time for the evening meal then it was out on a foot patrol. A couple of hours into the patrol a message came over on the radio. To all stations, Bomb reported in Carlisle Road. Their patrol was tasked to block off the western end of Carlisle road whilst another patrol blocked off the eastern end. This was done to prevent danger to traffic and people who might wish to use that route. Felix was in attendance. Felix was the code name given to the bomb disposal officer. He walked into the doorway of a shop with his explosives sniffer dog. He forced the door and they entered the shop. There was an almighty boom as the front of the shop disintegrated. A shower of glass was hurled across the road. Felix and his dog followed the glass at an altitude of about four feet. They landed on the pavement at the other side of the road. His support team rushed over to administer first aid whilst Matt and the patrol gave cover. That night, eleven bombs went off in various premises in Carlisle road. They learnt later that it was the IRAs way of wishing the outgoing unit a 'Bon Voyage' and the incoming unit a 'Welcome to Derry'.

Both the Felix and his dog survived but it took a long time to heal, even longer to get their hearing back and both were eventually invalided out of the Army.

There were one or two of the advance party who didn't get out and learn the ground. These people stayed within the relative safety of the car park until the squadron arrived. This inability to realise the importance of getting out to learn the local area was to have almost fatal consequences a couple of weeks later.

The personnel of the car park camp were responsible for manning an observation post situated on the corner of the main city wall. The city wall was about ten to fifteen feet wide at that point and had a metalled road running along the top of it between a door in the car park wall and the observation post. Known as the car park OP, it was sturdily built and could stop a bullet. Access to the OP from the car park was through the door in the wall, out along the road for about thirty yards and into the OP. The problem was that the move from the door in the wall to the OP was in full view of the Rossville flats and there was a Sniper in the flats who dearly wanted a British Soldiers scalp. There was a blind spot however and the only way to the OP was by using it. Matt opened the door in the wall and in one fluid movement ran through at the crouch. At the far side of the road was a retaining wall which would shield him from the Snipers view. Diving for the base of the wall, Matt heard the double crack as two bullets passed over his head. On reaching the safety of the wall, it was a simple task to crawl along it's length to the OP. Returning was simply a reversal of the procedure. Never once in the three months they were there did anybody get to the OP without being shot at and nobody ever got the sniper.

Twenty Six Squadron arrived and the old unit moved out. The changeover was spread over a couple of days to ensure a seamless operation. Then one bright sunny morning, Twenty Six found itself living within the walled city of Londonderry starting its 'peace keeping tour'. If only they knew what lay ahead.

Later that night everybody in the car park could hear what sounded like a war being fought in some other part of the city. A hundred and some odd rounds were being fired, some single shot and some on automatic. There was more than one weapon firing and the sounds of RPGs could be plainly heard.

The RPGs or Rocket Projectiles were Russian made anti-tank weapons. The weapon consisted of a shoulder mounted launcher from which the anti-tank high explosive projectile was fired. It was a recoilless weapon which had a danger area to the rear where the back blast from the rocket emanated. That meant that it could not be fired from inside confined spaces or with a wall to the rear.

During the time the squadron spent in Londonderry, it was an unusual occurrence if no RPGs were heard during a normal day. The norm was one to three a day.

The walled city had four large gates set into arches through which the access roads ran. The four main roads were in the shape of a cross with the crossroads in the centre of the city being known as The Diamond. Not to be outdone, one of the Catholic areas outside the city known as The Bogside also had a crossroads which was named the Little Diamond. These four access points were manned. Two of them for twenty four hours a day and one of them during daytime only. The daytime one was called Butchers Gate and great care was needed by the oncoming gate guard when opening the gate in the morning. It was the closest gate to the Rossville flats and sometimes had a bomb attached to the outside of it. When an explosive device was found, Felix was called and everybody retired to a safe distance for a smoke. Once the bang or controlled explosion had occurred car alarms were reset and windows were closed whilst normal service resumed. As for the other gates, the southern gate was used for incoming traffic only with exit from the city being through the western gate. The northern gate next to the car park was never opened to traffic but was used by pedestrians. These four gates communicated by radio but intelligence reported that the Provisional IRA were able to listen in to the radio nets. Clearly this situation had to be addressed. The only way to ensure security would be to install a telephone in each gate and run a dedicated wire from the command post to each phone. The only place the cables could be run securely would be around the top of the city walls. Any person attempting to tamper with them would be easy to spot. It was also difficult to get around on the top as the walls were covered in coils of barbed wire and lights. Matt arranged for the lights illuminating the top of the wall to fail one night for a couple of hours and climbing a ladder at the southern gate he crawled into the centre of the coiled barbed wire. Armed with only a half mile pack of wire and a 9mm Browning pistol he knew that if any bad boys spotted him up there, there could be no escape. He would be trapped inside an entanglement of barbed wire. He could feel his backside puckering up and he felt naked as he crawled in a clockwise direction slowly around the top of the walled city. He crawled to the western gate then repeated the ordeal from the western gate to the northern gate. From there it was an easy safe run into the command post. Into the warmth and safety for a brew and a fag. Back outside it was only one gate to go. The Butchers gate outside Rossville flats. Using the dark and the cover provided by the OP, Matt set off crawling at the base of the wall as much as possible. Past the flats and down to the gate. Phew. Made it, he thought as he climbed down the ladder and tested the phone.

One afternoon Matt was in Fountain Street. A fiercely protestant area on the opposite side of the city walls to the Bogside. The kerb stones were painted Red, White and Blue and large murals of King

185

Billy adorned the walls of buildings. A message came over the radio warning of a bomb that had apparently been placed in a bakers shop in Bishops Street Without, not far from the car park. A small patrol was dispatched to investigate. The experienced man in that patrol was one of those who chose to spend his advance party time in the car park. His unfamiliarity with the area caused him to take what he thought was a shortcut. It wasn't. The men were led through the bakers shop where the bomb was situated. Matt heard the boom from his location and listened as the radio erupted in pandemonium. That explosion cost them three men severely wounded with multiple fractures, lacerations and grazes. They, like the Felix in Carlisle road that first night, through no fault of their own, learnt to fly.

Matt was down at the southern gate with the sniffer equipment one Saturday morning. It was a busy time and a lot of vehicles had been pulled over for sniffer checks. Matt was checking for 'Car Bombs' or any attempts to smuggle explosives into the city. He noticed idly that there were a lot of people milling about but thought nothing of it. It was a Saturday after all, thought Matt. Without any warning, one of the Royal Ulster Constabulary police men shouted at Matt to cover him and ran into the crowd. Matt looked around him. All the patrol were busy dealing with minor incidents. Matt caught the eye of one of the patrol and shouted to him to give him back up as he sprinted off to catch up with the policeman. The policeman had by now arrested a wanted man and the crowd around him were starting to turn nasty. Matt ran up and together they walked slowly backwards towards the only cover available. A space between two sentry boxes with the city wall at the back. There was just enough room between the boxes for two men to stand. Matt and the policeman stood shoulder to shoulder with the prisoner boxed in behind them. The crowd in front of them numbered some two to three hundred people and had turned ugly. Some of the crowd were screaming for the prisoners release, whilst others were threatening death to 'Youse English Fucking Soldier'. Matt had his rifle and was well aware that one of the prizes sought by the IRA was a rifle, preferably complete with the owner. The crowd was so close now that Matt thought that they were really going to attempt a capture. To say that he was frightened was an understatement. He was out on a limb, alone to protect a policeman and retain an arrestee. Matt cocked his rifle and fed a live bullet into the chamber. He did it aggressively making sure that the crowd could see and hear his action. He was ready to use it if necessary, as a last ditch attempt to save his life or the life of the policeman. He shouted to the crowd to get back or he would fire; and he would, make no mistake. He called on the radio for help and just as he was starting to give up, the southern gate guard came pushing through the crowd. At the same time an armoured car reversed through the crowd and backed up to the sentry boxes. The crowd melted back realising collectively that the moment of initiative had passed. Matt said a silent prayer of thanks, gratefully climbed aboard the Pig and decided to have a Hamlet moment. He shakily lit up and hungrily sucked the cigarette smoke too deep into his lungs. It could so easily have been much worse he reflected. I should not have allowed myself to become separated. If somebody wants to do that in the future then good luck to them he thought. I'll never do it again.

The next day the search team were called to the command post and briefed for a search. It was just within the walls and was an unoccupied building in Bishops Street Within. Matt briefed the team on who was responsible for which part of the operation. Their method of entry, clearance for booby traps and the conduct of the search itself was outlined by Matt. The protective cauldron in the form of two eight man patrols was in place as Matt and the team made their way to the house with ladders, tools and rope.

Matt climbed the ladder. He hated this bit. He could so easily be climbing up to expose himself to a waiting sniper. Matt would be going alone. Should he set something off, he would be the only casualty. Once on the sloping roof, Matt removed enough slates to allow him to drop through into the loft. He moved through the loft to the centre of a room underneath and cut through the ceiling beneath his feet with a saw. He now uncoiled the rope and tied the end to a beam. Using the rope he lowered himself on to the floor beneath. He now used the jemmy or crowbar and levered up enough floorboards to get his body through and once more cut through the ceiling below. He lowered more rope. Climbing down, he could see he wasn't finished yet. The house had a cellar. He repeated the technique of going through the floor being careful to lift floorboards and not apply any downwards pressure. He climbed down the rope and eventually stood on the cellar floor. He stood still for a few moments and smelled the air. He was trying to detect the smell of explosives which in this area was called co-op mix. It smelt strongly of marzipan. All he could smell was damp. Good he thought. Now it was time to climb up the stairs but first Matt needed to check for booby traps or switches behind and underneath each step. It was quite gloomy down in the cellar but he didn't dare use a torch in case light sensitive devices were being employed. He had to work by feel. Any pressure switches would be placed so that any weight on the stairs would actuate them. There were none so matt climbed the stairs to the next obstacle. The rear of the door on the cellar side was next but that was also clear. Matt could not use the radio to transmit progress reports as there could be a device sensitive to RF energy. He could hear the command post getting impatient but he ignored them and concentrated on the task to hand. Entering the living room Matt checked underneath the window sill for any pressure switches. There were none. Next he had to clear the rest of the stairs then come back down and clear the ground floor. Coming back down he moved carefully from room to room, attempting to lift floorboards before placing any weight on them. Open doors were checked by using a mirror to show what was behind the door. Closed doors necessitated a return trip upstairs to cut another hole in the ceiling so that the rear of the door frame was exposed. It took Matt about two hours to clear completely the inside of the building. When he was finally satisfied, he opened the front door and let the search team in. One of the squadron officers had by now joined the team and Matt wasted no time in getting him back outside, explaining that he could still be blown up. He was not happy about the length of time this was taking. It was the first proper search he'd been involved with and Matt could see that he clearly had no idea of what was involved. There was a shout from upstairs and Matt looked up just as one of the team looked out of the window and beckoned Matt up. Matt cut short his discussion with, I'm needed inside. Nobody must be allowed to enter this building until the team have declared it free from explosives and booby traps. He added a hasty sir then went through the front door closing it firmly behind him. Upstairs in the loft Matt was handed a mirror and a torch. Matt checked the eaves and could just make out two rifle butts. "Can you get to the other end to check for pull wires", said Matt. "No, it's impossible", answered Jock. "Okay", said Matt. "Lets get Felix in to check this out before we move anything". The team moved outside and Matt got onto the radio to call the Felix. Once on scene the bomb disposal team questioned Matt and his team closely. They were satisfied that the team had done their job properly and entered the building. Matt and the team waited at the front door and had a cigarette. About an hour later Felix came down carrying two rifles wrapped in newspaper. There's more stuff up there he said as he gave Matt and the team the rifles. Matt left one man to guard the weapons as he and the rest of the team went back in to finish their search. In all, the team recovered two Lee Enfield Martini-action rifles plus one hundred and nine rounds of ammunition plus two eighteen inch bayonets. Not a bad result for an afternoons work thought Matt. Back at base there was a debrief where Matt made sure that everybody understood why it took so long to search a locked up, unoccupied house and why he was unable to give updates over the radio for at least the first hour of a search. If anything untoward happened, Matt assured them, they would know. They'd be able to hear the bang from anywhere in the city.

One of the local characters was a sergeant in the Ulster Defence Regiment. He was a very Pro-English protestant. His name was Sgt Harpic and he could often be seen at the city exit gate trying to sell his illegal liquor poteen, to the lads manning the gate. It was home made stuff and it could send you blind. One night at about eleven he came to the gate and reported his car missing.

If a car were stolen in Londonderry, it usually ended up packed full of explosives and was usually set off by the IRA to cause the maximum impact or damage for the media to report on. An all stations call soon went out and the roving patrols looked out for the car. After about twenty minutes it was found. It was parked up against a kerb. Sgt Harpic wasn't happy because it wasn't parked where he'd left it. Felix was called in to deal with a possible car bomb. A defensive cauldron was set up around the area and Felix set up his wheelbarrow. The wheelbarrow looked like a large toy tank. It was controlled remotely and had lights and a television camera on board so that the operator could see where it was going. It also carried a double barrelled shotgun or disrupter and a device capable of delivering the equivalent of a shotgun blast but without the pellets. It was also capable of delivering a jet of water. Wheelbarrow was deployed and it trundled up to the Triumph Herald. There was nothing to see inside the car and so the wheelbarrow was set up to blow the boot off in case the explosives had been set there. A call came over the radio. "All stations, stand by for a controlled explosion in orange street". There followed a deep boom then a second explosion as the rear of the car ignited in a brilliant pale blue flame. The petrol tank then went up and the whole car became a mass of red and yellow flames. Just as Felix reported that secondary explosions had been observed, Sgt Harpic UDR was seen with his head against the wall. He was beating the wall with his fists and repeating over and over again, "oh shit, oh shit". When pressed on the matter, Sgt Harpic had suddenly remembered where he'd parked his car before he went to have a drink. It had been found where he'd left it and to make matters worse, the car boot had been full of poteen, ready to sell on. He had so to speak, lost everything.

Notice came through of a regimental operation to arrest a wanted man from inside the Rossville Flats. Two Two Regiment along with Twenty Six squadron would silently surround the complex and secure it by two thirty in the morning. Matt and his team under guidance, would make their way to the wanted man's address up on the fourth floor and at three a.m. Would, without any warning break down the front door, get up the stairs and charge in to his bedroom. He would then be arrested and instantly lifted out of the flat. He'd be taken downstairs and whisked away to a police station in Belfast. Oh, and he'd probably be armed. The operation went like clockwork. By the time the occupants of the Rossville Flats had woken up and realised what was going on, the troops were long gone. They found themselves shouting at thin air whilst the rest of the city slept on.

One of the tricks the IRA used was to get little girls of about eleven or so to plant bombs in shops. The IRA would give a girl and her accompanying friend a plastic shopping bag; usually on a Saturday. Inside the bag would be a bomb with a timer already set and ticking away. Somehow, the timers had been previously smuggled in to the city. The explosives were made up from sugar and other items common to households. The girls would be instructed where to go and given a phone number to ring. They'd also be given quite a lot of money. The girls would go into a shop along with all the other shoppers and place their bag behind a counter inside. They would then get clear of the area and phone the number given. They'd be told to go home where a present would be waiting for them. The IRA having received notification that the bomb had been placed, phoned their local pre-arranged hot line to a newspaper office and informed that there was a bomb in such and such an area and would explode at, etcetera. If there was enough warning the troops would clear the area of civilians and call the Felix. He would sometimes send in his wheelbarrow. He would sometimes go in himself or sometimes stand back and wait for the bomb to go off. His decisions depended on many factors. Paramount of course was the safety of the local people who were often shouting abuse. Whilst all this was going on, intelligence men in plain clothes would be mingling with the crowd ready to point out known terrorists for the troops to arrest or taking photographs of any unknown players who acted furtively or suspiciously. The troops were never bored on Saturdays.

 One Saturday morning as Matt was preparing to take up his usual post at the entrance gate for the traffic, he was called to the CP. Briefed to cover the bus station instead of the main route in to the city Matt asked why. As far as he was concerned, him being there with the gelignite detector served as a good deterrent. People could see him working there and knew that he was diligent with his searches. Someone on the squadron was not doing 'joined up thinking', he thought. With a heavy heart Matt went out of the city gates and down the hill to the bus station. It was a fair way and there were only two of them. This is stupid and bloody dangerous thought Matt. He got onto the the radio to tell the CP that he was returning to repair his broken sniffer when there was the mother of all booms. Matt looked towards the city and saw what appeared to be a car engine block coming down towards the earth from a great height. Ominous black smoke rose up and Fire Engines could be heard making their noisy way towards the city. A car bomb had driven through the gate in the form of a VW milk float. The troops manning the gate could only carry out a cursory check as they had no gelignite detector and so the milk float complete with hidden bomb had got through. Matt was furious. It had obviously been reported to the IRA that Matt was not at his post that Saturday and that presented the golden opportunity to cause maximum disruption within the city. Several large department stores were destroyed that day but Matt never heard a thing about the person who had decided to redeploy the sniffer that day. The ranks had closed and had become silent.

One day there was a tip off from intelligence. A bomb would be placed in to a jewellers shop not far from where the VW milk float had gone up. The idea was that a bomb would be placed and in the ensuing confusion after the explosion a robbery would take place. They would need to set up a covert OP overlooking the shop. They would be watching to see who went in with a plastic bag and came out without it. They planned for three days and that night they took up residence in the cellar of a bombed out shop opposite the jewellers. There were five of them altogether and they spent the next three days over the weekend in occupation watching the shop. They used black plastic bags for human waste and ate cold food washed down with water. After day two it became difficult to keep up the levels of concentration whilst observing and by the time day three was over they were heartily glad to be moving out. Nothing happened during their time in the dirty damp darkness of the bombed out building and going back into camp to bright lights, hot food, hot tea and hot showers was like going to heaven.

Every Saturday since the milk float car bomb, they'd saturated the streets with airmen. Every few yards along each main street there would be one or two of them. Each airman had a shop to watch and would note the people going in and going out. Who went in with a plastic bag but came out without one was the million dollar question? And one day there he was. A man in his twenties had gone

193

into a chemists shop on the corner of the Diamond and had come out without his bag. As he hurried away with what seemed to be undue haste, Two airmen blocked his path. He turned back and there were two more who were pointing their sub machine guns at him. Unless he wanted to commit suicide, it was time to give up. He was placed up against a wall in a stress position as one of the airmen went back into the shop to clear it. Once cleared, the bomber was marched back in at the point of a gun and made to pick up his bomb. He tried to protest but the airmen were in no mood to take any prisoners. Walking back outside, still at gunpoint he was made to walk into the centre of a piece of waste ground and defuse it. He was then taken away with his bomb to the police station for formal arrest. The next morning, in the UK newspapers, this story made front page news. British troops inhumane treatment of Derry Bomber, the headlines proclaimed. Matt and his mates couldn't recall a single reporter near Londonderry that day. In fact they hadn't seen any for weeks. The message went out loud and clear to the IRA bomb makers though. If you want to plant bombs, make sure you're ready to defuse them when caught. That effectively put an end to the anti-handling devices on bombs for a while.

Thus far in the tour they had one Felix and his dog wounded. One Felix and his helper from Darlington killed. Three airmen seriously wounded in one incident and three more injured when a device was placed in a pub which went up when they were trying to throw out drunken patrons. One of the roving patrols had been shot at in broad daylight and they all had run the gauntlet having to cross sniper alley on many occasions when they had to visit the OP. Many occupied and unoccupied searches had been carried out each with its own particular different type of danger. It was getting close to the end of the tour and with only a week to go, Matt was diverted from his patrol area one night to rendezvous with one of the squadron officers outside the main city exit gate.

" Corporal Jenkins, he started". "This pair of houses across the road require us to investigate a problem". "The house on the right", he went on, is occupied by a Catholic family". "The house on the left is empty and has been empty for about twenty years". Before Matt could say anything, the baby officer carried on. "Lights were seen in the empty house tonight and the Catholic family are worried that someone might have placed a bomb next door". As you know, we are right on the edge of a Protestant area". "So what do you want me to do about it sir", said Matt? "I want you to go in and check it out to ensure it's not been tampered with", said the baby officer. "The best thing to do is to move the family out into a hotel for the night and search the place in the morning", said Matt. "We're not going to do that came the reply", "you are to carry out a search". "What, conduct a search of an unoccupied building at night, where you suspect a booby trapped Improvised Explosive Device might have been placed", asked Matt, incredulously? "Yes", came the reply. "But I don't have my team with me", said Matt. "You can take SAC Jones with you", came the reply. "Sir, with respect, he's not fucking trained and I can't take him". "Corporal Jenkins, you are to search that building now and that's the end of the discussion". Matt was furious. Once again a commissioned officer had over ruled his trained experts so that it could be demonstrated that he could carry out any tasks given to him without making any waves. His obstinacy over his career prospects taking precedence would probably cost lives tonight and it would probably be Matts. He knew that if he refused to carry out this task, even if he was subsequently proved right to do so, the charges and courts marshals that would follow would ruin any chances he might have of any real future in the Regiment. The commissioned officer who had ordered Matt to carry out the search might get a rap on the knuckles but ranks would close and it would be Matt who suffered in the long run.

Okay, thought Matt lets take five minutes out and have a think about this. It was out of the question risking an untrained man so he needed to be ditched. If this is a set up or 'come on' then there will be light sensitive devices. The floorboards might have pressure switches and there could be trip wires. He'd need a piece of fourteen gauge wire to hold between his fingers to sense that particular 'gotcha'. Matt sat silently and thought through all the options open to him.

"Right sir, I'll need my search equipment", said Matt. "Would you get onto the CP to get it sent out in a landrover"?

Ten minutes later the vehicle arrived. Matt got the baby officer to evacuate the family next door in case it all turned to worms and briefed the lad allocated to him. Matt neatly took out one of the four panels in the front door by removing the beading and used a sink plunger to suck the panel out. Using the mirror, Matt then checked around the inside of the door frame. Clear as far as he could see. He then gingerly put his arm inside and gently felt around. Nothing. He removed the second lower panel and the centre strut. As he crawled through slowly, he attempted to lift each floorboard in turn before placing any weight on it. Using the piece of fourteen gauge wire he felt gently forward for any trip wires. To get his body in completely took an age. To move far enough forward to get his untrained man in took another age. He had briefed him that once he was inside the building he was stay by the door and guard it. He was not to let anybody in under any circumstances. Matt slowly moved forward. It was totally black. The sweat ran down his face and dripped on the floor as he inched his way forward. He reached a door to his left then froze as he thought he heard a sound. He stopped breathing and cocked his ear towards where he thought he heard the sound. There, coming out of the silence of the night came the sound of a ticking clock. "Jim", he whisper shouted, "get out now".

Empty twenty years my arse thought Matt as he took cover on the other side of the road behind a skip. He drew on a cigarette as the bastard baby officer got onto the the radio for Felix. An hour later the Felix arrived and having briefed him Matt remained behind the skip and took no interest in any more of the proceedings. Eventually the Felix came out and sat beside Matt on the pavement. He lit a cigarette and showed Matt an old fashioned alarm clock. Matt couldn't believe it. "What the fuck", said Matt. "That clock must have been here for the last twenty years", said the Felix. "Your movement must have caused just enough vibration on the floorboards to set off the last bit of the spring". "What on earth were you doing in an unoccupied building at night", he asked? Matt told him. "Right, leave it with me", he said and walked away. Matt never found out what happened 'in camera' that night but the baby officer kept a low profile for a few days. The eye healed well though.

With a week to go Matt and four of his men found themselves on standby for 'Snatch' duties. Word was that there was going to be a riot in the Bogside area. They would go into the riot to make arrests. They waited until called at the northern gate. They would not have the luxury of an armoured car and protective shields. They would be chasing on foot. They were dressed in gym shoes, green uniform, flack jacket and beret. They were armed only with a baton. Matt told them to stick with him and not get separated. He had the only radio. They waited for about six hours before the call came. It was late afternoon and they could hear the noise of the rioting people. They broke cover and ran down the hill towards the crowd. The crowd was streaming back towards the Bogside from the direction of the Creggan area. They were running fit to bust. By the time they got down the hill the crowd were gone. Dispersing instantly as if they were a divine wind or school of fish. Matt realised that the crowd had dispersed to leave them as targets for the sniper at the Rossville flats. They were in the open. Run shouted Matt. Back up the hill they raced expecting at any moment to hear the crack of rounds going by. They made it. All of them but they realised that they'd been subjected to what was known as a 'come on'. It could have had a tragically different outcome. Matt often wandered why they were not fired on that afternoon. The Rossville flats sniper had missed his or her, golden opportunity.

Chapter 19 - Back to Germany

Spring had arrived in Londonderry and the area took on a promise of the summer to come. The Orange marchers had whistled and drummed their way through Londonderry and it was time to go home. Nobody dropped their guard though. A moment's inattention could still yet be fateful.

One morning whilst it was still dark, handover complete, they boarded the white coaches and made their way to RAF Aldergrove. They were met by the familiar faces of the resident RAF Regiment squadron lads. Over a brew, they were told excitedly about an RPG that had been fired at the camp about three weeks ago and had 'they' seen any action yet!

Eventually they climbed up into the body of the Hercules transport waiting on the tarmac and strapped into the red-webbed seats that ran down the sides of the aircraft. Some hours later they climbed out of the noisy, smelly tube of the fuselage and walked into the squadron area at RAF Gütersloh. They handed in their weapons, then clambered aboard the waiting transport and were taken to the married quarters. Matt sat down in his lounge with his wife and family. It was the strangest thing. The strangest feeling. He couldn't relax, neither could he quite believe he was here. He was not wearing a flack jacket and he felt naked without his rifle. He had to remind himself that it was over. He was safe. He lit a cigarette but could not bring himself to go near the windows. The last few months had changed him. He knew that for sure, when one sunny morning whilst relaxing on the settee, he heard a deep boom, boom. Without a seconds hesitation Matt leapt up and dived on the floor behind the settee. Having sheepishly got up to the looks of surprise of his wife and neighbour he realised it was only one of the base Lightnings going through the sound barrier overhead.

There were many amenities and differing sports available at RAF

Güttersloh and Matt chose to go Gliding. He joined the club as winter set in and they flew when the snow was hard on the ground. One day it was so cold that the canopy could not be closed until the very last second before take-off, otherwise their breath would have frozen on the inside and they'd have been flying on instruments. That evening, when they put the aircraft to bed back in the hanger, Matt checked the outside thermometer: it had risen to minus 14° Celsius, the warmest it had been that day. In the spring, the aircraft went back to their mother club at Detmold, and Matt had to hitch hike or walk to get there.

 He soloed one sunny, quiet evening in March - on his twenty-sixth launch. Completing left and right-hand circuits, he qualified for his A and B certificates. He flew three solo flights that evening and on each he was amazed, on looking around, to find the back seat empty. He never again managed to pull off such smooth landings as he made that evening.

 The Inter-services gliding championships were held at Paderborn that year and Matt attended, along with other new pilots, to crew for the competitors. The day's task had been set and the competitors had all flown off. Matt was one of the pool of retrieve crews just hanging around waiting for a call. A great big black cumulus nimbus covered the sky from horizon to horizon and lightning flashed in the distance. 'Anybody want to fly?' came the call from the duty pilot, 'There's a winch and a Swallow needing use.' Matt called out and was waved over. He had often helped to launch gliders into conditions like this at Swinderby, when he was a kid. That RAF station was home to East Midlands Gliding club at the time. Several pilots had climbed to goal heights inside 'cu nimbs' and Matt was now interested in finding out about conditions under the cloud. I should be okay if I stay on the airfield boundary, he thought, and if I suddenly get strong lift or sink I can turn in and land - in fact, as nothing is using the airfield I could land in any direction. Cockpit checks completed, the winch cable was connected. 'Up slack,' he called and the winch driver, following the signals from the launch point, took in the slack cable. When it tightened, Matt called, 'All out'. The Swallow moved forward, then accelerated and lifted. Matt pulled back very gently and waited until he'd climbed to about 50 feet. At that point he gently rotated into a 45° climb. Looking out at the wingtips relative to the horizon showed him the climbing angle. Checking the speed and looking out to the side all the way up, Matt was careful to lower the nose and release the cable before he disappeared into the black cloud. He turned left and cleared the winch. He had a 900 feet launch which was not bad with the cloud base as it was. He turned downwind. My, thought Matt, this is bumpy. There was no real lift to speak of and no bad sink either. Matt carried on downwind and turned on to the 'base leg' of the circuit. He turned onto finals. The wind suddenly backed as a squall and reversed its direction. The air which had been flowing over his wings providing lift suddenly flowed the wrong way, instantly robbing the lift. Matt's clue came as the nose pointed earthwards and the Air Speed Indicator (ASI) registered zero. As he hurtled earthwards his speed suddenly picked up. The only thing that's going to get me back, he thought, is speed. He was by now pointing towards the airfield with 60 knots indicated. He kept the nose of the glider pointing at a spot just before the main road that crossed the end of the airfield at the Cement works end. At the last minute he lifted the nose and gently lifted over and and back down onto the airfield. He came to a halt and allowed the wing to lower. He unstrapped, then lifted off the canopy. The other club members had reached him by now and as Matt shakily lit a cigarette, he was being bombarded with questions. 'What happened?' they asked. 'We thought you'd bought it,' said another. Matt couldn't bring himself to speak. He sat on the grass, quietly drew on his cigarette and tried to make sense of what had just happened. He couldn't get over seeing the ASI suddenly dropping to zero as he totally lost control.

It was now turning into a warm German summer and the events of the previous year in Northern Ireland were behind them. The station was in the throes of its Minival, Maxival, Taceval season and a Mini had just been called. The squadron deployed to its war positions and the day wore on at a measured pace. Exercise injects were being acted upon to practise those, who it was felt, needed the practice and eventually, a halt was called for the night. The station personnel could go home until the morning but Twenty Six was to remain deployed for the night. Furthermore, the squadron CO ordered that no alcohol was to be allowed. Everybody gratefully pulled off their charcoal, anti-chemical suits and set about establishing a routine for the evening. Matt was called to the phone. 'Cpl Jenkins,' said a voice at the other end. 'Yes,' replied Matt. 'Hello son,' said his father. 'Dad, where are you?' said Matt. 'I'm at VAS for the moment just seeing the aircraft squared away for the night. Do you fancy a beer?' 'I can't,' said Matt, who then explained about the continued deployment. 'Well could you get a couple of hours off?' said his father. 'Hang on,' said Matt, 'I'll call you back in a sec.' Matt put the phone down and sought permission from the sergeant to absent himself for two hours. No problem, he was told, just be back before midnight. Matt phoned VAS and his father picked up the phone. 'Okay,' said Matt, 'I'm clear until eleven.' 'Fine,' said his dad, 'get changed and I'll meet you in the Officers' mess beer garden in forty minutes.'

For an off-duty airman to go and drink at the officers' mess was a crime of monumental proportions. It was unheard of. To do so whilst he should still be on deployment and on duty was a crime of even greater magnitude. On a double-count of drinking alcohol when expressly forbidden by the CO and to do it in the Officers' mess as well, was crime exceeding even biblical proportions. Matt didn't give it a second thought. It was dark as he got to the billets and changed into slacks and a jacket and tie. He made his way around to the rear of the mess and spotted his father sitting with two other people on the other side of the beer garden. Matt walked up and his father greeted him, then introduced a Wing Commander and a Squadron Leader. Both were his father's pupils converting to the Beagle Basset aircraft. A beer was ordered and Matt had a pleasant time chatting and listening to these senior officers at the table. During a lull in conversation Matt recognised a voice at the table behind them. It was his CO. Oh My God, thought Matt. Tell me it's not true. He stole a glance behind him. It was his CO and deputy squadron commander sitting one table away, drinking a beer. If I'm discovered, thought Matt, my feet wouldn't touch the ground until they'd cut me down from the rope. The cheeky bastard's banned us airmen from alcohol but there he is, with the second in command having a drink. Matt leant forward and whispered to his father the bad news. 'Don't worry son,' his father said, 'if push comes to shove we've got enough rank at this table to sink the pair of them.' Yes, thought Matt miserably, but you don't have to live here when you've gone. Shortly afterwards the CO and deputy went inside. Matt took that as his cue to leave. He said his goodbyes and thank you's, looked about him once more to make doubly sure the coast was clear, then left. Breathing a huge sigh of relief, Matt went and changed back into uniform and made his way back to the command post.

During the Olympic Games on the 5th September 1972, at four-thirty in the morning, Palestinian commandos broke into the quarters of the Israeli team at the Olympic Village in Munich. They were armed with automatic rifles and immediately killed two members of the Israeli team. They also took nine others hostage. Over the next twenty-three hours, the nine hostages were murdered, as was a German policeman.

Five of the Palestinian terrorists were killed.

As the shock waves reverberated around the world, 26 Squadron were warned to standby for multiple deployments at flight strength. 'Control and Reporting' flight found themselves heading for RAF Wildenrath to provide armed protection for the station. They were thirty strong, which gave them enough men for three patrols at full section strength plus a headquarters element. The station already had an RAF police section, along with dogs, who provided the static guards. C and R flight patrols would be highly mobile and in contact by radio to a control room. They had airfield crash maps which provided an effective way of directing roving patrols to any incident site. It was September and it was hot, both day and night. They provided cover twenty-four hours a day and the on-duty or active patrol could be called immediately to attend any incident. The station tannoy was also used to pass messages to the patrols if they were uncontactable by radio.

Once a year, each RAF station completed for the Jolliffe Trophy. It was presented to the station demonstrating the highest standards in catering. On this, the judgement day, the Airmen's mess would be resplendent in a new coat of paint and have fresh-cut flowers on tables. The cooks would be dressed in clean crisp whites, and taught to smile. The food would also be hot.

It was into this ambience of catering efficiency and bliss that Matt and his mates went for lunch and joined the queue at the servery. They were carrying their weapons but they were unloaded, with the magazines stowed in bullet pouches on their webbing belts. Matt took a plate and noticed that it was hot for a change. He then noticed that the cook was smiling. Matt looked around him, then back again. Bloody hell, thought Matt, I think he fancies me. Matt chose Steak and Kidney pie and moved on down the servery. Just then the tannoy clicked on.

'Stand by for broadcast, stand by for broadcast,' came the metallic voice. 'Patrol alpha three, report to grid Romeo Seven immediately,' came the message. Before it could be repeated Matt and the patrol had dropped their plates on the nearest tables and were running for the vehicles parked outside. The quickest way for Matt was through the window and that's what he did. They jumped into the vehicles and roared off in a cloud of dust towards area Romeo Seven. It was the sports field. On arriving, they were surprised to find their flight commander already there. Matt was briefed as patrol commander that two terrorists were holed up inside the cricket pavilion. Matt looked at the wooden pavilion, the Married quarters behind it, and the trees around the sports field. 'Is this real, sir' asked Matt, 'or is it an exercise?' 'It's real,' came the reply. Matt knew that the last thing he was going to do was to fire towards the married quarters and so, he briefed the gun group to take up a position on the left flank and to start firing as soon as in position. Matt and the rifle group would give covering fire meanwhile, so that the gun group could move into position. Just as Matt was about to give the order to open fire, the flight commander shouted 'Stop'. It was an exercise after all. Just then the Squadron CO and deputy squadron commander came out from behind some trees and walked up. They were visiting for the day. 'Well done,' said the CO, 'carry on.' Matt turned on his heel and made his way across towards the Land Rovers. He was furious. What was the point in calling an exercise during a real deployment? Why take the chance, when live ammunition is loaded and the rifle section are about to give real covering fire so that a loaded machine gun can move into position?

They mounted up and headed back to face the cooks who were, by now, unamused and unsmiling once more. Even the pie was cold but, by this time, the judges had left the Airmen's mess and all had returned to normal.

One dark night there was a report of an intruder inside the bomb dump. Once again, Matt's patrol deployed. Forming up just inside the gate, they moved into an extended line - each man side-by-side so that they could fire to the front without the risk of hitting their buddies. As they slowly moved forwards into the woods, Matt stressed once again the importance of keeping the line straight. No-one must get ahead or drop behind. If one person stopped then they all stopped. Matt had the radio man beside him. 'Okay Mac,' he said to the operator, 'let the CP know that we've started the sweep.' Mac got onto the radio. They moved forward into the night. It was so dark that Matt could only just make out the men immediately to his left and right. He noticed that Mac was starting to get ahead. 'Mac,' he whispered. He looked again and stopped. There was no Mac, he'd disappeared. 'Mac,' he called out. Louder now. 'Down here,' came a voice from beneath him. Matt looked down but couldn't see a thing. 'Nobody move,' said Matt as he knelt down and felt the ground with his hands. Mac turned on his torch and there, about ten feet below him, Matt could see Mac. He was sitting in the bottom of a concrete ditch. Radio smashed beside him. They got him out and went back to the vehicles. Matt scrubbed the sweep as it was too dangerous to be in there walking about at night. If there are any intruders in there then let the dogs have a go, he thought. A visit to the medical centre found Mac detained overnight for observation. At least he'll get a decent night's sleep, observed Matt. Clean sheets as well. If I had known, I'd have fallen in as well.

Not long after he arrived on the station, Matt learned from one of the Lightning squadron lads that he could put his name down for a flight in the Lightning T4. Matt asked that his name be put forward but, by the time he had served nearly three years on the station, the flight had not been forthcoming, nor did it look like happening. One day, on Station Routine Orders, a small inclusion at the end stated that volunteers were required to sell copies of the annual issue of the RAF Magazine. The person who sold the most would get a trip in a Lightning. It was a no brainer to Matt. He reported to the officer in charge of the project and promptly took half the available magazines thinking that the other half would be distributed amongst more than one person. He sold his quota within a week and so, went back for the remaining magazines. Nobody else had volunteered, so Matt took the rest. He sold those too and so, he got his trip in a Lightning. Ninety-Two's T4 was unserviceable, so the CO phoned up his opposite number on Nineteen squadron and arranged to borrow theirs. Matt knew most of the airmen who worked on the aircraft line. They gleefully handed him a sick bag to stow in his pocket and helped him strap in. The boss climbed into the left hand seat and when all was ready, gave Matt the okay to start. In the T4, the engine start buttons were on the right hand side of the aircraft and couldn't be reached by the boss. Matt had had a thorough brief and a few dry runs on the simulator before he'd even got near the real thing. They started up, taxied out to the end of the runway, lined up, turned on the power, then released the brakes. The aircraft shoved Matt in the back all the way down the runway with its tremendous acceleration. The boss lifted, pulled up the wheels then rotated and allowed the aircraft to climb vertically in cold power. They turned left and flew south in formation with another three Lightnings. It was an incredible experience. Matt was flying it and asked if he could do a slow roll. Yes, came the reply, but take it easy. Matt slow rolled, at Mach .95, and the aircraft felt like it was on rails. They slowed down and descended to low level. They were over the Hennezee river and Matt was flying the aircraft at 300 feet and 450 knots. They were heading north towards the Mohne Dam. The boss said 'I have' and Matt held his hands up to show he'd let go. They crested the rise in front of them and there was the dam. They'd come onto it at right-angles to the lake. Once more the boss rotated into the vertical, rolled off the top and set course for base. They flew high to eke out the best mileage from the thirsty engines and hit the airfield with the runway about 30° off the aircraft nose. They curved in on the approach but were instructed to go round by Air Traffic Control. 'This is going to be a bit tight,' said the boss, referring to their fuel state, as they went around again. This time they came in to a 'full stop' landing. They taxied back to the dispersal and shut down. The ladders were placed against the aircraft sides and Matt thanked the CO of NinetyTwo Squadron for a trip he would never forget. Climbing down the ladder he was greeted with, 'Blimey, you were a long time for a Lightning, especially a T bird'. Matt smiled and handed back the sick bag - unused.

If the Russians ever crossed the East German Border, the plan was to use natural features to the allied NATO forces' advantage. The Russian tanks would be funnelled or condensed into 'Killing Zones' by the mountains, hills and other geographical features present in the Nord Rhine West Falia region of Germany. Each year an exercise was held which involved thousands of British troops and other assets. As part of this massive deployment, air defence units were exercised as well as anti-tank personnel. As a result, Twenty Six Squadron became a tiny cog in this very large machine. Their exercise role would last for three weeks and would find them covering a large part of Germany looking towards the East. Known as Exercise Quick Train, the guns moved each night to new locations or designated vulnerable points. The OPs had to move to provide early warning as well and needed to be set up by midnight each night, to be ready for first light. The start of the third week found Matt and his chums in the Hertz mountains. Covered in forest, the whole area was navigable only by using loggers' tracks. These wound their convoluted way up through the forrested hillsides in a switchback fashion.

Matt's OP crew consisted of himself and two airmen. They had a Land Rover with a trailer containing their packs and camping equipment. One evening Matt had been called to a briefing with the other OP commanders; given his new grid reference he was sent on his way. Everybody was running late and time was becoming scarce. Matt grabbed his men and fresh rations then set off. He briefed them on the way. They reached their area or, rather, the bottom of a hill in their area. They needed to set up the OP at the top. A little way up the track it forked, so Matt took the turning off the main track and stopped. 'Okay chaps,' he said, 'we'll unhitch the trailer here and you can get the meal on. Whilst you're doing that, I'll take the Land Rover to the top and carry out the recce. I'll be back within the hour, then we'll eat and move into position.'

Matt drove up the side of the hill using the switchback track. It was steep but soon he came out on the top: it was a plateau covered with dry grass. He found the grid reference to be beside a wood and having done so, he set off back across the plateau towards the track leading down. It was now getting dark. Suddenly, the Land Rover smoothly rode up what appeared to be a ramp. Matt tried reversing, rocking and jumping but nothing worked. He was stuck. Getting out he had a close look. The engine sump had ridden up the exposed stump of tree root. Now, both front wheels were clear of the ground and there was just not enough traction on the rear wheels to pull them off. The only way to get off would be to jack up the front of the vehicle sufficiently to place enough logs under the front wheels to clear the stump. The jack was in the trailer. Matt knew he had to get down the hill for help. He checked that he had the map and compass. He checked he had water. He checked for food, but chocolate would have to do. He checked his rifle. There was a problem - he only had blank ammunition. Matt removed the blank-firing attachment from the end of his rifle and put it in his pocket. He cocked the rifle placing a round in the chamber ready to fire. If he met any animals on his way back down, a blank fired straight into the eye or the ear would kill it, hopefully. Mind you, the animal would have to be pretty close for you to be able to do that, thought Matt, and I don't aim to get that close to anything that might be wandering around here tonight. It was dark by now and Matt made his way towards the track. He started down and the trees closed above him blocking out most of what little light still remained.

He could just make out the track as it was composed of a light sandy earth. He walked down it silently. He had entered a new world. Shadowy and dark. Just then came a crashing and banging noise from down the slope of the hill. A creature moved uphill across his front and stopped on the track about ten yards away. Matt could just make out a dark blob against the light sand of the track. The hair on his head and his arms stood on end as he remembered, from long ago, those Hertz mountain bears in the zoo at Hamm. He stood rooted to the spot as he realised that he was no longer outside the cage looking in. He was, in effect, inside, looking out.

He stood frozen to the spot for what seemed to be hours. The creature stayed still as well. This could not go on, thought Matt. Someone has to make a move. It was the hardest thing to do and in abject terror, convinced he was going to die, Matt walked towards the bear. 'Yaar,' he shouted and it shot off down the slope. 'Fuckin hell,' thought Matt, 'Yee Haar.' His heart was going so fast he thought it was going to come out of his chest or explode. He walked down the track, his mood getting lighter with every step he took, until he rounded the next corner. The creature was waiting for him on the track once more. Matt now knew that if he approached it, it would go away and that's precisely what happened. Matt walked around each bend, with the creature getting closer and closer each time, until Matt reckoned that the next corner would be showdown time - time to start shooting his blanks. As he approached the corner, Matt realised that it was the track fork where the lads and the trailer were. He could even see the lights. He said a silent prayer of thanks as he walked into the welcoming circle of bright light which was the camp site. Matt explained what had happened to the vehicle and detailed Jordie to bring the jack and jack-handle. He told Ginger to bring the rope and as they walked towards the track junction, Matt told them about the meetings he'd had with the Hertz mountain bear. 'Yeh, yeh,' they said, 'a good story but your not getting us on that one, ha ha, ho ho.' They turned onto the main track and started to head up the slope. There was a tremendous crashing and banging below them as something made it way onto the track in front of them. 'You see,' said Matt, 'what did I tell you?' 'Jordie? Ginger? Where are you?' shouted Matt. They had vanished. 'Down here,' came one voice. 'I'm right behind you,' said the other. They gathered themselves and slowly walked up the track. Matt had lost most of his fear by now as he'd been joined by two other juicy morsels which he was sure would be tastier than him if the bear chose to snack between meals. They made their way ever upwards, repeating the meetings around every corner. The creature just took a straight line directly up the hillside so it was waiting as they rounded every corner, getting ever so slightly closer each time.

'Right, here's the plan,' said Matt when they'd reached the top. 'We're not going to go into this like the Keystone Cops. We all need to know what each of us is going to do and make sure we don't mess up.' No one needed a pep talk. They were high enough on adrenaline already. 'Jordie, you go in the passenger's side door. Ginger, you go in the back and I'll go in the drivers side door. As soon as we get inside, I'll start up the engine then hit the horn. You, Jordie, put the headlights on as I hit the horn. On the count of three, go.' They ran to the Land Rover and the plan went like clockwork. Matt started the vehicle and hit the horn. At the same time, Jordie turned on the headlights and there in front of them, caught in the main beams, was a herd of reindeer. 'Fuck, fuck, fuck,' said Matt. 'Fuck fuckety, fuck, fuck, fuck,' said Jordie. 'I dinna fucka believe it,' said Ginger the Jock. 'Fuckin bear, my arse,' the lads chorused.

Passing round the cigarettes, they contemplated the evening so far. 'You know, we could just about make the midnight radio check if we're slick,' said Matt. 'Now where's that jack, Jordie?' 'What jack?' said Jordie. 'That fucking jack I told you to bring up here,' said Matt. 'And the rope?' said Matt to Ginger, hopefully. Ginger denied he'd been told to bring any rope, so Matt gave them the good news.

'Get back down that fucking hill and bring the jack, jacking handle and fucking rope back here as fast as you fucking well can.' He left them in no doubt what he wanted …... yesterday.

 Eventually, they got the vehicle off the tree root stump and drove back down to pick up the trailer and equipment. They made it back up to their OP position but they were late and missed the midnight radio check. When the flight commander came later that morning to find out why they'd missed the radio check, Matt could only tell him, sheepishly, that somehow the Land Rover had got stuck on the top of a dry mountain plateau the night before and it had taken a long time to extricate it. He didn't tell him about the adventures along the way or the many meetings with the Hertz mountain bears. No, he decided, he'd play down the hero bit for now.

Chapter 20 – Further Training

Matt was warned that his Tourex was due in approximately four months. He would be posted to RAF Catterick to join the Further Training II, or FT II, course. Having passed the RAF education tests, he was qualified to the rank of sergeant should he ever get promoted. Before he stood a chance of that happening he first had to pass the FTII. He had been selected for the course which due to start a couple of weeks after Tourex. Ever since he had been on Twenty Six, Matt had followed the fortunes of those corporals who had left the squadron destined for the FT II course. Not one had passed. Not one in three years. The feedback was that it was a physically demanding course and the failures just couldn't keep up or reach the required standard. Matt was determined that he was not going to fail through a lack of fitness. He stopped smoking and went for a run every night. He started off with three miles and worked up to an average of five. It nearly killed him but, as he told himself, the pain was caused by his lack of fitness and that was entirely his fault. The family flew back together and Matt hired a car to get them all from Luton to the Married Quarters allocated to them in Middleton St George. They moved into a house opposite where they had lived before they moved to Germany and it felt like they'd never been away.

Matt and the rest of the course moved into the hutted accommodation on the edge of the airfield where they were briefed on the course, the next morning's timings and general course admin. It started with the normal sort of classroom lectures but they had noted that, on the first afternoon at 16:00, they were to parade outside the billet dressed in tracksuits for PT. They got changed and waited for one of the directing staff to arrive. It was one of the Para sergeants and he didn't look like he would be taking any prisoners that afternoon. 'Right, form up in threes,' he ordered and they set off on a run around the airfield. It wasn't long before it could be seen who was fit and who had paid lip service. After about twenty minutes they stopped and went through a series of exercises. They started running again, then stopped again for more sit ups and press ups. Matt suddenly realised that the directing staff sergeant was using the breaks for a breather. He was puffing as well and was red in the face with exertion. They set off again and the sergeant suddenly said, 'Okay, those of you who want to run on can.' At that, Matt and about six others ran off. It was much easier without the squad and their ridiculously slow pace. Matt and another lad ended way out in front and had completely recovered by the time the main group came puffing in with retching and groaning in the ranks. Matt had got the fitness thing under control. The course was difficult and demanded restraint from Matt. During one exercise the directing staff were demonstrating how to 'pull' a suspected Improvised Explosive Device. Matt knew they were so totally wrong that anyone trying to use their technique would surely be blown up. It was obvious that they'd never been trained and had never had to do it for real. They'd probably never been to Northern Ireland either. Matt started to say something and was told to shut and learn. If he wanted to pass the course he'd better wise up!

The final exercise was split into two phases. Between the two phases, the course was to return to their billets and sleep for eight hours. But, at the end of phase one, Matt and a couple of others were taken off the course because their squadron had been warned for Cyprus. Dismayed to be pulled off at that point, because they would have to start the course again in six months' time, they went home to Middleton St George, dug out their tropical Khaki Drill uniforms and equipment, got changed and reported back to their squadron. No sooner than they were ready to deploy, the squadron was released from standby. So, with a mixture of irritation and relief, Matt and the other two returned home to change back into course attire. Having done so, they reported back to the course and met the other students who, refreshed and ready to go, were clambering on to the back of waiting trucks. By this time, Matt and his colleagues were knackered and it would be another four days before they could get a proper night's sleep.

At the end of the course they found out whether they had passed or failed in the usual way. The ones left sitting were congratulated, then told to sod off. The failures queued up outside the course commander's door. Matt, having been left sitting, said his goodbyes and reported back to his squadron.

He'd been posted to Forty Eight squadron. They were equipped with the Tigercat Missile system - a land-based version of the Seacat. It used the OP system of early warning: effectively the same as the guns but with many more OPs pushed out much further. Matt joined an OP flight, the work taking on a familiar pattern.

On one deployment they were heading for Germany for two weeks. They would be living in the field and this time, unusually, they would not be taking their missile systems. They would be acting in their 'field' or 'infantry' role.

The Harrier Jump Jet had been newly deployed in Germany and tactics were still evolving. The Harrier squadrons deployed regularly, away from prepared airfields, and into the woods and forests of Germany. The aircraft used local roads to take off and land and camouflaged hides were constructed along the edges of the roads and woods. Each of these aircraft sites had to be defended and to guard against surprise attack, a ring of OPs was set up at about five to six kilometres out from the aircraft sites. These Ops, manned by the RAF Regiment, would provide early warning and in some cases interception of any attempted infiltration by saboteurs.

Matt along with the rest of C & R flight were there to provide the 'enemy' forces on one of these Harrier deployments. One morning, in high summer, Matt was briefed to take five men and an umpire on a patrol. Their objective was to get as close to the Harrier aircraft as possible and place dummy explosives on the ground underneath it. They had to start from a given grid reference which placed them eleven kilometres out from the aircraft sites. Matt started by carrying out a careful map reconnaissance. He noticed a large dyke running from about the seven kilometres range down to about the six kilometre mark where it veered off. It was the only bit of usable cover he could see but, of course, the friendly forces would have access to the same information as him. He decided to chance it anyway. If they got caught, there was always tomorrow. Matt briefed the troops. On top of the standard briefing headlines of Ground, Situation, Mission, Execution et cetera, he stressed aircraft safety and movement in the close proximity of aircraft. He ensured everybody had their water before cocking their weapons and setting off. It was a hot day and there was no cover. Sweat formed in dark patches on their clothing as they moved in single file towards the dyke. Entering the dyke and out of eyesight of anybody up at ground level they took a short break and had a drink. Progress along the dyke was good. They could see the far end and there were no surprises along the way. They reached the point where the dyke turned sharply and Matt lifted his hand to call a halt. Inching up to the top with his binoculars, Matt motioned to the umpire to stay down below the parapet until he'd had a quick look around. Matt pulled clumps of grass from around him and poked them into the camouflage net on his steel helmet. Careful to break ground amongst the long grass, Matt slowly inched his way up careful not to make any sudden moves. He started scanning with his binoculars, looking for any movement that would give any position away. He motioned for the umpire to come and take a look and continued to scan. There, what was that. A flash of sunlight had caught his attention. It was as if the sun was reflecting off glass. It came from a position about a kilometre to their front. Matt now scanned the ground between him and the suspected OP position. There was a hedge that would provide some cover. They would need to move round to the OP's flank to stand any chance of getting through the OP ring anyway. They broke cover and moved off, all running at the same time in a crouch for the hedge. Moving along the hedge, Matt listened and watched the OP position for signs of discovery. There were none. Eventually, they crawled to the edge of a shallow dugout and peeped over the parapet. The dugout contained a field telephone, about a dozen empty Amstel bottles and two sleeping bodies. The patrol moved back to discuss the next move. Matt couldn't believe his eyes. It was corporal Smith and Minging Charlie. Giggling quietly, they circumvented the OP and made their way towards the parked aircraft still five kilometres away and reached their objective without any futher dramas. The attack was judged a 100% success for Matt and his patrol. The umpire was an RAF officer attached to the Harrier force. He was incensed that the Harrier Force depended on the two sleeping drunks of the RAF Regiment for their security. This time the pair had been caught out by an independent umpire through their own lack of professionalism. Matt couldn't say that he felt sorry for them.

The deployment ended and another one began.

The squadron vehicles were lined up once more along the perimeter track in convoy order. They were going to Germany on exercise with the Harrier force, again. The men had said their goodbyes to wives and families. They would be away for a month deployed around the Wildenrath area. Word came for Matt and one of his mates to report to the Station Commander immediately. Fearing the worst, Jim and Matt ran to the station headquarters building and reported to the Station Commander's adjutant. Matt was marched in first, where he was congratulated on his promotion. He couldn't believe what he was hearing. Matt, a sergeant. Jim was next and when he came out he was grinning from ear to ear. Making their way back to the convoy via clothing stores, where they were issued with the shoulder-mounted chevrons which they wore proudly, they sauntered back towards the vehicles. 'Oi,' came a shout obviously meant for them. 'Get a move on, we're leaving.' Matt and Jim jumped into their Land Rovers and the convoy set off. No-one knew yet but Jim and Matt grinned all the way to the ferry port at Hull before they, now as sergeants, walked past the gaggle of corporals and reported to their surprised Flight Sergeants on the quayside.

Chapter 21 - Life as a Brand New Sergeant

Vehicles and men were loaded and they set sail, courtesy of the North Sea Ferries group. An overnight sailing saw them waiting to disembark under the harsh arc lights of the cold, wet dawn. Formalities over, the convoy set off and that afternoon rolled into the gates of RAF Wildenrath. Matt knew the station like the back of his hand from the 'Black September' deployment days, of course. What he didn't know, however, was the inside of the sergeants' mess. Matt and Jim found their rooms. It was great. One room each. None of these twenty-man rooms ever again. They met, as detailed, in the bar for pre-dinner drinks and Matt caught himself mentally pinching himself. It was like being elevated to the standards expected, nay demanded, in civilian life for the first time. Two short days later the squadron moved off into the field and began the exercise. Matt and Jim were still not stretched and realised just how cushy this life as a sergeant could be. Time flew past and within a couple of weeks they found themselves homeward bound once more. Matt's family had a surprise. A corporal had walked out of the door and a sergeant walked back in. The rise in pay that came with the promotion now put them into the bracket of being able to afford a mortgage, so the first weekend home found Matt and his family looking at Plot 13 in a new development going up in the village of Eaglescliffe, near the town of Yarm in County Cleveland.

Matt's flight was now top heavy and someone had to go. The Tigercat Fire Unit flight had a vacancy for a Number One or Fire Unit Commander. A short interview later, Matt was moving his kit from the OP flight into one of the Tigercat system bays. He had been placed in charge of Alpha system. He had a lot to learn but as the weeks rolled by Matt soon came up to speed.

The Tigercat system was an antiquated guided missile system. It was one of the secrets disclosed to the Russians during the Vassel and Christeen Keeler sex scandals in the late 1950s. The guidance frequencies could be changed just before launch and they were kept secret. The launchers carried three missiles and were specially built by 'Short and Harland' of Belfast. They were an adaptation of the Navy Seacat system and they fired the standard solid-fuelled Seacat missile. The effective range was 3.75 kilometres but this was reduced if the aimer used large control inputs. The hydraulic oil used to move the control surfaces was exhausted from the rear of the missile every time a control input was given. This meant that it couldn't take on a crossing target as there wasn't enough oil to maintain the necessary control deflection. In its favour, however, was its warhead. This consisted of 37.5 lbs of RDX/TNT in a 60/40 percentage mix. It had proximity fuzing as well as contact fuzing and with a bang that big, it would bring down anything it hit. If it could only get to catch it.

Matt now started taking an interest in promotion prospects and after asking many oblique questions to other sergeants and flight sergeants, discovered that 'if you kept your nose clean and achieved good marks on your annual assessments, provided there was a vacancy and provided that you had the most seniority, it was possible to make it to flight sergeant in just over seven years'. With so many 'variables' involved, a more usual time span was about eleven years. Matt didn't want to wait that long and so he started looking around for a loophole in the system. The first thing he needed to do was to take more RAF exams. He put his name down for the next sitting of the Administration and Organisation Part 4 exam and swotted each night for the next three months. As he went in to sit the exam he bumped into the sergeant who had taken them on their PT whilst on the FT II course. With him was the other course sergeant and between them, they wasted no time in telling Matt that he didn't stand a chance of passing with his inexperience. Matt passed. They failed. Matt had a warm feeling within and smiled to himself when he found out. They would also have read the results when they were published in Station Routine Orders.

In due course, Matt learnt that the squadron would be deploying to Northern Ireland again. They were to be based at RAF Aldergrove which was co-located with Belfast Airport. They would be operating as a field squadron and their patrol transportation would be Land Rovers and helicopters. One of the tasks they would carry out would be the setting up of 'snap' vehicle control points to stop and search cars. They would be airlifted in swiftly by helicopter in the event of a tip off that weapons, explosives or wanted persons were being transported. There would also be quick reaction force on permanent standby in case reinforcements were needed. Foot patrols and mobile patrolling would fall under their remit. They trained for some three months to become efficient in the execution of these tasks.

Chapter 22 – Back to Ireland

The squadron flew out to Aldergrove and after Londonderry, Matt could see that this was a cushy number. He was going to find out that it had its own set of dangers though. Matt worked in the Intelligence cell collating and assessing different reports to get an overall picture of what was going on in their area. This formed the basis of tasking patrols to particular areas and functions. Information came from various sources, one of them a local who would only meet at night in the middle of deserted countryside. Mostly though, information was written intelligence snippets and direct observations from the patrols.

One day, Matt received word that the local informant wanted a meeting. A place and a time was set up and a double Land Rover patrol was briefed. They moved into the area. It was dark and raining and close to some houses which were part of a secluded hamlet. The cauldron or defensive screen was deployed and a vehicle checkpoint set up. The informant's car was noted entering the checkpoint and it pulled over to one side. Matt started the tape recorder hidden under his flak jacket; he opened the car door, checked inside and got in. 'Are there any problems?' was Matt's first question. 'No. no,' came the reply. The informant went on to talk about mostly inconsequential stuff but Matt was after information about home-made guns being manufactured at the 'Shorts' factory in Belfast. Nothing was forthcoming, so the night was a bit of a washout as far as Matt was concerned. Later, back at base, the general consensus of opinion was that they had been set up to keep them busy in one area whilst something or somebody had been moved through another area.

One night, Matt was on duty in the command post when the duty officer came in. It was 01:00 hours and during the quiet hours, the duty officer was normally expected to be contactable from his bunk. He only came into the command post if something was 'going down' or he wanted a cup of tea. This time it was none of those. 'I've just been informed there is a coffin that needs to be searched in the main airport warehouse,' he said. Matt knew that one of the ways of smuggling arms into the country was by using dead bodies that were being repatriated. 'I'll need you to escort me, sergeant Jenkins,' he said. 'Fine,' said Matt, handing over the command post to the corporal. He collected a portable radio so that he could keep in touch with the command post, grabbed his rifle and went outside to the vehicle. It was a still, freezing cold night and the grass was white with frost as they drove around the airfield to the civilian complex which was Belfast Airport. They located a large shed, as big as an aircraft hanger. The duty officer showed his paperwork to a disinterested civilian guard and they went inside. It was vast and it was cold. They located the coffin and under the harsh overhead mercury lights, unscrewed the lid. Matt could see that the duty officer was uncomfortable but he had to carry out his unpleasant task and search beneath the body in the coffin. As he pulled back the shroud covering the body and started to run his hands down the sides of the body, Matt suddenly said, 'Hang on, didn't he move just then?' The duty officer jumped back then swore in a most un-officer like way. Matt kept a straight face - just. Afterwards, whilst travelling back in the Land Rover, they discussed the night's events and both agreed that it was not a very pleasant task searching dead bodies in the middle of the night. Unless, of course, it started moving!

It was now Christmas day. It had been agreed that the senior NCOs would carry out the helicopter patrols on Christmas day. The morning passed without incident and the afternoon patrol was set for 14:00 hours. The forming up point would be next to the control tower. Matt and the patrol waited at the appointed hour and the helicopter arrived. The patrol commander was absent. This officer was renowned for his short fuse and incandescent temper, so they waited. They were motioned across to the helicopter by the pilot and as they climbed aboard Matt informed the loadie that they were waiting for the flight commander. The loadie pointed out quite rightly that the flight commander was late and what were they going to do. Matt said, 'Let's go.' He'd crucify us if we were late thought Matt. They took off and headed for their patrol area. Ten minutes into the flight the loadie shouted in Matt's ear that the flight commander had arrived and wanted them to go back and collect him. Matt said, 'Okay, but put us down in that field next to that road over there so we can set up a VCP.' The chopper landed and they jumped off. It rose with a clattering roar and headed back towards the airfield. Silence descended once more on the cold but peaceful countryside. They lay on the ground around some bushes having taken up 'an all round defence' on exiting the aircraft. From behind them in the centre of the bushes came a sound. 'Psst.' Matt looked around. 'Psst,' louder now. 'Behind you,' came a voice. Matt looked around and there lying on the ground in the middle of the bushes were two very drunk Irishmen. 'Would you loike a drink?' said one of them, offering a bottle of Bushmills whiskey to Matt. 'Thanks,' said Matt taking a swig and passing the bottle on. 'What the fuck are you doing out here in the middle of nowhere with a bottle of whiskey on Christmas day?' 'Ta be shore,' said the Irishman, 'if we knew dat den we wouldtent be here at all would we?' came the reply. Matt shook his head in disbelief. They weren't armed. They had no radios. There were no wires running from their position. They were just two drunken men in the middle of a field and no matter how incongruous it may seem, Matt decided to leave it as one of life's little mysteries. The chopper returned with a great clattering roar shattering the silence and Matt, along with the rest of the patrol, jumped aboard. The boss was on board and Matt could see he wasn't happy but it was too noisy inside the helicopter to understand anything he might be saying. They flew over a farm and a woman came running out waving a sheet to attract their attention. The pilot landed nearby and the loadie jumped out and ran to her.

He ran back and jumped in. After talking to the pilot on the intercom they took off and the loadie uncorked a bottle of wine and took a swig. He passed the bottle to Matt who took a swig and passed it on. It went around the cabin then up between the pilot's legs. It disappeared for a few seconds then came back down into the cabin through the co-pilot's legs to do the rounds once more. They flew around the airport then headed down to Nutts corner. They landed in a very large front garden of a private house surrounded by a very high hedge. The pilot shut down the helicopter and climbed down. 'We'll be here for about half an hour,' he said. 'Enjoy.' The patrol trooped in through the front door to be ushered into a large room. On a table were bottles of wines, spirits and beers. They were invited to help themselves by the genial host, who was obviously a friend of the pilot. They helped themselves to drinks and food. It turned into quite a party but, all to soon, they said their Thank You's and climbed back on board. The pilots started the helicopter up once more and they flew the short distance back to the airport. On arrival they were ushered into tents where the squadron had arranged a reception for them as they were the ones working that Christmas day. Their weapons were taken away to be handed in to the armoury and they were shown the spread awaiting their return. The trouble was that by that time they had consumed so much booze in such a short space of time that they had difficulties standing up without swaying and giving the game away. Matt reluctantly accepted yet another beer and sausage roll and moving through the tent, drank the beer and ditched the empty can. He crept out of the tent and made his way back towards the sergeants mess. Climbing into bed that afternoon, the rest of Christmas day and night passed in oblivion - but it was a great patrol they had that Christmas day.

There was a report of an empty farmhouse near the perimeter of the airfield. It had been unoccupied for some years but now lights had been seen over a period of two weeks. It was suspicious activity and Matt had been in a similar scenario before. This time, it would be different. Matt took a foot patrol out and they observed the farmhouse for a day. The next day they returned and moved close. Carefully walking around the outside of the building whilst checking for tripwires or other telltale signs of booby traps, Matt chose an entry point. He set up the patrol in a defensive posture, taped up a small window pane and broke the glass. There was hardly a sound and hardly any fallen glass. Gently removing the broken slivers still sticking to the tape, Matt now eased a small compact mirror into the hole and inspected the inside of the window frame. Left right, up and down. There was nothing there to indicate any nasty surprises. He put his hand in and lifted the handle. The window swung out and Matt climbed in. He had one of his original search team with him from the Londonderry days and he accompanied Matt. Together they cleared each room as safe. In one of the rooms it was clear that someone had been living there. It was pretty basic but too clean to have been tramps or wine'os. They resolved to keep the place under observation but also to keep their distance until lights were seen once more.

Three nights later lights were reported again. Matt with his search man and covering patrol moved silently to the farmhouse. This time, after setting the patrol into position, Matt took his man and the patrol commander with him. They entered through the back window and crept along the corridor. Matt had his 9mm pistol in his hand. It was cocked and ready. They arrived at the room that had light coming out from underneath its door. They looked at each other, Matt nodded, slowly grasped the handle and in one movement opened the door and leapt in. As he leapt to the side he could see two men. They were in the bed. Matt moved towards them pistol at arm's length, ready to fire immediately. The patrol commander was already on the radio and footsteps were running up to the front door. They'd taken the precaution of unlatching it on the way to this room and the covering patrol now took up residence. Matt wasn't concerned about booby traps any more as the two men in the bed were hardly likely to be blowing themselves up. They were unceremoniously bundled out of the building and taken away for questioning. The farmhouse was locked up until the morning when a thorough search would take place by the police and the reasons for the occupation established. Back at base Matt thought over the nights events. Would he have pulled the trigger, he thought. Yes, he certainly would have if it had been necessary. He was ready to shoot and the men in the bed knew it. I would rather face a Court Marshall for not reading out the yellow card than attend my own funeral, he thought. As for the prisoners, one of them was a known Provisional IRA wanted man, so all in all the night was a 'goodun'.

There were other incidents that took place during the tour. Some raised a laugh, some were sheer fright and some were suicidal boredom. Some were just suicidal.

One morning, Matt was out on patrol with two Land Rovers. A radio message came through that some men with guns had been seen down by the loch and would he go and investigate. They hot-footed it down to the water side, dismounted near a large group of people and went to enquire as to who had seen and reported the group of armed men. As they approached, it dawned on Matt that the large group of men, numbering some twenty or so, were the armed group. They were all carrying shotguns. Gentle enquiries revealed that they were out on an organised duck shoot and yes, they had firearms licences for the shotguns. If the group had had bad intentions, Matt and his five men would have been badly out-gunned. On informing the CP that the group were legitimate, Matt returned to base. Walking back into the CP, Matt enquired as to who had sent him and his men to investigate that one. The Flight Sergeant told Matt that he had ordered the patrol to investigate ... so what? Matt asked him how many people were in this armed group and the Flight Sergeant admitted that he didn't know. Matt suggested that, in future, the CP staff find out more about a potential incident than they had done this day. and preferably before sending six armed troops to investigate twenty-plus armed men who, in this country, could have had less than innocent intentions. This advice, coming from a person who ranked as junior to the Flight Sergeant, did not go down well but Matt was adamant and politely held his ground. He was sure that the run-in would have repercussions later but he didn't dwell on it for too long. The tour ended and they returned to the depot and home.

Matt learnt from the orderly room that volunteers were being sought for an eighteen-month course with the Army. It was called the Long Gunnery Staff Course and apparently, was the most difficult of courses to pass. You could be failed at any time during the course but - and here was the clincher - if you passed you would be sent to one of the new Rapier squadrons being formed. Each squadron had an establishment for a flight sergeant who had qualified by passing this course. Qualified sergeants could be expected to be promoted into this post. With such a carrot being dangled, Matt thought it was a no- brainer. Whilst he doubted his ability to pass such a difficult and infamous course, he resolved to give it his best shot. If they wanted him off it, he would have to be carried off it, kicking and screaming all the way. Matt applied for the course and eventually received a syllabus, a start date and a posting notice. He was over the first hurdle. He bought some books and started to self-study his worse subject - maths - in the evenings. The Flight Sergeant was delighted to let him go as he considered Matt to be a 'clever dick' after the run-in over the duck shooters. 'No respect,' he thought, as he said good riddance to Matt. 'Better men than you have failed that course sergeant Jenkins, so you watch out because when you get back I'll be looking out for you.' 'Yes, Flight,' said Matt, realising he'd been dismissed. He closed the door gently behind him.

Chapter 23 – The Gunnery Staff Course

Matt was posted to RAF Locking in Western Super Mare. The Number One School of RAF Radio Training. There he met the rest of the RAF Regiment contingent. Two of them he knew well having served in Butterworth with one and in Londonderry with the other. For three months they studied maths and electronics. They felt like their brains were being taken apart and put back together as the course progressed.

They had two civilian instructors. One taught maths and electronic theory and the other gave practical demonstrations to back up the theory. As a course, they looked forward to the practical demonstrations because they usually went wrong. When they did, they provided endless opportunities for side splitting silent hilarity. Looking at each other made it even worse when the smoke from yet another failed experiment started to rise gently. They never let on to the instructor but they all thought that they'd suffered a ruptured stomach muscle on more than one occasion.

They learnt that electronic circuits had smoke going through the wires. Everything worked fine whilst the smoke was contained within the wires but should it escape and become visible then the circuit would invariably stop working. From their observations, there could be no other conclusions. Then one fine afternoon they had this theory disproved. It was a mistake in the first place to put a bunch of Regiment sergeants on a sunny Wednesday afternoon in a classroom. The experiment was a demonstration of the waveforms present when a double diode valve was rectifying AC to pulsating DC. A large student oscilloscope was hooked up to the circuit and it was all switched on. There was no smoke. Good thought the instructor. There was also nothing showing on the oscilloscope either. The instructor went across to the oscilloscope and fiddled with the controls. Still nothing. "Perhaps the valve's not seated in it's holder correctly", said Matt helpfully. They all watched in eager anticipation as the instructor moved across to the experiment. He placed his left hand in his pocket. This was a necessary precaution to stop himself from touching anything with his left hand. If he did touch something with the left hand he could electrocute himself as the current travelled down the left hand side of his body, through his heart and then to ground. They watched as he wiggled the valve. Nothing. In his eagerness to get everything working he forgot the basic safety precaution and removed his left hand from his pocket. He grabbed one part of the circuit board for support and wiggled the valve again. Suddenly he jumped up as he strapped his body across the valve and received 300 volts for his troubles. Matt could have sworn that he'd seen the instructors eyes go round like a fruit machine before he said something very naughty and dismissed the class. They almost couldn't contain themselves. Fortunately they did wait until they were out of earshot because when the black humour came, it caused tears to course down their faces.

Later during the course they were introduced to the type 88 radar. It was a monster of a Radar. It had a mercury filled rectifier valve and was like something out of Flash Gordon. It stood about three feet high and buzzed and flashed blue. They were suitably impressed. One of the students on the course, who had been learning quite a bit lately said intelligently, "looking at that wave guide, this radar must have quite a low frequency". "That's not the wave guide", said the instructor, "that's the air conditioning trunking"!

The receiver was one small draw in the room full of electronic wizardry and was amazing only because of it's small size.

There were six of them at Locking competing for five places. Matt was one of the four who passed. One failed completely and one, who was the best on the course decided that it wasn't for him. Matt and three others found themselves heading towards Larkhill.

Christmas had come and gone. Matt had moved into the mess at the Royal School of Artillery at Larkhill and the first day of the course arrived. They reported to the Basic Science and Technology wing and commenced three months of Locking style maths and electronics. There were three main characters involved with the students now. Two were tutors. One they christened Dougal because like the dog in the Magic Roundabout, he walked round in circles most of the time. The other they christened Hogsey because it sounded derogatory. The third person was a lab technician who wheeled experiments in on trolleys and took the used ones away. They called him 'Lurch'. There were others but these three were the main players. The one who stood out the most because of his obvious ability was Dougal. He taught at the local university.

One of the first and most basic of experiments was to connect a car battery up through an ammeter to a lamp. This was connected through plates suspended in a glass jar which was filled with distilled water. The intention was to show a zero current flow when the distilled water was added. When an impurity such as salt was poured into the water, current flowed and the lamp lit. Matt spotted Lurch one lunchtime wheeling the trolley in with this experiment on it. They had seen this one at Locking so Matt knew what was coming. He came back from lunch making sure he was the first in and poured most of the salt into the distilled water. Hogsey conducted the experiment that afternoon to the amusement of the Blue contingent and the consternation of the Brown contingent. The latter of course had no idea as to what should have been happening but Lurch got a bollocking whilst protesting his innocence.

It was hard going as the standard was high. Each Monday morning there was an exam. The pass mark was usually set at seventy percent. This exam each Monday ensured that every weekend was spent studying and not playing. One failed exam meant that you were off the course and they lost a few of the Army lads during this time. Two more were taken off the course after eleven months due to a failure during the Basic Science and Technology or BST leg. It had taken that long for the results of one of those Monday morning exams to catch up with them. The Blue or RAF Regiment contingent all seemed to get through okay and they moved on to equipments. They started off with the Bofors 40/70 anti aircraft cannon. Matt knew less than any body else on the course about the gun. He had successfully managed to escape the horrible things for years. Now his chickens came home to roost. He had to learn and fast. The instructors were amazed at his lack of knowledge and constantly singled him out when asking questions. This is where I now really work, thought Matt. This is the 'carry off kicking and screaming bit'. Matt did get through that leg and passed after a respectable performance in the final practical tests. There was nobody more surprised than him.

The course moved to Wales to fire the Bofors at the Royal Artillery Range at Manorbier. It was strange having the whole firing point available for just one gun but it was a worthwhile exercise in the end. They learnt about stoppages for real and experienced a 'Creeping Breech block' malfunction at first hand. The situation occurred as the aircraft was turning in to commence it's run but before the firing run was announced. A round fired from the gun without any human intervention and passed low and to the left of the oncoming aircraft. Indeed a creeping breech block was suspected and the gun number four was inserting the 'Breech Block Locking Bolt' when the gun fired and sheered the bolt. The number four was left with a surprised expression on his face whilst holding the sheered off end of the bolt. Fortunately the aircraft was not hit and recovered to base whilst an inquiry took place. The cause was worked out to be a Creeping Breech Block, with the order to insert the Locking Bolt given when the Breech Block had travelled too far for the Bolt to be effective. When the Breech Block reached the top of its travel, the firing pin actuated as normal and fired the round in the chamber. The recoiling Breech Ring sheered off the end of the Locking Bolt. The next day it was business as usual but the knowledge that Matt gained that week served him well over the coming years.

 Next came the Rapier Guided Missile leg and this time it was a level playing field. None of the other students had any previous experience with this equipment. Matt finished near the top. Then they spent a couple of months learning the shoulder launched Blowpipe guided missile system. At the end of that leg the course moved to the Royal Artillery Range situated in the Outer Hebrides on the island of South Uist. There they fired the live Blowpipe and Rapier missiles. They had fired the Bofors at the range in Manorbier in Wales some months before so the Hebrides was the final deployment of the course. Christmas was once more approaching and posting notices were held pending formal publication of the results. Matt and the rest of the RAF Regiment contingent learnt that they had all passed and back at Larkhill a small ceremony was held where they were presented with their certificates. At the same time, they were given their postings. Matt was going back to RAF Catterick to become the Wing Assistant Instructor in Gunnery or AIG working with and teaching the Bofors 40/70 gun. He was the only person on the course to be posted into a Bofors job. He would be teaching it and running the Manorbier range with RAF Regiment personnel who had been weaned and had grown up with the damn things. Oh joy, he thought but on the plus side he learnt that he had also been promoted to Flight Sergeant. He couldn't believe that he'd passed the course, been promoted and sent to the guns all in one go. It was in some respects a bitter sweet pill and he knew that his testing times were yet to come, when the hairy old gun sergeants started asking carefully scripted questions to test his level of knowledge.

Chapter 24 – Ack Aye Jesus on the Wing

The Wing started working a rotation system with three, mini, gun squadrons. Each mini squadron had four guns. They trained first at RAF Catterick then carried out live firing on the range at Manorbier in Wales. From there they returned the guns to Catterick, then flew to Belize in Central America. Arriving at Airport Camp, they took over the guns at the International Airport from the squadron that was returning. This deployment was mostly a posturing exercise to dissuade Guatamala from invading. The off going squadron moved back to RAF Catterick and after leave, started training once more to be ready for the next Manorbier, Belize deployment. During all of this, Matt also had to organise the Tigercat training and get the aimers of this optical system qualified by firing a live missile. As the systems were kept at RAF Catterick and would only be deployed if there was an invasion, the aimers had to go to sea with the Royal Navy and qualify from a ship. Matt's routine revolved through the training cycles of both the gun and the Tigercat personnel. After training at RAF Catterick he conducted the range at Manorbier as the Wing AIG. He then travelled to Belize and oversaw the handover and 'shake down' exercises. During this time he controlled the changeover of the Tigercat personnel, then moved back to the UK to start with the next Squadron.

On the range he wore a white hat. He wore it so that he could be seen instantly and clearly by everyone on the firing point. If a gun had a problem that the number one or gun commander couldn't rectify then he looked for the AIG. The AIG then assessed the problem. If the problem could be rectified and a lesson taught at the same time, the AIG would do so at that point. If he deemed the gun unserviceable, then he would authorise the armourers team forward to repair it. On the first range firing camp after taking over the new post, Matt found himself wearing the white hat. A firing run had been called. The gun safety men were behind the guns calling 'safe to shoot' whilst brandishing their 'dead man switches'. The observers were behind them waiting to call the 'fall of shot'. The guns started firing. Immediately, one of the guns had a stoppage. Matt looked but kept out of the way. The number one would not learn anything if Matt jumped in straight away. He walked slowly away but waited for the call. It came, so Matt walked back and observed the gun from the rear. If the breech was open and ready to feed a round and fire he would see daylight. He couldn't. He reminded himself that the lack of daylight could also be due to a partly or half fed round. Matt went around the front of the gun and felt the position of the outer extractor release lever. The breech block was up so the gun was safe. Matt now mounted the gun platform itself. He could see the result of a loading error causing a jam in the mechanism. A safety device had actuated and rounds were damaged. Other rounds were mixed up with the gun mechanism and the whole thing looked a mess. 'What have you got here number one?' Matt asked. 'A mess Flight,' came the reply. 'Do you want to fix it or would you rather I do it?' said Matt. It was a test and Matt knew it. This particular chap had tried to catch Matt out every time he had walked past the gun back at RAF Catterick. He seemed to resent such a young Flight Sergeant. 'I'd like to learn from the expert,' said the sergeant. 'Right,' said Matt. 'Number six, fetch me a number eighteen mil open-ended spanner from the tool kit.' He was handed the spanner. Matt undid the four bolts holding the top plate of the left hand side of the hopper. He gently removed the rounds from the gun, one by one, and handed them to the number six. He then reset the 'Hopper Feed Slipper Safety Device' and re-seated then tightened the four bolts once more. Handing back the spanner, Matt jumped off the gun and called for the number one for a private chat. They walked a little way behind, out of earshot. Matt pointed out that that stoppage should never have happened. It was down to poor drills and the number one was responsible for the training of his men. There was nothing else to say. The number one knew he was at fault. He had also seen a stoppage cleared in a way that he had never thought of and knew then that this AIG person was not someone to 'bullshit' or try and catch out. He seemed to know his stuff. Word soon got around amongst the gun number ones and Matt realised that he'd received the finest training in the world when it came to the Bofors 40/70.

Matt's time in Belize during each handover/takeover lasted about a fortnight. Usually during a weekend, a trip out to the Cayes would be organised. Off duty men would load up a local boat with half an empty oil drum, charcoal, food and beer. They'd take their snorkelling kit and a long sleeved shirt to shield them from the sun later when they had sunburn. The day would be spent on a small island under palm trees snorkelling, drinking beer, eating and more snorkelling. The waters were crystal clear and warm. The colours of the reef and fish were stunning and it seemed like living in paradise. It wasn't of course. There was no drinking water or shelter and he realised that life would quickly pale if one were shipwrecked there. In the three years that Matt spent at RAF Catterick he made thirteen trips to Belize.

It was during these trips that Matt discovered the Tigercat system's deployment documentation consisted of three grid references on an Ordinance Survey map. That was it. No serious reconnaissance appeared to have taken place so, if there was an emergency deployment at any time in the future, Detachment Commanders would be running around in the dark like headless chickens looking for a grid on a map, the route to which led through a swamp. He resolved to rectify the omission.

Matt surveyed three sites for the Tigercat systems at the airport. He obtained aerial photographs of the airfield and on three of them, he marked each site and the route to be taken to it from the aircraft pan. He did this in case they had to deploy off an aircraft, in a hurry, where the 'numbers ones' had no experience of the area. The primary and secondary firing arcs were also marked. Radio frequencies, missile crystals for the secret guidance frequencies and other essential pieces of information were kept in three brown envelopes and marked - each with the call sign of the detachment number.

One afternoon, back at RAF Catterick, the balloon did go up and they were ordered to deploy to Belize. Guatamala were rattling their sabres and threatening to invade. All personnel went home, donned their tropical kit, packed a bag and said goodbye to their families. 'We'll be a couple of weeks,' Matt told his family.

They drew weapons and ammunition, then left Catterick by road and drove in convey to RAF Wittering. There they were loaded onto C130s. They took off and headed out East over the Atlantic. They refuelled at Gander in Newfoundland then headed South. Refuelling once more at Nassau in the Bahamas they flew from there into Belize. The two aircraft landed and the three Tigercat systems quickly deployed into pre-surveyed positions according to their marked-up aerial photographs. Six live missiles were issued to each Fire Unit initially. Matt helped out with getting the spare missiles safely into the bomb dump. Arriving back at the pan to collect another load, Matt was taken to one side by the squadron commander. 'What is the maximum height these missiles could be dropped onto concrete and still be okay?' he asked. Matt had a horrible sinking feeling. 'How high have they been dropped then sir?' said Matt. 'Over there,' he indicated with his chin. Matt looked. There was an aircraft loading trolley full of pallets of live missiles. One of the pallets was sitting on the concrete pan, not the trolley. The retaining catches had been stowed and the pallet had rolled off - from a height of several feet. 'The maximum you could drop those, sir, onto concrete would be twelve inches,' said Matt. 'They've been dropped from about four feet and are now unserviceable. They're probably in a dangerous condition as well and should be kept away from other ammunition until an Ammunition Technical Officer has had a look at them.' 'Could we use them up first?' said the CO. 'If the rocket motor casing's cracked they'll go haywire on launching. The gyros are probably shot as well so there'll be no guidance anyway,' said Matt. They were okay for missiles at the moment, so Matt was not overly concerned that they may run short.

Gradually life settled into a routine and when the invasion had not occurred by the third week, the gun and missile system crews started taking it in turns to have twenty-four hour 'admin' breaks. After six weeks, the alert state was lowered and the air defence manning was lowered to one Tigercat system and three Bofors guns. The original couple of weeks deployment eventually stretched to six months.

During this time, the Tigercat flight had a flight commander known to all as 'Golly Gosh'. He was given that nickname because he never swore. On one occasion, as he was showing a high ranking visitor round the site, he opened the door of the accommodation hut. The handle had just been painted, it was a booby trap. He looked at his black, freshly painted palm and uttered the expletive, 'Gosh'. Towards the end of the detachment, the flight started working working normal shifts with one fire unit only now deployed. Every Monday 'Golly Gosh' would come into work in a foul mood. He was like a petulant child until lunchtime. After Monday lunchtime, until the end of the week, he was fine. Each day Matt used to walk around the airfield and visit each gun and the resident Tigercat detachment. He did it just to keep morale up and show his face. He surveyed 'in' each gun so that the slant range to a target on any given bearing could be accurately assessed. One time he surveyed 'in' the airfield radar. Pilots had complained of it being out by 2° when using the extended runway centre line. On yet another trip, instructions came through from the boffins at Malvern to survey six sites in case the Rapier was ever to be deployed there. The Rapiers did eventually deploy there and Matt was rewarded with the knowledge that he did the survey work.

The Bofors were finally phased out, having given over the task of Short Range Air Defence to the Rapiers. The mini gun squadrons were disbanded and one of the Tigercats was given to the RAF Regiment museum whilst the rest went into storage.

The last squadron to pass through Belize with the Bofors were, of course, also the last squadron to fire at Manorbier. Matt watched the final gun fire the final round and collected the final empty case for a souvenir. The CO immediately asked the gun number one to give him the empty case of the final round fired, which in good faith he did, but it wasn't the real one. Matt had it and he watched with interest later as that (nearly) 'final' empty case, suitably polished and mounted on a wooden plinth was presented to the Wing Commander after the final disbandment parade of the guns and squadrons. He smiled to himself many times over the next few years as he sat at home and glanced at his fireplace to admire a gleaming, empty case holding the pokers and fire irons.

The final parade was held, the final gun fired its blank rounds in a salute, a drive past of the squadron vehicles took place, then it was all over. Over the next few weeks, the equipment was handed back to stores and the inventories were closed down. It was goodbye Guns and Tigercats, or was it ? The 'Fat Lady' had not yet sung and she would not be denied, but Matt wouldn't find that out until a later date.

One evening at home in Eaglescliffe, the phone rang. It was a friend of his wife. She answered as wives have a propensity to do and after a short while, said to Matt, 'Do you know what's happened to Adrian?' Matt, who knew him well, was at a loss. 'Here, talk to her', said his wife, 'Adrian didn't come home from the last detachment and she's worried.' Matt took the phone. 'Hello Annette', said Matt. 'That effing bastard didn't come home when the squadron returned,' screamed Annette. 'What's the bastard up to? Tell me, you must know,' she accused. 'There's a wife and two children here to think of and he might be lying dead somewhere.' 'Matt thought not but couldn't throw any light on the matter. With promises to ask official questions when he got back to RAF Catterick, Matt thankfully put the phone down. The lady in question was a short plump Irish girl from Belfast. Her accent was so thick one could cut it with a knife. She was also very loud. She liked to play fast and loose around the married patch and Matt suspected that Adrian had just had too much and left her to it. The next evening the phone went once more. It was Annette once more. The RAF were giving her ninety days notice to quit her married quarter as Adrian was no longer in the forces. He had completed his twenty-two year term and had elected to be discharged in Belize. She was sobbing and wailing on the phone. Matt handed the instrument to his wife and allowed his ear to cool down. The next day, Matt made some discrete inquiries with people who knew Adrian. It was true that Adrian had become disenchanted with a wife who pleasured so many other husbands whilst her own was away. It was also true that he had met a girl in Belize who wanted to share her simple life with him. He arranged to get his discharge and after he'd collected his gratuity, he bought himself a smallholding just outside of the Belize International airport. He bought some piglets, then negotiated with the Army at the airport camp to take away their swill and slops every day. The Army cooks were overjoyed at this simple solution to their hygiene problem and so, each day, Adrian collected the stinking waste food. Adrian, in turn, fed this food to his pigs and when they were big enough, he offered them back to the Army at a much better rate than the imported stuff which came overland in stressful conditions. Adrian had it made. Most days he could be found in a hammock on his veranda sipping local rum with a pretty young girl waiting on him, hand and foot. Other days he would be helping to deliver piglets that were swelling at the same rate as his profits. They grew fatter and fatter as they feasted on the rich food being thrown away by the various messes at the airport camp. The the wheel turned the full circle and Adrian hired other farmers to look after the pigs and supply his growing need for expansion.

Matt was posted once more. This time to RAF Bruggen in Germany and 37 Squadron equipped with the Rapier missile system. He was full of misgivings. If he had been posted fresh off the Gunnery Staff course straight to Rapiers then the knowledge would be fresh in his head. Instead he had been posted to, and had frantically learnt the one thing he had started off hating but finished off quite enjoying, the Bofors. Going onto the Rapier system now meant he had that vertical learning curve to surmount, again. Ah well, thought Matt, if you couldn't take the joke, you shouldn't have joined up!

Chapter 25 – 37 Squadron

RAF Bruggen was situated near the Dutch town of Roermond on the German Dutch boarder. It was home to three squadrons of the Speycat Jaguar single seat bombers. Surrounded by thick forests, the airfield itself could only be seen from the air and It felt like working in a park. The family lived in Roermond Holland and the camp was in Germany. This caused some problems. The children's school was on the base in Germany and they had to cross the boarder twice a day. For this they needed passports. It was difficult to make the youngest children understand the importance of not loosing their passports. They were only five, seven and eight after all. The passports were carried in pouches hung on chords around the neck and life sometimes became a little fraught when the children wandered into the house after school without the pouches visible and of course, the passports absent.

One warm summers day, Matt came home to find the whole family outside the house. Thinking that they were locked out Matt enquired smilingly as to what might be wrong. An hysterical wife informed him that there was a 'Dragon' in the house. Matt slowly and quietly opened the front door. Nothing there. He peeped into the postbox cupboard next to the front door and there it was; a baby Dragon. Well, a lizard really, and not a very big one either. He caught it and gently carried it out of the house where he let it go. The children thought the episode great fun but the wife only sniffed and went inside, looking around suspiciously for its mate.

Walking across the compound towards the headquarters flight for the first time Matt had to negotiate a path through the four deployed Rapier fire units of 'B' flight. The men were carrying out tests and checks to determine their serviceability. One of the corporals caught Matts eye and said, 'excuse me flight, this Tracker is failing it's TV Confidence Test'. Matt couldn't remember the TV Confidence test let alone how to carry it out, so he said, 'have you done the test according to the book'? 'Yes flight', said the corporal. 'Have you repeated the test', said Matt? 'Yes flight', said the corporal. 'Then snag it and get an engineer across to look at it', said Matt. He walked the remaining few yards to the HQ block and went gratefully inside to 'Arrive'. Matt realised during that short conversation just how much he had to relearn after nearly three years of not seeing a Rapier. He guessed at a later date that he had neatly avoided showing up his ignorance that day by his response to the corporal.

The squadron was under the command of the Supreme Allied Commander Europe. This meant that they could be ordered to deploy anywhere in NATO. They did not belong specifically the the station they were based at. They normally deployed though to defend RAF Bruggen, their base. Deployments were interesting however. They deployed off base which took them to the edge of the woods surrounding the airfield. They set up their Rapier equipment on farm tracks in the border area between the two countries. They had special passes to allow them free movement in the border area. They had to present these passes when demanded to by the German and Dutch border guards who patrolled the area. These guards sometimes lay in ambush for people who chose to cross illegally instead of through the customs posts situated on the main roads. Smuggling cigarettes and booze, the locals waged a constant war of stealth whilst trying to outwit the guards.

Movement through the thick forests with Land Rovers and trailers to support the fire units 'In the field', would usually be by means of the loggers trails which frequently ran into large clearings. Four or five trails would run off from the edges of the clearings so one had to ensure they were on the right trail when they departed the clearing.

The station had the normal run of Microvals, Minivals, Maxivals and Tacevals so deployments were frequent. The HQ complex during deployments was also located in the forrested area but was on the base itself. Half buried buses and coaches were camouflaged in amongst the trees and power was provided by a twenty seven and a half KVA Meadows Generator.

It was at the deployed HQ complex at 'oh five crack sparrows' one morning that the squadron moral was raised a few notches whilst waiting for breakfast. It was dark, damp, cold, miserable and raining. Large drops were coming off the trees whilst twenty or thirty men stood in a sodden line holding their cold mess tins. They were waiting for the cook to finish getting breakfast ready. Matt went up to the head of the queue to find out what the hold up was. He found that the cook was working like a 'one handed paper hanger' and was nearly there with the production of breakfast. 'Do you need a hand cookie', said Matt jokingly. 'Why, can you cook', retorted the cook? 'Can I cook', said Matt in an aggrieved tone? 'Let me tell you, I'm that good, that when I whistle The Last Post, the eggs jump out of the tray, crack themselves together in mid air and fall into the hot pan to fry'. 'When they're done I whistle Yankie Doodle Dandy and they jump from the pan into the waiting mess tins', giving it a double axle with a triple toe loop along the way, said Matt. 'Now, do I get the job', asked Matt? 'Nahh mate, said the cook, you fu*k abaat too much'!

'Breakfast, shouted the cook to the queue'. Those within earshot chuckled as they temporarily forgot the discomfort of the morning. Indeed, they visibly perked up over the exchange between the Flight Sergeant AIG and the Senior Aircraftman cook. Temporarily at least, moral had climbed.

One nil to the cook!

On every squadron there were those with evil minds or the time to hatch evil plots in the name of good clean fun. These plots were usually painstakingly worked out down to the last detail and usually involved a newcomer to the squadron. And so it was one morning when a new lad arrived and was placed into 'A' flight. His detachment sergeant sent him across to the engineers to help out as a general dogsbody for the rest of the day. The scene was set! He reported to the engineering flight and was sent out to help an engineer who was levelling the fire unit. The engineer was tut tutting as he turned the fire unit this way and that. 'We need a new levelling bubble', he said. 'This one's unserviceable'. 'Nip across to squadron stores and tell the storeman that the fire unit levelling bubble's u/s'. The lad dutifully made his way across to the stores and delivered the message. The storeman started rifling through his stock cards. He stopped and shook his head, sucking his teeth he declared that the last bubble had been used a week ago and he had not received any replacements yet. 'Here, take this stores demand note to the station technical stores and bring one back', said the storeman. Our erstwhile lad now walked the mile to the station stores and after a few enquiries found the technical stores. Presenting himself at the desk he passed the demand note across the counter. 'you can't get that item without a chit from SCAF', said the grim faced storeman. 'Hang on whilst I make out this requisition', said the storeman. Our lad exited sheepishly and went to hunt out the Supply Control and Accounting Flight for this required chit'. It was just around the corner and presenting himself at the desk, the lad handed over his now accumulating pile of papers. The corporal duly signed the sheath of papers, added a couple more forms for good measure and sent him back to the squadron storeman to have them stamped. The lad now walked the mile back to the squadron then returned and presented his completed paperwork to the technical stores storeman. He was given a black plastic bag filled with water. It was sealed and had a NATO stock number written on a piece of white tape attached to it. 'Don't drop it', said the storeman, 'it's the last one in stock', he said. Our hero now made his way back to the squadron. By now, word had got around. There were people hiding everywhere. Looking out from the rear of the fire unit bays and the darker side of rooms, a hundred or so pairs of eyes remained hidden but watchful. Enter now our hero walking through the squadron gates hot and tired. He reported to the squadron stores for the item to be booked in, then had it issued to him. He signed for the bubble then took it outside to the waiting engineer. 'Where have you been', asked the engineer. 'I've been waiting ages for you to get back from stores'. 'It's a long story', said our hero wearily. 'Here', he said, handing over the plastic bag. 'Thanks', said the engineer. 'Why don't you go and get a drink from the canteen whilst I fit this', he said. Our hero gratefully retired and the engineer split the bag, emptied its contents down the drain and threw the plastic in the bin.

Nothing was said about the incident for weeks until one morning when men were being detailed off for jobs. Our young hero had by now been taught to level the launcher and had obviously worked out that he had been the victim of a prank that hot day in May. He volunteered to work with the engineers again that day and climbing up onto the roof, he waited with a water filled condom, above the door to the engineering shed. He didn't have to wait long. The door opened and out walked the squadron storeman. He'll do thought our hero. The condom was dropped with spectacular results. The storeman almost had a heart attack as this voluminous rubber sac hit his head and burst. The realisation and shock of the water hit him next as the roars of laughter reverberated around the compound at this impromptu comedy act. Our hero scrambled down, went up to the soaking storeman and said, 'you look like you've lost your levelling bubble mate, would you like to borrow the one you issued me'? 'Even better, would you like to send out an engineer to get it'?

In about nineteen eighty or eighty one, the then Prime Minister, Margaret Thatcher, gave the Zambian nation a shipment of arms. These consisted of Bofors 40/70s guns and Tigercat missile systems. The Zambian operators and technicians needed training on this equipment and that training was set to take place at RAF

Catterick. One bright sunny October morning Matt was called in to see the squadron commander. 'Ah flight, take a seat', said the CO, after Matt had gone in, saluted and stood. Matt took off his beret and sat. This is not normal, thought Matt. Wonder what he wants? It didn't take long to find out. The CO opened up the batting with a brief outline of events that had led to this interview and informed Matt that he'd like him to go to Catterick to oversee and carry out the training. The first thing that struck Matt was that he'd just been 'asked'. It had never happened before. Since joining the forces he'd always been ordered. Matt realised that he'd be poorer whilst at Catterick because he would loose his 'Local Overseas Allowance' (paid whilst he served in Germany), for the duration of the detachment. He pointed this out and was told that some other pay arrangements would be made to cover most if not all of the loss. For this discussion to be taking place at all, Matt thought, something must be going on somewhere within the 'upstairs corridors of power'. 'Sir, I'm not sure about this', said Matt. 'Zambia has borders with Rhodesia. Whatever the political feelings are against Ian Smith, I can't forget that he's an ex RAF officer and a decorated ex Battle of Britain pilot to boot. I for one am not at all happy at the prospects of having to teach Zambians to shoot down aircraft of Ian Smiths' Rhodesian Air Force.

A couple of days later Matt was crossing the compound when the CO appeared and motioned Matt over. 'Let's take a walk flight', said the CO. Matt fell into step as they walked to a quiet spot. 'I've been in touch with Wing', said the CO, 'and whilst they understand your views, you will be going'. 'The orderly room is making the arrangements as we speak'. 'I for one sympathise with you but I trust you'll complete the job to your usual high standard'? 'Yes sir', said Matt. The subject had been taken out of Matts hands. By turning the whole thing into a formal detachment order, the powers that be acknowledged that this was not something that would or could be done by favour.

Matt reported to RAF Catterick two weeks later and after he'd 'arrived', he made his way across to the old Tigercat garages. Matt could see that he was not the only 'old boy' to be detached back for this event. He met many familiar faces and one of them filled Matt in. The three Tigercat systems were being refurbished to an 'as new' standard. The guns also. Spares which a year ago were impossible to get hold of were now appearing from the far flung corners of England. Looks like quite an operation thought Matt. Matt was summonsed to see the Flight Lieutenant in charge of training and was briefed. They had a week to get the equipment that they would use for training ready. The rest would be refurbished as the training went on so that by the time the training had finished the men and equipment could return 'en bloc'.

It was getting cold now as November was knocking at the door. The leaves had left the trees bare and the chill wind was starting to pick up. Crows wheeled above the airfield hangers which housed the guns and cried out with their raucous voices. It looked and felt bleak after the warm October of Germany. A coach pulled in that night from Heathrow airport. It's heating was full on and it contained the shivering Zambian contingent. They were outfitted in civilian clothes bought locally in Africa. One short sleeved shirt and lightweight slacks did not auger well for their survival in England. They were taken to stores and issued with standard UK disruptive pattern uniform and boots and the next morning they were taken into M&S in Darlington to obtain something more appropriate for the English climate. This was all paid for in cash by an English accounts officer using public monies. Who would settle the final bills, Matt had no idea.

On the first morning of the course, the Zambian contingent were paraded. Matt took the Officer in charge to one side and asked him to separate out the technicians. An RAF chief technician was stood to one side ready to receive them and separate them out into their various trades. The Zambians had been asked to provide two radar techs, two hydraulics techs, two electricians and two mechanical engineers. The officer realising that they could not fulfil the brief called for volunteers. Everybody put their hands up so the officer chose eight men to fulfil these posts. Matt lifted his eyes heavenwards and noted that the chief did the same. Matt grinned as the newly fledged techs were handed over. Matt next asked for the missile men. These were selected using the methods. The remainder would be trained on the guns.

After six weeks of intensive training the gun crews could 'talk the talk'. They still had Manorbier get through though. The Tigercat aimers were sent off to sea to fire with the navy and the 'gunners' went to Wales. When the first gun fired the first round of the first firing run, the gun crew were so frightened by the 'BOOM', that they leapt off the gun as one man and fled, leaving the loaded gun gently revolving through the safe arc behind it. The instructors made the gun safe and it was generally agreed that they should have obtained some blanks for training whilst still at Catterick. The techs never got trained. They just had no idea and (not surprisingly) were incapable of getting their heads around 1950s technology.

As a footnote to this episode, one senior RAF Regiment officer went to Zambia on a visit a year after the arms shipment. An air raid occurred whilst he was there. Out of the six guns, only one was able to fire and that stopped after one round due to a loading error. Of the Tigercats, there was nothing to be seen.

It would seem that the Rhodesian Air Force were safest when Zambia had anti-aircraft guns and missile systems to misfire!

Back at Bruggen, Matt started studying for GCEs in his own time. His aim was to get decent passes at grade 'C' or above in five subjects. He eventually achieved his aim but it took a lot of work to 'self study' the subjects and get the results he demanded of himself. He would limit himself to one day a weekend for studying and the other day for gliding. The family usually spent both days of the weekend at the gliding club. Matt progressed through the gliding training. Aerotows became second nature and Matt preferred them to Winch launches. He passed his Bronze 'C' and started to fly further and further out from the base. One day, the airfield needed to close to gliding activities because two Jaguars were landing from the UK. The airfield would be closed for an hour so Matt elected to fly the K18 and soar in the area of Venlo for an hour. He made it without any problems and noted that he'd been flying into wind to make it. Getting back should be easer. The Chief Flying Instructor came onto the radio and asked Matt if he had a Barograph fitted. Matt affirmed that he had and was told to try for his fifty kilometre cross country flight. He was instructed to head North to RAF Laarbruch and then land about two kilometres further on. Matt set off, again into the wind, tracking the Maas Canal. He found Laarbruch with six hundred feet to spare and was sorely tempted to keep going. It was a fifty 'K' attempt after all but with a large airfield below him and an unfamiliar small field ahead of him he had insufficient height to get a good look at the proposed landing area before being committed to land. He reluctantly decided that Laarbruch was the only choice for a sensible person to land and so after forty eight kilometres of a fifty kilometre flight completed, he landed. He told himself that there would always be another day but he was still gutted.

Number thirty seven squadron continued its never ending routine of exercises at half strength. The rest of the squadron was taking its turn defending the International Airport in Belize. One day a planned new issue of Tracking Radars occurred. At one per fire unit it was a significant amount of extra equipment. This now bought the squadron up to full 'Blind Fire' capability. A fire unit detachment could now shoot down a target in fog or at night without ever having seen it. A tremendous amount of training was necessary to get all the detachment crews up to speed with this new equipment but soon the depleted squadron was deploying with full Blindfire system capability. About a month after the squadron was re-equipped, orders came through that one of the Tracking Radars was to be trialled in Belize. The wing commander wanted to know just how a Tracking Radar would stand up to the conditions prevalent in Central America. Matt would be taking it out and would ensure its integration with the fire units currently 'in theatre'. He would also train the fire unit detachment crews. This gave the added bonus that when the deployed half squadron returned to the base in Germany, they would be fully trained and ready to face the annual categorisation board that was going to be held. Every man on the squadron would be tested in their primary role and it was vital for the squadron to achieve a pass. Incidentally, it was also vital for the squadron commanders promotion prospects that a 'Pass' be awarded. An added bonus was that the fire units would be guaranteed to to be fully compatible with the Tracking Radar.

The route out was from Bruggen by road to Wildenrath. From there a C130 cargo aircraft from Air Support Command would transport them to RAF Lynham. After an overnight stay at Lynham they would strike out across the Atlantic to Gander in Newfoundland. They would overnight at Gander then take off for the US military base at Homestead situated near Miami. Another overnight stay would then preceed the flight to Andros in the Bahamas. From the Bahamas they would fly the last leg into Belize International Airport.

Because of the security classification of the Tracking Radar, it was accompanied at all times by two plain clothed but armed RAF Policemen. Matt knew them from his time some years before at RAF Gütersloh and they whiled away the long hours of flight by yarning to each other or 'pulling up a sandbag and swinging the lamp' as it was known. Matt was delighted to have them guarding the Tracking Radar during their overnight stops as it left him free to sleep in a bed and enjoy whatever the local night life had to offer. On the first night at Gander Matt ate lobster at the Motel. It was the first time in his life he'd eaten lobster and it was a monster. After the meal, there was no room for anything else so Matt paid his meagre bill and retired to bed. At the aircraft the next morning they boarded and Matt noticed that they'd been joined by a dozen or so Gurkhas. They would be flying with them all the way to Belize. Another long day passed as they droned on South, down the coast of America. They landed in the late afternoon and Matt was doubly glad that the RAF Police were guarding the Tracking Radar and not him. They were accommodated in a 'Howard Johnson' Motel which was a 'dry' establishment. The Gurkhas were now under Matts charge. He'd been briefed to look after them by the captain of the aircraft and told not let them get into trouble during their overnight stay. After enquiring at the Motel desk, Matt and the Gurkhas were pointed towards the Holiday Inn, next door and after a shower and change all thirteen of them headed out towards the bar. I don't know about keeping them out of trouble thought Matt but with a dozen Gurkhas around me this evening I guess I'll be the safest man in Miami. They enjoyed ice cold beer and huge steaks accompanied by fresh crisp salad and baked potatoes with sour cream dressing. Matt thought about the RAF Policemen left on the plane whilst he ate his meal and as he did he smiled, raised his glass and toasted their dedication. The next morning after a large breakfast 'American style', they arrived back at the aircraft and greeted the dishevelled policemen. They had now been on the aircraft for two days and nights using a chemical toilet for the essentials with bottled water to wash and drink. Their food consisted of flight rations in cardboard boxes and their moral had sunk to a fairly low ebb. They flew to Andros and were on the ground for an hour. They off loaded equipment to a Navy detachment there that was going to be used on submarine equipment trials.

During the last five or so hours into Belize the policemen told Matt how much they hated the hot, humid, stinking place. In their words, if Guatamala were the backside of the world then Belize would be about five hundred miles up it.

After such a long trip the aircrew were planning to become 'unserviceable' when they got back to Nassau in the Bahamas. It would probably take three days to fix the aircraft before they could fly back to the UK. It was this chance of catching a few days paid holiday in the Bahamas that prompted the policemen to volunteer for this job in the first place. They had earned it on the way out and by god, they were really looking forward to their just rewards on the way back. Barring anything major of course, whatever unserviceabilities they carried into Belize they would nurse them back as far as Nassau before grounding the aircraft. They landed in Belize and Matt was met with a suitable towing vehicle. The Tracking Radar was taken to the squadron compound and put to bed in a secure lock up. That afternoon on the way to the mess Matt glanced across to the airfield and was surprised to see the C130 still sitting on the pan. After a shower and a meal Matt caught the transport down to Belize city. There were only two air conditioned bars in Belize city and Matt chose the one by the sea front. The view was nicer. Walking into the bar, Matt ordered a beer and peering around in the gloomy bar lit only with a few dim lights Matt recognised the two RAF policemen sitting nursing a beer. Matt walked over. 'Hi guys, what are you doing here'? 'Kite's u/s', said one of them. 'But I thought you weren't going to go u/s until you got back to Nassau', said Matt. The policeman explained to Mat that a strut had broken on the landing gear during that last landing in Belize. The aircraft couldn't even be taxied until a spare was fitted. The spare part was on it's way from the UK and should be here in about three days or so. 'So what about the aircrew', asked Matt. 'Oh another C130 arrived and took them to Nassau but the crew chief had to stay with the aircraft', said the policeman. 'Meanwhile, you're stuck in Belize for the duration', smiled Matt. 'Aye', they both chorused glumly. 'We're quite looking forward to getting home now', said one of them.

Matt spent a month in Belize ensuring that the Tracking Radar worked with the fire units. On two of the Rapier systems, parts needed to be changed for a successful integration to be achieved but eventually all the systems worked well and all men were trained up. They needed to be because the squadron would be facing it's annual categorisation test when the Belize detachment returned. Matt said farewell and climbed aboard a VC10 for the return trip. The flight back was vastly different to the flight out. On the way, Matt reflected that he had now completed fourteen trips to Belize. That meant that he had crossed the infamous 'Bermuda Triangle' twenty eight times and he was still here to tell the tale.

Back in Germany the detachments eventually returned bringing back with them a Tracking Radar that was still serviceable after six months of constant night and day use. The squadron passed it's annual categorisation board, so all in all it had been a worthwhile trip. Apart from two disgruntled RAF policemen that is. Wonder if they've managed to get out of Belize yet, mused Matt.

Two and a half years at Bruggen came and went, then towards the end of the final six months Matt stepped out from behind one of the soundproofed generator running booths. He was deep in conversation with one of the engineers. 'Look out', shouted the engineer who at the same time grabbed Matts arm and pulled him back. A landrover sped past running over his outstretched foot. He felt the wind from the closeness of the vehicle and realised he'd had a close one. His foot hurt like hell and he sat down on the concrete floor. 'Who the hell was that', exclaimed Matt. 'He just came flying through the compound gates'. 'He was going much to fast'. Matt ended up in Sick Quarters then was taken by ambulance to the British Military Hospital in Rheindahlen near Münchengladbach. He was returned to the squadron that afternoon with his foot and lower leg sporting a large white plaster cast which he wore for the next six weeks.

One day Matt had a phone call. It was a sergeant from the postings office at RAF Innsworth in Gloucester. How would he like to go the the Outer Hebrides for two and a half years, he was asked? Well, said the voice on the other end of the phone, he'd have to volunteer to go but 'records office' would promise him his choice of postings at the end of it. 'I'd quite like to go to Cyprus after the Hebrides', said Matt. 'Okay', said the sergeant, 'we can fix that up'. 'We'll send you the paperwork in a couple of days then'. 'Okay', said Matt. Sure enough, two days later Matt was asked to go to the squadron orderly room to fill out some paper work. His posting came through. He was going to the Outer Hebrides for two and a half years to work on the Royal Artillery missile ranges. He would be living in the mess but first he had to get his family back to their home in Eaglescliffe and place the three younger children into boarding school.

One sunny morning the house was handed over and Matt took the family to catch the flight back to the UK. All of their possessions had already been shipped so there was only the caravan left. Matt drove back to Bruggen and retrieved the caravan. He was using it as a removals van so it was pretty full. He also had a pair of parakeets in a cage. The cage was hung up so the birds would have a swinging time on the way home. He hitched up the caravan and set off. What with his foot still in the plaster cast and the birds swinging in the cage, Matt realised that he'd have to take it easy on the way back. Eventually he made ferry port of Zeebrugge and was loaded for an overnight crossing of the North sea. It was a calm crossing and the morning saw Matt offloaded and heading for customs. This should be interesting thought Matt. Matt pulled up next to the customs man. 'Anything to declare', asked the official. 'Yes', said Matt. He declared the cigarettes and the bottle of whiskey he had then declared the birds. 'Bring them out please', said the customs officer.

Matt scrambled inside to retrieve the cage. 'Glad to see the door's wired closed', said the customs officer. 'Do you have an import license for them', he asked? 'Yes', said Matt producing the paperwork. 'Do you know that you have to have a visit from a vet within forty eight hours of arriving home and the cage must be locked for another six weeks', said the customs man? Matt nodded. 'You will require regular visits from the vet to certify that the birds do not fall ill during the quarantine period', he went on. Matt affirmed that he was aware of these requirements and replaced the cage in the caravan. Next followed the formalities of importing his duty free car and caravan into the country. That took another half hour. By the time he set off, Matt had been detained for one and a half hours at 'Her Majesty's Pleasure'. He set off on the final drive home. Only about two hundred and fifty miles to go. Over the next six weeks or so, Matt kept a close eye on the birds. He noticed that the female or the hen, was the dominant one of the pair. She would spend the day squawking and pecking at the cock. He would keep moving out of her way to sit at the far end of the perch with the resigned look of a henpecked husband. One day the family came in from a shopping trip and Matt idly wandered over to the cage and looked in. The Cock was sitting on the perch with a smug expression on his face. The hen was lying on her back on the bottom of the cage. She was as dead as a doorpost. Brown Bread, right proper she was. Fortunately the quarantine period had finished some time before, so Matt didn't need to report the suspicious death. She had just tried it on once to often thought Matt. It'll be a lonely old life for you now me old cock thought Matt . It'll be a bit quieter too.

Chapter 26 – Hebridean Adventure

It was night, it was raining and it was getting cold. Matt was queuing for a ticket on the Caledonian McBrain ferry for a crossing from Oban to Loch Boisdale in South Uist. The ferry sailed at ten pm and it was now eight thirty. Matt arrived at the little glass window of the ticket office and knowing that it was usually slightly cheaper to buy a return ticket than singles Matt enquired as to the cost. He reasoned that as he was posted to the Outer Hebrides for two and a half years, he would be using the return portion at some time in the future. 'Er, how much is a return ticket to Loch Boisdale please', Matt asked the ticket seller. The little old ticket seller looked up at this 'Sassenach' with a mixture of scorn and pity. It was obvious that the specimen had been born with no brains at all. He said clearly and loudly in a Scottish brogue that carried to the waiting queue, 'why, it's exactly twice the price of two singles'. There were sniggers behind Matt as he bought his single ticket and walked back to his car.

The drive had taken nine hours from Eaglescliffe in county Cleveland to the ferry terminus in Oban. His route had been through some spectacular countryside along the way. He had driven over the Pennines on a clear cold day and reaching Penrith he'd headed North to the boarders. In Glasgow he took the motorway through the city and over the Erskine bridge. Continuing North, Matt drove up the side of Loch Lomand before heading West then South down the Mull of Kintyre and into Oban. The ferry sailed overnight and so the next morning Matt drove off the ferry at loch Boisdale. Matt drove to the island of Benbecula. The drive took about forty five minutes along a single track road to the Airport on Benbecula and the army camp.

Benbecula camp provided the domestic facilities for the men and women who manned the Royal Artillery Missile firing range on South Uist. Situated just outside of the village of Balivanich, the camp provided accommodation for the hundred or so army personnel there along with their dependants or families living in the married quarters. A separate detachment lived and worked on St Kilda, an island situated fifty miles out in the Atlantic. St Kilda had been depopulated early in the twentieth century and during the harsh winters, the army were the only human inhabitants. Cut off by storms for weeks at a time, the detachment manned radars. These radars sanitised the outer edges of the danger envelope of the missile firing range when the larger and more powerful ground to ground missiles were fired. Any intruding vessels were shepherded out of danger by Range Safety Boats. Russian 'fishing' vessels bristling with aerials usually refused to move and so under those circumstances, firing had to stop until the area was clear. On days such as these when everything stopped, Matt couldn't help but think that if the firing of the larger missiles were to continue regardless, the Russian 'fishing' boats might leave the area of their own accord. At high speed.

The detachment on St Kilda were not the only people to get bad weather during the winter. Matt and the rest of the firing point team used to have to cross the causeway between Benbecula and South Uist every day to get to to work. Some days they had to turn back as heavy green seas were driven over the top of the causeway by the storm force winds. Occasionally they would go for a week without being able to get across the causeway.

There were four launch areas controlled by the 'Taj Mahal' or Range control as it was known locally. Matt worked within a department consisting of an officer in charge and three senior NCOs. Beneath them they had a Womens Royal Army Corps sergeant, two female corporals, two female lance corporals and a handful of ladies or privates. They spent the days in their reinforced concrete bunker and controlled the missile firings in a safe and orderly manner. Matt was initially employed as the flight safety officer. Because of the allusion to the RAF uniform colours he was known as the 'Blue Destroyer', whilst the Royal Artillery Staff Sergeant who controlled the firing inhibits, was known as the 'Stopper'.

Their day to day work consisted of controlling Rapier missile firings and ensuring that the rules governing Launch Area Safety were followed pedantically. There were three main consoles within the concrete building where the Launch Area personnel worked. One dealt specifically with Launcher safety and was known as the LASOs console. One console dealt only with monitoring the Rapier systems health. The telemetry provided a permanent record of the firing by means of an Ultra Violet or UV chart recording. The third was the 'Visual Flight Safety Officer' or VFSO station. This consisted of lines engraved on perspex which denoted the safe firing arcs. The VFSO looked through this and visually monitored the flight path of the missile. If a missile went rogue or looked like it was going to cross one of these lines, the VFSO was provided with a button to press. This blew the warhead on the missile and removed the guidance commands. The LASO could prevent firing and could cut down a missile in flight if necessary. When a firing day commenced, the girls went down to the fire units and mounted TV cameras. These were controlled from the LASOs bunker and provided close up pictures of the firings. They also monitored the operators sight picture so that the LASO and the VFSO could see what the Rapier operator could see. The girls also manned the telemetry console during firings. They would bring in the camera equipment at the end of the firing day and in between firing runs they gossiped and knitted the day away.

Rapier missile firings were carried out from either Launch Area 1 or Launch Area 3. The Blue Destroyer usually ran LA1 and the Stopper LA3.

One day as Matt was climbing the stairs after having been down the firing point, he heard the boss shout. Flight, I've heated your dinner up in the microwave. 'Bastard', shouted Matt. Matt knew that he only had salad. The boss knew that too. He'd looked. Matt ran up the stairs two at a time but to no avail. The lettuce was black and liquid. The potato was still hard but his sweet, the Kit Kat having been removed from its silver foil wrapping was melted nicely. Matt waited for his chance to repay the kindness but the boss was not going to let his guard down. One day lady luck smiled on Matt. He realised that the boss was engrossed in a girlie magazine. As quick as a flash he popped the bosses lunch into the microwave. 'I'm just nipping down to the firing point sir', Matt shouted over his shoulder, whilst running down the stairs. 'Would you hit the timer for me on the microwave for lunch please'. The boss walked across with his eyes still fixed to the centre page spread in the magazine, reached out and turned on the timer. Matt waited at the bottom of the steps until he heard the explosion from the microwave oven upstairs. As innocently as possible he climbed the stairs once more. 'Have we over cooked our eggs today sir', he asked, with undisguised glee? The door was hanging off the microwave oven. It had exploded. The boiled eggs were just to much for it to take. 'Oh dear sir, it looks like you'll have to buy a new microwave oven to replace the one you've just destroyed'. 'I mean, that sort of damage could hardly be construed as fair wear and tear could it'. 'You f**king ***ker', yelled the boss. Matt smiled and picked up his plate of salad and choice cold meat cuts. 'Now now sir', said Matt. 'Language like that is not becoming of an 'awficer' like you now is it sir'. ' Especially a commando person who we mere paras look up to and down sir'. 'Is it now'. 'You just wait', said the boss but Matt just grinned. It was a special relationship between them both because the boss was an ex ranker. He understood and liked Matt for who he was and what he represented. The younger members of the section however hadn't a clue about the 'Blue destroyer' or his Regiment and thought that the Women's Royal Army Corps and the Royal Artillery were the only units worth representing in the British army. Matt was going to show them the light but the time had not yet come.

One day Matt was carrying out the duties of LASO, controlling the missile firings. The Rapier radar wasn't working and the system number one had been slewing the system manually. This run was no exception. Matt allowed the launcher to go to its Tracking state and glanced at the boresight camera monitor screen. He could see that the operator was tracking the target smoke but Matt was puzzled by the change in colour. It had changed from red to white. Ah well thought Matt. Everything's pointing in the right direction. He lifted the final firing inhibit and reported 'Inhibits Off'. The operator pressed the firing button and the missile after the usual one second delay lifted up it's skirts and leapt off the launch rails. There's something wrong here thought Matt as the missile didn't follow the usual track downrange. Instead it went almost vertically upwards. Matt stood up and leaned forward to get a better view, then he spotted it. The operator had fired on the con trail of a transatlantic passenger jet. Matt blew the missile immediately. There was never any danger of hitting the jet because the missile had not been allowed to fly for long enough. Whilst some would argue that the aircraft was too high to be hit, Matt wasn't so sure. The thing was that a few hundred people were now walking around who would never know that they had had a live missile fired at them as they flew in from America.

Best not let the daily papers find out thought Matt. They'd blow it out of all proportion and have a field day with that story. I could just imagine it now, said Matt to the boss. 747 fired on by Englands finest as it approaches Scotland. No worries though, they missed.

Matt had joined the gliding club at Benbecula. The club had one two seater glider and two club members and Matt was one of them. The other member was the chief flying instructor. Their method of launch was a 'piano wire' cable attached to a landrover belonging to one of the visiting units. The vehicle was driven along the the runway with a safety man watching the aircraft for speed up or slow down signals. Because flying was limited to the vagaries of the weather in the Outer Hebrides, there were not many 'legal' flying days. Matt managed to get a weeks gliding course at RAF Biscester near Oxford and so found himself sharing a K18 with another solo pilot for the week. All launches were by aerotow and they both managed to fly for at least two hours each day, free. At the end of the course, Matt was asked to report to RAF Uxbridge on the outskirts of London. RAF Uxbridge dealt with Matts administrative matters whilst he was posted to an Army unit. He reported to the officer in charge of the orderly room. A Warrant Officer who informed Matt that he'd been promoted. He was now a Special Acting Paid Warrant Officer and 'congratulations sign here'. Matt signed, left and headed to clothing stores for the new rank epaulettes, beret and hat badges. He had a warm feeling all the way back to the Hebrides. At 36 years of age, he must have been the youngest ground trade Warrant Officer in the Air Force.

 Orderly Officer duties came round and Matt stood his turn. It was the evening of his duty and there was a formal mess dinner taking place that evening. Matt of course was unable to attend but between his scheduled trips to the Range head he was able to stand at the bar in the mess and enjoy a Coke-Cola. Tall wooden partition doors separated the bar from the dining hall and as Matt sipped his drink he could hear the muted roar from the dining room coming through the closed partition doors. Seems to be going okay, thought Matt. Just then, the noise got louder, as if a door had opened into the dining room. Matt looked round and sure enough a door had been opened. The strange thing was that it was one of the diners and he was crawling. He reached the bar side of the door, closed it and stood up. 'Gawd, I'm desperate for a piss' said Sgt Crisp as he got up and walked towards to toilets. Sgt Crisp had broken a cardinal rule. You never got up and left a formal dinner. The only exception was pregnancy. Matt smiled to himself, Sgt Crisp would have to return without being detected. He would certainly be for the high jump if he were caught.

After dinner, the tale gradually came out. It would appear that when he left, the people around his now empty place quietly caught the attention of the Mess manager. He in turn realised what had happened and had the waiters covertly remove the food, place setting, glasses and chair from the place at the table formerly occupied by Sgt Crisp. He returned on his hands and knees to his now empty place at the dining table. As he had no chair he had to half kneel and half crouch. Not wanting to be discovered, he went through the motions of eating without props. Eventually Sgt Crisp got bored with the proceedings and decided to have a cigarette. This was another Taboo. He held the cigarette under the table but the Regimental Sergeant Major known as the RSM, smelled smoke and wrote 'Three extras' on a napkin and passed it to his left. As the napkin made its way around the table, each recipient, not knowing what it was about, shrugged and passed it on. When it got to Sgt Crisp he looked up to find the RSM staring intently at the progress of the napkin. Shit, said Sgt Crisp, gotcha replied the RSM and so it was that he earned himself three extra orderly sergeant duties.

Later on as Sgt Crisp and Matt visited the Gents, Sgt Crisp continued to bemoan his rotten luck to Matt. ' It's a good job the old wanker didn't know I'd got up and left for a piss as well', said Sgt Crisp and from the locked stall behind them, Matt heard the voice of the RSM. Make that another seven extras for taking the piss and three more for the wanker. Report to me in the morning, at my office Sgt Crisp. Matt smiled, shook his head and left for his Range head checks.

One day Matt was at work and stood at his console. He was watching the 'Into Action' sequence of yet another Rapier detachment crew on the firing point. One of the girls on the section came and stood beside him. 'You blokes get it easy in the raff compared to the army', don't you sir, she said? 'What do you mean', said Matt, keeping his voice level. 'Well you have a cushy life for a start', she said.' None of the hardships of being a real soldier', she added. Matt reminded her that he was not in the raff. He was in the Royal Air Force Regiment and he was very much a soldier, only more professional than most. A few of the girls guffawed and smirked at this. 'How would you know anyway', said Matt. 'You racks never have to do anything more difficult than knitting anyway', said Matt. 'We're not racks sir', said one of the girls. 'You screw racks to the wall and to call us racks is an insult', 'sir'. 'Precisely', said Matt and in the same vein, I'm not raff'. 'Okay', said the girl. 'Seriously sir, just what, do the RAF Regiment do then'. Matt spent the next few minutes filling in the gaps in the girls education then said, 'If I were to organise an exercise to teach you new skills, would you all take part', he asked. 'You bet we would said one of the others, we never do anything apart from come here each day and man these boring consoles'.

'Right', said Matt. 'Give me a couple of weeks and I'll work out a plan with some details'. 'You'll need to carry out some extra training pre-exercise, to ensure that you'll be able to exercise the skills you'll need but that will be part of the work up phase'. 'If you can master the basic skills then we should be ready in about three months or so'.

Matt wanted to involve other agencies involved with running the ranges and to this end he went to the various heads of departments and outlined his proposals. No one would be forced to go on this exercise but there would be a limit to the number of volunteers Matt could take. The activities that would take place involved being dropped off from the transport on the first day with one group walking over Bheinn Hecla and another walking over Bheinn Mhor. They would camp overnight at a Bothy and on the second day they

264

would walk out to RV with an Armoured Personnel Carrier or APC (heavily disguised as a white 29 seater Army bus). This would transport them to a secret location where the Army Catering Corps had prepared a hot meal cooked in field conditions. A hot and hearty stew was on the menu with spotted dick and custard to follow. They would then once again board the buses and be transported to Loch Boisdale. There they would RV with a submarine (heavily disguised as a Range Safety Launch) and be transported to the Island of Barra. They would be disembarking in Castle Bay and setting up camp on the far side of the bay. The tentage and rations being pre-positioned. The next morning there would be a signals and orienteering exercise followed that afternoon by a River Crossing exercise. The following day, they would recover to camp and be ready for work on the Monday.

For an itinerary as ambitious as Matt proposed, a mountain of administrative work needed to be climbed. He would be involving the REME, Royal Signals, Royal Artillery, WRAC, Catering Corps, Range Safety section, Padre, Air Sea Rescue Helicopter (if necessary) and of course himself representing the Royal Air Force Regiment running the show. It took Matt three months of planning and negotiating with the various agencies involved to get all his 'ducks in a row' but he got there.

Meanwhile, whilst all the planning and administration was going on, normal work continued. Matt slotted half day training exercises in to his busy schedule where he took the girls out and taught them how to use a compass and map. They came unstuck once when Matt deliberately took them through an area of 'known magnetic abnormality' in the hills overlooking the Sounds of Erriskay. A ship with a cargo of whiskey bound for America had come to grief on the rocks in the Sounds many years before. This was due to the compass being affected by the magnetic abnormality in bad visibility at night. The troops learnt a valuable lesson about maps and common sense that day.

The exercise day came and the troops paraded in a state of high excitement. Matt checked the packs of both men and women to ensure that everybody carried all the equipment he'd stipulated. It was all essential and nobody was allowed to carry anything that was not. He announced to all that if there was anybody who was not fully fit, they should declare it now and not risk going. If they were ill or injured it would compromise the exercise and they would have to call out a rescue helicopter from the Scottish mainland to lift them out if they couldn't be carried out. At that point a REME Major asked Matt if he minded if he tagged along. He would like to see how his troops handled the physical and mental stress when they became fatigued in cold wet conditions. Matt agreed but he stipulated that the Major had to come as a Craftsman and not a Major. Matt was not going to give over his command after all the work that he'd put into it. The different transport vehicles set off with thirty soldiers plus a Craftsman Smith and headed for their different drop off points. Reaching theirs, Matt and his team of WRACs jumped off the transport at the foothills of Bheinn Hecla and having sorted out their kit, they shouldered their packs and set off. Some miles further down the road, the Sergeant Major and his team were doing exactly the same thing adjacent to Bheinn Mhor

The higher they climbed, the steeper it got. The women who had talked constantly since they left the vehicle started to quieten down as they ran out of puff. Eventually there was a silence that matched the mountain. Every time they saw a crest they were convinced that the slope would ease off after they passed it. They learnt that the slope just continued to increase. The climb now became steep but they could see the top and they flogged on. They were climbing on their hands and knees when one of the WRACs decided that she couldn't go any further. It hurt to much. The top was only a few hundred yards by now so they sat down on the grassy slope to catch their breath. 'I can't go any further', said the girl. 'I'm pregnant'. Shit, thought Matt. He looked at one of the corporals in the group and raised an eyebrow, a silent questioning gesture that he hoped would provoke a response. She shook her head as she looked him straight in the eye. The shake was almost imperceptible but it was there. Okay so this was a cop out. He talked to the girl earnestly and pointed out how far they'd come and how little they had to go. She was having none of it. She wouldn't go one more step. Matt knew better. He could be obstinate too. After all, he'd learnt a valuable lesson from Bully Bill some years before. Matt stood up and slung his pack on his back. He then took the girls pack and slung it across his front. Then he grabbed the girl by her wrists with both hands and started to walk backwards up the slope towards the top. The girl fought him with all her might. Matt dragged, cajoled, shouted, gave earnest encouragement, smiled but continued up the slope. The girl fought all the way, screaming and yelling that she could not and would not be made to do it. As Matt neared the top, two of the men came down and with one at each side they made the summit. They all stood in silence as Matt doubled over to catch his breath. 'You see', he said at last, 'you could do it'. 'I knew you could do it'. 'The only problem was that you didn't know that you could do it'. 'And if I hear any more nonsense about you being pregnant, I'll insist on you being tested at the medical centre when we get back'. The girl was quiet and couldn't meet Matts eye. She had understood at that point, that 'quitting' was not a word in Matts vocabulary. They walked on down the other side of the mountain and about three hours later, they made the first RV, the Bothy.

One of the Signallers ran up the track and got hold of Matt to tell him that a helicopter had been tasked to rescue one of the girls in the group going over Bheinn Mhor. Eventually it landed and dropped off the second team. Matt then discovered what had happened.

The going became to tough for one of the WRAC in the second group. She announced that she was unable to continue. A radio message was passed back to the 'Taj Mahal' stating that they had a 'Broken Female'. This was received as a 'Broken Femur' which caused the rescue service to swing into action. The group were plucked of the mountain side and flown to the medical centre. The aircrew were more than a little annoyed when they saw the casualty get off the helicopter unaided and walk past the waiting doctor.

Matt was incensed but would have to deal with it after the exercise. The helicopter flew off back to the mainland and Matt turned back to the exercise.

'What are we having to eat tonight', asked one of the girls after Matt had got everybody to gather round. 'Barbecue', replied Matt. 'Where's the meat', she asked suspiciously. 'Right here', replied Matt reaching down and grabbing a dead rabbit from a pile the lads had stashed under a bush. After the expressions of revulsion had died down Matt gave them a talk on survival and food. As he talked, he skinned the rabbit. A fire had been lit so Matt suspended the rabbit above the flames using a pole. He told the assembled troops that the choices were hot delicious meat or cold hunger for tonight's meal. In any case he wanted them to try 'survival rations' as they had another strenuous day tomorrow. No body apart from the Sergeant Major had any idea about the plan for the next day. Those that wanted to, ate and went to bed. Those that didn't want to just went to bed. Matt arranged a guard rosta for the night then turned in.

Reveille was at 05:00 the next morning Matt got up and put some water in his mess tin. He placed it on the still glowing embers and after a few minutes was rewarded by hot water for a shave and tea. Next he cleaned his boots working a waterproofing compound called 'dubbin' into the leather. He put clean dry socks on and replaced his boots. Next he chivvied up his group to get ready then he gave the orders for the day.

They set off for the RV with the APC. The girls were now map reading for themselves and they made slow but steady progress. Matt had to stress the urgency of making the RV on time. If they didn't, the transport would leave without them. Nobody relished the thought of being abandoned out in this hilly craggy countryside and so they made their RV. It was a hard walk and had taken over three hours. The troops were beginning to learn that life in the 'raff' was perhaps, not the cushy number that they had first thought it was. They climbed gratefully aboard the bus and were surprised at how warm it was after the keen wind outside. The bus set off and took them to the RV with the Catering Corps. When they realised what was going on, moral went sky high. Matt called them together and explained to them that they had just experienced first hand just how hard it could get travelling over rough wet terrain. Some of them were limping and Matt stressed the need to look after their feet. 'Before anybody eats', said Matt, 'I want you to attend to your feet and your boots. And that's precisely what happened. Matt noticed that quite a few 'spectators' had come to see the troops. The base commander, a Brigadier was there with his wife. The Padre was there and assorted heads of departments showed an interest. One of the Captains was talking to an exchange USAF officer who was most impressed at the troops activities before they ate. 'Our boys would have gone straight for the chow', he announced.

They finished their meal, cleaned up and climbed on the coach once more. They set off for Lock Boisdale and there was an excited ripple of conversation when they stopped at the docks and transferred to the waiting Range Safety Launches. The trip to Barra took about an hour and several of the girls revisited their lunch on the way. After what seemed an age, they motored into Castle Bay and tied up at the wharf. They unloaded their packs and also a large plywood crate. Matt made them carry this to the camp site along with their luggage. They knew better than to argue by now and so they meekly did as bid. Matt had a surprise. The box contained a Guitar, charcoal, steaks, sausages, bread rolls, beer and pillows. They set up camp as the sun started to set then Matt set into action the plan. All the troops were paraded. No exceptions. They would be going out on a route march and would be back about midnight depending on fitness. Matt expected some 'leakers'. He expected some to try and sneak off to avoid the march. What they didn't know was that the Sergeant Major would be marching them half a mile to the pub and after an hour would be marching them back again. By this time Matt would have got the Barbecue going and broken out the beer.

Matt read out the guard rota for the evening and the marchers set off in gloomy silence and disappeared around the bend. Matt sat on the edge of the box and quietly smoked a cigarette. He didn't have long to wait. Two girls came out from their tents. 'Oh dear', they said. 'Did we miss something'. 'Where is everybody', they asked innocently. 'Get over here you two and give me a hand shouted Matt. He pointed out to them that their behaviour in thinking they could pull a 'fast one' had caused them to miss the fun. Now they would be staying behind and doing chores. He set them to work getting the fire going, getting the food set out ready for cooking and generally making sure that the camp was neat and tidy ready for the troops return. He didn't give them a minute to themselves and a couple of times they asked to be allowed to go on the march. The second time Matt said 'don't tempt me', so they shut up. Exactly an hour later the party that had set out thinking that they were going on a route march returned and the fun began. The rules were; before anybody could eat, they had to entertain the remaining troops. Then they had to cook their own food. The entertainment could be carried out by sections or individuals. Some sang, some did comedy sketches but all had a great time except two who had the 'Mickey' taken unmercifully. Matt reminded them that reveille would be at 06:30 and turned in for the night. The next morning dawned bright and clear which was more than could be said for the sore heads being nursed. After the ablutions they were formed up into their respective teams and set off for the orienteering and signals exercise. The Royal Signals parties were sent off to the tops of the hills once more as relay stations in case of any communications problems. Before the morning was out each group would have walked around the island.

That afternoon the assembled personnel were told to change into underwear and the one piece 'boiler suits' Matt had made sure they had packed before they left camp. He made them take all their kit in their packs and they set off for the 'River Crossing' exercise. The point at which the crossing would take place was a narrow stretch of water which fed an inlet or small harbour. The water flowed fast as the tide went in and out but at slack-water it was still for about an hour. They arrived on site and dumped their kit on the grass. Matt now demonstrated how to make up a floatation pack. He'd been taught in Malaya some years before. The assembled troops now learnt why Matt had insisted on them bringing the poles with them. He spread his groundsheet or poncho cape on the ground and piled all his equipment into it. He then laid one of the poles on top and rolled the free edges of the poncho around the pole. When he had finished it resembled a short fat sausage. He now used the 'Para' cord to lash each end of the cape to the pole. Having seen how it was done, the troop now made their own. Matt took one of the girls

271

flotation pack and gave her his. He tied a rope around his waist and holding the flotation pack under his arm he jumped in and swam across to the other side. He was met by the Sergeant Major who took the rope from Matt and tied it off on a large rock. Matt went back and climbed out of the water. 'Right', said Matt. 'Who's next?' One by one they jumped in and swam across. All except one who had a fear of drowning. No amount of persuasion would get her to go into the water. They made their way back to camp. Moral was once more sky high. The night followed much the same pattern as the previous night but with more abandon applied to the acts. Much later, sitting around the camp fire, the men of the REME were sitting with their arms around each others shoulders swaying gently whilst giving a sentimental rendering of 'I'm dreaming of a White Christmas'. There's no snow shouted some wag. Craftsman Smith now came into his own with inspirational initiative. He grabbed a feather pillow and his knife. Hey Presto, there was snow. He waved it above the singers who redoubled their efforts in the sudden snow storm. Matt smiled, shook his head and went off to bed.

 The next morning the place looked as if a chicken massacre had taken place. The place was covered with feathers. Matt crept silently over sleeping forms and found the Craftsman Smith's back pack. Matt removed the Majors rank tabs and crept quietly away. Reveille was sounded and after a cold breakfast they struck camp. After the equipment was piled up on the jetty they all marched back to the camp site. Matt got the Sergeant Major to dole out the black plastic bags. It resembled an out of work chicken farm. There were white feathers everywhere. Matt addressed the troops. 'Right', he said. 'This place is covered in assorted litter and feathers'. 'I want you all to form a line on your hands and knees and pick up every single piece of rubbish including the feathers'. 'We will not be leaving, until this field is as we found it'. Craftsman Smith made a dash for his back pack. 'If you're looking for these Craftsman Smith, forget it'. Matt held up the Majors shoulder tabs. 'You were the one who caused this mess so it's only fair that you help clear it up'. Craftsman Smith shrugged his shoulders and joined the line. Half an hour later the field was green once more and half an hour after that they were at sea. Most of them had breakfasted on the boiled sweets that came in the compo ration boxes. A few of them demonstrated a phenomena only seen at sea. They were being sick over the side but despite their breakfast of boiled sweets it was still coming up diced carrots.

They were met at the Boisdale docks by the bus which bumped them over the single track road back to camp. It was lunchtime when they arrived but before getting off the bus, Matt addressed the troops for the last time. 'This afternoon is your free time to sort yourselves and your kit out'. 'Tonight there is one last parade'. There was a collective groan. 'You are to parade in the NAAFI bar at 19:30 hours'. There was a cheer. 'And I'm buying the first round'. A very loud cheer erupted. Matt climbed down from the coach, made his way to his room, dropped his kit and crawled into a hot bath. He lit a cigarette and reflected over the last few days. It had been fun but it had also been hard work at times. The people who went, had learnt something about themselves. Even Craftsman Smith. They found out that they were capable of doing things they wouldn't have known they were capable of, if they hadn't have been stretched to their limit. A couple of people also learnt that trying to get out of what seemed to be an unpleasant task could prove be counter productive. That evening they all met in the bar and Matt bought the first round. Moral was as high as he'd seen it in a long while and all had a great time swapping 'war stories' about 'their' exercise.

Some weeks later during a lull in missile firing one of the girls came up to Matt. 'You know sir, we've been talking about that exercise you took us on', she said. 'Is that so', replied Matt slowly. 'Well we're all agreed', she said. 'About what?' said Matt. 'It was the most enjoyable time we've had since we joined the Army', she said but we are all agreed about one thing'. 'Which is', said Matt. 'We will never, ever, go on exercise with you again......ever'.

Matt smiled and turned back to the console to continue his cushy life in the 'raff' whilst the 'racks' made the tea.

On the 2nd of April 1982, Argentina invaded the Falkland islands. Despite the efforts of the American Secretary of State, Alexander Haig. The shuttle diplomacy between London and Buenos Aires failed. The then Prime Minister, Margaret Thatcher announced that Great Britain would not stand for this act of aggression against a British territory. A Task Force was put together from all three services and sailed via the Ascension Islands into the South Atlantic. They were charged with retaking the Falkland Islands.

The mobilisation effect was even felt in the Outer Hebrides where peacetime firing restrictions were lifted. Missile firing was now conducted in the open and 'T' Battery of the Royal Artillery arrived to fire and prove their equipments before going to war. 'T' Bty did not have a bad weather capability and relied on the visibility being good enough to engage targets using the optical Tracker. 63 Squadron of the Royal Air Force Regiment on the other hand did have the 'Blindfire capability' and they also fired to prove their systems on the Hebridean Ranges. Both 'T' Bty and 63 Sqn travelled down to the Falklands with the task force but only 'T' Battery were landed. Matt scratched his head over that one. 'T' Bty couldn't fire at night or during bad weather. That didn't leave too many opportunities to defend the troops. Needless loss of life must have been caused by the decision to keep 63 Sqn at sea when they could have been providing day and night all weather cover for the men and ships.

Back in the Hebrides, Matt noticed that the RAF Vulcans had started using the range for practise bombing runs. It was always at night or at twilight. The huge delta winged bombers would appear silently at low level and would only be heard on departure.

After the initial flurry of the 'T' Bty and 63 Sqn firings the range became very quiet. No units were coming through now and absolutely nothing was happening on the Range. The Firing points were silent and would continue to be so until the end of the war. Matt lost count of the number of times he'd phoned the postings people, telling them that he was wasting his time going to an empty office in the 'Marie Celeste' each day. He'd be much better employed working at something useful in the Falklands than sleeping his days away where he was. Each time he phoned he got the same answer. 'Wait out', said the disembodied voice at the other end. So Matt 'Waited out', twiddled his thumbs and continued to do nothing.

Matts brother was down in the Falklands as a 'Fighter Controller' on HMS Glamorgan. The ship was hit by a Land Based Exocet Anti Ship Missile. Thirteen crewmen were killed in that attack but fortunately the ship survived. Matts brother, who was not on board that day was in 'Bomb Alley' instead. He was on another ship looking out using the on board search radar for hostile aircraft activity. It was his job to vector the Sea Harriers onto the Argentinian aircraft before they could do any damage. It seemed to be a case of the 'Devil or the deep blue sea'.

Meanwhile back in the Hebrides, Matt was so bored doing nothing that he used to volunteer to be Orderly Officer and so was a popular chap whilst the war continued.

It was on one such stint that he found himself down at LA1 one Sunday morning. He was required as part of the duty to visit the Range head twice a day. He'd decided to call in to LA1 and make a cup of tea. There was nothing else happening. He'd just settled down with a good book and his tea when the phone rang. The only people who knew where Matt was were the guardroom staff. Matt had a funny felling as he picked up the phone. 'Warrant Officer Jenkins', said Matt into the mouthpiece. 'Sir, we've got a problem on St Kilda'. 'What's the problem', said Matt. 'Sir the 2i/c phoned and told us that OC St Kilda has been injured and we need to organise a casevac flight'. 'Okay', said Matt. 'Go ahead and call the Air Sea rescue helicopter from the mainland'. 'Oh and warn the doctor to stand by, I'm on my way back and should be there in half an hour'. Matt replaced the receiver, threw his tea down the sink and locked up the building. He made his way back to camp and a guardroom that was buzzing. Matt got hold of the orderly sergeant and asked him if he knew what had happened. 'What had caused OC St Kilda to be injured badly enough to call for a casevac', he asked? 'He was hit by a flying frozen chicken', came the deadpan reply. 'Go on', said Matt slowly, 'tell me what happened'. 'Well', said the sergeant, as far as I can tell, this is how it goes'.

 When the seas are really rough, the resupply vessel is unable to land essential supplies. Some times the detachment can go weeks during the winter months before supplies and mail can be delivered. When this happens, as an emergency measure, an aircraft is chartered to make air drops of essential supplies. This was one such occasion. Apparently, OC St Kilda was on top of the hill next to the DZ talking the aircraft in. He was on the ground to air radio giving instructions to the pilot.... Left a Bit....Right a Bit.....Okay.....Let her go. Trouble was, he got it ever so slightly wrong and the bag hit the DZ and split open. One of the frozen chickens ricochet off the Land Rover windscreen and hit him in the shoulder. He's in a bad way, apparently.

 The helicopter arrived and as it took on fuel and the doctor Matt briefed the crew on the events leading up to the casevac flight. The helicopter took off for St Kilda and on the way back flew the casualty straight to Glasgow. It transpired that the casualty had multiple fractures of the arm and collar bone that required steel plates to be screwed in to the bones to hold them together. It was some six months before the ex OC St Kilda was seen at Benbecula again.

 The camp swimming pool was closed for repairs. It had been shut for some weeks and was likely to remain shut for the foreseeable future. There weren't many types of exercise that Matt enjoyed as much as swimming. In the winter months, the pool was a godsend. Running was just plain silly in sixty mile an hour winds and activities in the gym were boring repetitious exercises. The day was a non working day the weather was so bad that Matt and the crew couldn't get across the causeway between Benbecula and South Uist. They had returned for the day and Matt had gone to find a cup of tea in the Mess kitchens. The mess cleaning staff were sitting in a circle having their mid morning break and Matt was offered a cup of tea. He thanked the lady and sat down. He chatted with the group and bemoaned the loss of the pool. They tut-tutted and shook their heads in as if they were Olympic swimmers being denied their only training facility. Matt smiled at the good natured sympathy the old ladies were extruding which along with their smiling faces gave Matt a warm feeling inside. Later on, he met one of the cleaners in the corridor. 'Oh hello', she said. 'I know where you could go swimming if you wanted'. 'Really said Matt', racking his brains but not recalling any mention of public baths on the islands. 'Yes', she said. 'Lord Granville, lives near Sollas in North Uist'. 'He lives in a Round House', she added. 'He's got an indoor pool and I'm sure he'd let me use it if I asked'. 'I used to cook for him and his wife'. 'Well, it would be nice to swim again but do you think you could get permission to use his pool', said Matt. 'I don't think it'd be a problem', she said. 'I'll phone him tonight and let you know tomorrow'. 'Thanks very much', said Matt. 'I'll see you tomorrow then'.

The next day at work, Matt asked if anybody knew who this Lord Granville was up on North Uist. 'He's only the first cousin to the Queen', said one of the girls'. 'The Queen Mother is Lord Granville's aunt', she added. 'Why do you ask', she said. 'Oh nothing', Matt replied. 'I was reading something somewhere and I wondered if this chap was the same person'. That evening he met the cleaner once more. She said her name was Moirag and she'd phoned Lord Granville and it was okay to go tomorrow night. Matt would have to collect her from her home in Balivanich at half past six sharp and drive up there to Sollas. It would take about an hour. Matt was speechless. He gulped and nodded. 'Don't worry', she said. 'He doesn't bite'. At the appointed time Matt drove up to Moirag's house and collected her. She directed him to the Roundhouse up near Loch Roag, where the famous standing stones from pre-history were located and Matt discovered that it was indeed round. He drove into the round inner courtyard and parked up. 'This way', said Moirag. Matt followed Moirag through one of the doors into the house. He found himself in a corridor which ran around the centre of the Roundhouse. Rooms went off one one side as they walked a little way around the corridor. Moirag stopped in front of one of the identical doors then went in. Matt followed to be confronted with a heated swimming pool. 'Changing rooms over there', said Moirag, pointing to a couple of doors. Matt got changed and showered. He dived into the pool and instantly forgot that he was in a house, at night, in the Outer Hebrides. It might have been stormy outside but in the pool it was heaven. Moirag came out of the changing room and said, 'try this'. At that she walked over to a lever set into the wall and pulled. A wave machine started up. 'Bloody hell', laughed Matt. 'This place is something else'.

After about twenty minutes, there was a knock on the door and a butler walked in bearing a silver tray. He put the tray down and announced that Lord Granville thought they might like some home made fruit cake and a drink. Further more, he requested the pleasure of their company when they had finished their swim. The butler left and they got out and dried off. There on the tray were two pieces of fruit cake and two tumblers of what Matt discovered to be Malt whiskey. He turned off the wave machine and attempted to do the sustenance justice. They changed and made their way around the corridor once more. At yet another anonymous door, Moirag stopped and knocked. There was a muffled voice from inside and Moirag opened the door and stepped in. Lord and Lady Granville were sitting on a settee in front of a peat fire. She wore a plastic cigarette lighter around her neck on a piece of black cord and was puffing away as she sat in front of the fire. Lord Granville got up and greeted Moirag warmly. 'Hello', he said to Matt. 'And who are you?' Matt told him who he was and where he'd come from and was immediately put at his ease by the old Lord and his wife. They were ushered into chairs and conversation went on for some hours. Eventually it was time to say goodbye and so they took their leave. Driving back to drop Moirag off, Matt thanked her and reflected on the last few hours. Drinking the Queens Cousins' best malt and chatting like old mates. All because he bemoaned the loss of the camp swimming pool to the cleaners one day. It just goes to prove, he thought, it's not what you know in this life, it's who you know that counts.

After he left the Hebrides, Matt did some research and came across an obituary for Lord Granville; a perfect gentleman of the old school.

GRANVILLE James Leveson-Gower, 5th Earl of Granville, was first cousin to the Queen. His mother, Lady Rose Bowes-Lyon, was the third daughter of the nine children of the 14th Earl of Strathmore and Kinghorn. Queen Elizabeth the Queen Mother was Lord Strathmore's youngest child, and therefore Lord Granville's aunt. Educated at Eton, Leveson-Gower joined the Coldstream Guards, attaining the rank of major. During the Second World War he was stationed in North Africa and Italy, where he was awarded the Military Cross for bravery. It was apparent to all who knew him that he seemed perfectly content to live out his remaining days in the Hebrides where he enjoyed a healthy out-of-doors lifestyle. He was undergoing tests for a heart by-pass operation in London when he collapsed and died of a heart attack.

The 5th Earl of Granville, MC; born December 6, 1918, died on November 1, 1996.

Matts posting came through. He had requested Cyprus but the voice on the other end of the phone laughed and pointed out that that was the choice of most of the Warrant Officers in the Regiment. When Matt pointed out that the carrot dangled by the records office was, his choice of posting if he volunteered for the Hebrides, he was told that he must have misheard and he would be sent to Larkhill near Stonehenge in Wiltshire. Matt was angry that he'd been lied to but with another two and a half years with the Royal Artillery, he would be teaching the Gunnery Staff Courses. The wheel had turned a full circle and eight years after his own Gunnery Staff Course he was going to achieve his ambition and teach the courses himself. That almost made up for him missing out on the Cyprus posting. Almost but not quite.

'Where are you going', said the boss. 'Fort fumble', replied Matt. 'God help us all', said the boss. 'Amen to that', said the Staff Sergeant. 'My god, a blue uniform teaching our Gunnery Staff courses'. 'Standards must have dropped', said the boss. 'Watch it', said Matt. 'I haven't gone yet'. Eventually with all the goodbyes said and the camp clearance completed, Matt bought himself another 'single' ticket and caught the Caledonian MacBrayne ferry across the 'Minches' to Uig on the Isle of Skye. He drove the length of the island to the Kyle of Lochalsh where he caught another ferry for the short trip to the mainland of Scotland.

Away from the wilds of the North where the only things to see were bogs, sea, lochs, mountains and sheep. Back down South to civilisation he headed. His eyes feasted on trees and hedge rows with his smile getting broader with each passing mile. Even the rain seemed softer now and as he crossed the English Scottish boarder, the sun burst from behind a cloud and flooded the world with light.

Chapter 27 – Fort Fumble

As Matt drove through the gates of the Royal School of Artillery at Larkhill a sense of pride came over him. He had passed their exacting course all those years ago and had now been invited back to teach it. He pulled up outside Hardy block and went into the Master Gunners office to say hello. 'Hi Matt', came the greeting. 'Great to see you, how the devil are you ?' 'I'm fine said Matt'. 'Great to see you again Bill'. 'Stow your kit upstairs, you've got the top office', said the Master Gunner. 'Then I need to introduce you around the various interested departments and their heads'. Bill was genuinely pleased to see Matt. He had passed his course at a later date than Matt but the Army was a faster proposition for promotion than the RAF Regiment. They had known each other for a few years by now and were of equal rank but the Master Gunner, by appointment, was the senior person. It didn't phase Matt at all. He liked Bill and knew that he'd fit in. They made their rounds of the various departments finishing off with the Basic Science and Technology department or BST as it was known. The same instructors were teaching the same subjects to a Gunnery Staff course as they had done so many years ago, with Matt and his mates. The computers were newer however. Gone was the 'colossus' that used to cover the entire wall and used 'Teleprinters' for its input and program data. That computer had one thousand bytes of memory at it's disposal to run the operating system and programs. In it's place sitting on a small table was a state of the art BBC PC with 48 kilobytes of 'Random Access Memory' to play with. Matt shook his head in wonderment. They don't know they're born Matt said to himself, referring to the present students who were going through the BST leg of the course.

Back in his office Matt looked at the course programme. He would start to deliver his part of the syllabus in two weeks time. No problems, he thought. Let's get the equipment working first.

He noted that his first course would be an officers course. No chance that any of them would have any first hand experience of deploying a Rapier system. Their background would have included siting the equipment if he was lucky thought Matt. He had to turn them into Instructors Gunnery or IGs thought Matt. Thinking about the units he'd served with and the expertise or lack of, Matt decided that the officers on this course would be worthy of the title of IG when they finished. He would not be the person to let standards slip for the RAF Regiment. He reflected on this as he gazed idly out of the window. It dawned on him that he was looking at Stonehenge. He had a clear view of the 'Henge' which was some three miles away. This will get interesting mid summer, he thought.

Matt arranged for a full Blindfire Rapier system to be deployed in the equipment park for the next day then went back to the Mess for lunch. That afternoon, back in Hardy block Matt renewed acquaintances with the the other Sergeant Major AIGs. He was on first name terms with most of them and all were glad to see him. One of them came up to Matt for a quiet word and let it be known that he was posted away for a year to Nigeria. He wanted someone to pay his mortgage and house sit whilst he was away and would Matt like to do it? Matt agreed readily and a deal was struck. The next week would see Matt moving out of the Mess and into private accommodation in the local village of Netheravon.

The next morning Matt checked the equipment out and called the REME in to fix the various faults that had manifested themselves. He was not surprised. This equipment was only used for training and as such it got hammered. It took two days before the equipment was one hundred percent serviceable but to give the REME technicians their due, when they handed it back to Matt it was on top line. The 'FH70' field guns were firing from the valley just below the equipment park and Matt left the 'Mode' switch to 'Radar. One of the field guns fired a shell down range. The surveillance radar 'saw' the shell and passed the azimuth data to the Tracking Radar. The Tracking Radar slewed to the target azimuth. Within a second it had locked on to and was tracking the shell. The system automatically went into its 'Radar Tracking Mode' where the Missile Beams came up to point at the target. The whole missile system now followed the trajectory of the shell until impact. Considering that the missile system was designed to take out targets which were aircraft sized, getting on to and following a shell was not a bad demonstration of performance.

On the first day of the Officers Rapier leg of their Gunnery Staff course Matt repeated the demonstration. He stood them to one side and addressed the course, outlining what was about to happen. He then set the safety key to 'Arm' and the 'Mode' switch to 'Radar'. He stood back. The 'FH70' Field gun obligingly fired whilst the Rapier system locked on to the shell and tracked it to impact some fourteen kilometres away. They were suitably impressed as Matt addressed them once more. 'Gentlemen', he said. 'As you can see, the equipment is working as advertised'. 'Don't break it'!

As the course progressed so did the students. They became more proficient at the drills and the first night deployment took place. They moved out to a spot out on the Larkhill ranges and proceeded to deploy the system in the dark. About fifteen minutes into the operation a volley of cursing and swearing alerted Matt that there might be a problem. He walked quietly across in the direction of the noise and watched. He grinned in the dark. Everybody makes this mistake once in their career and they needed to make it here on the course where no harm would be done but a valuable lesson would be learnt. One of the course members was berating the crew who had deployed the Tracking Radar. The cables could not be connected as the Radar had been placed too far away from the Launcher. After more swearing and cursing, it was agreed to move the Radar closer to allow the cables to be connected. Moving that piece of equipment and redeploying it added forty minutes to the overall into action time. This meant that they were effectively late in providing the Air Defence Cover they had committed to at the briefing. The situation was not lost on the students either. They had made the most basic of errors which could have had far reaching repercussions if they had been on operations.

The Rapier leg of the course lasted for three months and Matt and his deputy whipped them into shape. Never letting up for an instant and never accepting second best. Eventually the end was in sight and the course moved up to the Outer Hebrides to enable each man the experience of firing a live missile. The practise camp went without a hitch. Each man fired his missile and at £ 30k a pop, made the most of the experience. Back at Larkhill the course 'Passed out' and twelve new baby IGs were born.

The next course Matt had was a 'Baby Officers' course. They were the Sandhurst graduates who had just 'Passed Out'. They had come to Larkhill for their basic equipment training. Rapier if they were 'Cloud Punchers' and Artillery pieces if they were 'Steam Gunners. These 'Young Officers' had their own mess as they could get a bit boisterous after the smell of the barmaids apron. They were known as 'YO-YOs'. They were kept separate because the more mature officers who lived in the Officers Mess proper, preferred to fall asleep over their beers without the interruption of these young lads and their high spirits. The course would be six weeks long but at least they would be a keen bunch. He paraded the course on their first day and addressed them. 'Gentlemen', he started off. 'I want you to understand that I will call you sir because I have to'. 'You, on the other hand will call me mister, because I've earned it'. 'Do not be late, ever'.

The first few weeks went normally, then one Friday afternoon during a break, a 'spokesman' from the course approached Matt. 'Er Mister Jenkins', he said. 'Yes', said Matt looking up from diagram he was studying. 'We were wondering if you would sponsor us on a charity walk this weekend to Oxford and back'. 'No problem said Matt', 'what's it in aid of?' 'We lost one of our colleagues at Sandhurst in a car crash', said the student. 'I see', said Matt. 'The problem was that he had his dog with him in the car when he crashed'. 'Go on', said Matt. 'Well, the car caught fire and the only thing left of the dog was ashes', said the now uncomfortable looking student. 'His girlfriend was pretty upset because it was her dog, so we're trying to get some cash together to buy an urn for the dogs ashes'. Matt wanted to get back to finding the fault on the piece of equipment he was working on. Known as the 'Flat Trainer', it was notorious for going wrong. He wasn't really listening to the story about the burnt dog so he said, 'okay, put me down for a fiver and let me get on'. Matt couldn't help but notice that the grateful student almost skipped out of the building with apparent glee. Hmm, must find out more, thought Matt as he pored once more over the data diagram of the Flat Trainer. Eventually, Matt was forced to call in the REME. He made his way back to Hardy block and called in on the Master Gunner. 'Bill', he started. 'Do you know of anything going down with the YO-YOs at the moment?' 'Funny you should mention them', said Bill. 'They are in a bit of trouble at the moment. 'Tell me more', said Matt. 'Well', said Bill. 'They had a bit of a night the other evening, too much sauce, young lads you know the sort of thing'. 'Well, said Bill. 'Things sort of got out of hand and they dispatched a raiding party into the main Officers Mess'. 'Go on', said Matt. 'This is getting interesting'. 'They raided a Majors room whilst he was at the bar'. 'They removed a large bureau from his room and set fire to it on the lawn outside'. 'They were caught and apart from taking it in turns to be orderly officer until they leave Larkhill, they also have to pay a collective charge of about three hundred pounds to replace the bureau'. 'Ah', said Matt. 'I get the ashes part of it now and proceeded to tell the Master Gunner about the sponsored walk and the cremated dog'. Matt went home that evening with a smile on his face. He was quite looking forward to Monday morning with its expected events and consequences.

The weekend passed pleasantly enough and soon Monday came around. He was up bright and early and into work. He was teaching in the equipment compound until lunchtime. When the morning break came around he dismissed the class and wandered off into the compound office to get a cup of tea. He was standing outside the office idly drinking his tea when some of the course approached. The story about the tragic accident was earnestly and sincerely told once more and Matt was asked to contribute the five pounds he'd pledged. Matt kept a straight face and told the YO-YOs to wait till later because now they had to take the Rapier system 'Out of Action'. The course took it out of action then Matt got them to put it back into action. Once it had been redeployed Matt got them to take it out of action once more. This sequence of events continued for the rest of the morning and through lunchtime. After lunch he dismissed the course but before he let them go to their next lesson he reminded them not to stop off on the way to get lunch. The Master Gunner was taking the next class personally and would take a dim view of any latecomers. A sweaty, tired bunch of baby officers left the equipment compound and headed for Hardy block. As they left, a few of them heard Matt mutter, 'an urn for burnt fucking dogs'. 'They'll have to get up earlier in the morning to catch me out with that one'. What they didn't know was that the Master Gunner had arranged for the course to be met at Hardy block by the 'Physical Training Instructors' or PTIs. They were going for a little run and it would last all afternoon.

Matts next course was an advanced Rapier operators course. When the course paraded, the students immediately recognised Matt from the Hebrides. Matt also knew some of the students and their deeds. One of the students on the course had shot down two A4 Skyhawks during the Falklands conflict with one Rapier missile. He had engaged the first aircraft head on and the missile had travelled down the air intake before exploding in the engine. It was flying at high speed and very low level. The wingman or second aircraft was following so close that it flew into the explosion and promptly blew up as well. After that performance the lad had been sent on an 'Advanced Rapier Operators' course. Matt shook his head in bewilderment. The ways of the forces were indeed mysterious sometimes.

Matt was reminded of another instance of decision making that had caused him wonder about the sense of it all. It was back in the Hebrides. Visiting units came through every two weeks for their Rapier Practise camps. If not Rapier then it would be some other system. Some of the WRACs had a high old time dating new fellows every couple of weeks and some of the girls were married. One in particular had been caught 'in-flagranta' by her husband who had taken a dim view of the proceedings. The subsequent naked chase with him yelling obscenities at her was the cause of some quite delicious gossip on the married patch for a while. He was eventually caught by the Military Police and locked up until he'd calmed down. The next problem was what to do with him. He had a promiscuous wife and he was a jealous husband. In one blinding flash of inspiration, someone in headquarters had a bright idea and posted him to St Kilda, fifty miles out into the Atlantic. Still, it was a bird sanctuary. The wife meanwhile, had a wonderful time before eventually running off with a soldier from a visiting unit. Perhaps there was wisdom in that decision after all.

Matts turbulent life had by this stage started to settle down. He had by now taught three Gunnery Staff Courses and various other courses. A long and vicious divorce was now over and Matt had remarried. Matt and his new wife lived on a farm in Netheravon and for once Matt was not worried that his 'ex' might might be still weaving her vindictive web. It was over. He setteled down to enjoy married life.

One Friday afternoon Matt was called in to see the RAF Regiment liaison officer. Known as the 'Granddaddy' of the RAF Regiment Gunnery Staff. He was an omnipotent being in that what he said went. RAF Records and postings listened to him. He was getting on a bit thought Matt as he went into the office and saluted. He was a corpulent man who sat behind his desk with a genial smile on his face. His grey handlebar moustache was impressive and he was on his last posting to Larkhill before retirement. Matt had worked with him on exercises in the past and so had built up a rapport. The interview started with Matt being informed that he'd been posted to RAF West Raynham. He would be demoted from Special Acting Paid Warrant Officer to his substantive rank of Flight Sergeant. Matt asked the inevitable question. Why? He was told that in the five years he had been attached to the Royal Artillery his annual confidential personal reports or ACRs had been penned by Army officers. The RAF would like to see some reports being written by RAF officers before they would consider Matt for promotion to substantive Warrant Officer. Matt was incensed. It felt as if the RAF thought that an ACR written by an Army officer was worth less than one written by an RAF Officer. That aside, Matt pointed out that he'd just got married and if he were allowed another six months before moving he'd be more than happy to 'fall in' and follow the party line. Alas, it was not to be. His date of posting had been set and he would be off in two weeks. Matt was dismissed and he made his way back to his own office. He was stunned. After his performance over the last five years to be treated like this felt like a betrayal. Like a yapping dog, he'd been called to heel. He made a phone call to records and postings that decided the course of action he would take. He filled out a set of forms applying for 'Premature Voluntary Repatriation' and walked back to the RAF Regiment liaison officer's office. He knocked and was called in. A surprised liaison officer accepted the forms and told Matt not to be too hasty.

He went to place them in his top drawer but Matt asked him to sign them once more. Matt pointed out, with politeness that submitting these forms for his release after the time he'd served in the forces was a right and not a privilege. He retrieved the signed forms, saluted and walked out. Back in his own office once more he posted the forms to records and postings then picked up the phone. An old pal of his who had been on the same course as Matt all those years ago now worked for British Aerospace and yes there was a vacancy in the Customer Training School. A few days later Matt took some leave and drove to Stevenage for an interview. He was asked when could he start and Matt replied, 'in about six months time'. He was asked to get in touch with the BAe Customer Training School again when he was a month away from leaving the forces. And so it came about that he changed his normal working dress from a disruptive pattern camouflaged suit to a lounge suit.

It had taken twenty four years to go from being a civilian to being a civilian. Mind you, Matt mused, there have been one or two experiences and scrapes along the way and perhaps one or two more than I have told people about. You never know he thought, I might even write a book about it all one day.